A Guide to Color Reproductions

by

Margaret Bartran

The Scarecrow Press, Inc.
New York and London   1966

For A. Yale Gerol, M. D.

Introduction

The choice of fine art reproductions available in the United States today seems to be at least double that of ten years ago.

This guide contains over 8500 titles of color reproductions that were listed in publishers' catalogs at the time of writing. This is simply a comprehensive report of the contents of publishers' catalogs, and it should not be considered promotional in any way.

To keep the book from becoming unwieldy it was limited to reproductions commercially printed in color on paper, available through distributors in the United States at prices quoted in U. S. currency. It is not meant to refer to any hand-made prints, already-framed pictures, black and white subjects, drawings, photographs, slides, postcards, book or magazine illustrations, or reproductions smaller than 7 x 5 inches. The list excludes foreign publications which are not stocked in the United States and prints which are apt to become unavailable in a short time, such as subjects offered only for the period of a special sale.

Titles are listed under the alphabetically-arranged names of the artists who produced the originals from which the reproductions were made. Next to each title are given dimensions in inches, vertical measurement first, of the largest size in which the print is available. This is followed by a publisher's symbol to indicate a source for ordering, and then by a price for that size. Smaller sizes are listed below that in diminishing order, with a source and price for each one.

The second part of the book consists of an Index of Titles. Titles are arranged alphabetically under the first important word of each one with a reference number referring to a number in the List of Reproductions in which the prints are numbered consecutively.

To avoid confusion English translations of titles in other languages have been used only as they were listed by the publishers, since these translations usually appear on the prints. If the publisher gave no translation, the title appears here only in its original language.

It is hoped that reproductions of black and white subjects and drawings as well as many fine oriental subjects which had to be omitted in this volume, can be included in a forthcoming supplement. The author would appreciate being reminded through the publisher about omissions, so that the combinations of this volume and a supplement will constitute as complete a listing as possible.

Abbreviations and Publishers' Symbols

AA	Aaron Ashley, Inc., Box 244, Yonkers, N.Y.
Ac.	Active
AJ	Arthur Jaffe, Inc., 3 East 28th Street, New York 16, N.Y.
AP	Artext Prints, Inc., Westport, Conn.
C.	Circa or About
CAC	Colonial Art C., 1336-1338 N.W. First Street, Oklahoma City, Okla.
CFA	Catalda Fine Arts, Inc., 15 West 27th Street, New York 1, N.Y.
DAC	Donald Art Co., Inc., Spencer Place, Mamaroneck, N.Y.
DP	Dietz Press, Inc., 112 East Cary Street, Richmond 19, Va.
ESH	Erich S. Herrmann, Inc., 3 East 28th Street, New York 16, N.Y.
Grav.	Gravure
H.C.	Hand Colored
HNA	Harry N. Abrams, Inc., 6 West 57th Street, New York 19, N.Y.
IA	International Art Publishing Co., 243 West Congress Street, Detroit 26, Mich.
MMA	Museum of Modern Art, 11 West 53rd Street, New York 19, N.Y.
NYGS	New York Graphic Society, Inc., Greenwich, Conn.
PENN	Penn Prints, Harlem Book Co., Inc., 221 Park Avenue South, New York 3, N.Y.
Pr.	Processed surface, smooth lacquer or brush strokes
Res.	Resident of
Tr.	Translation
WK	Walter Keane, 245 Woodside Drive, Woodside, California
RL	Rudolf Lesch Fine Arts, Inc., 225 Fifth Ave., New York, N.Y. 10010

v

ABBEY, EDWIN AUSTIN	American	1852-1911	
1. Castle of the Maidens	19 x 44	CAC	18.00
2. King Lear	20 x 46	CAC	18.00
	11 x 27	CAC	7.50
	8 x 10	AP	.50
3. Richard, Duke of			
Gloucester	22 x 45	CAC	22.00
ABBOTT, LEMUEL FRANCIS	English	1760-1803	
4. Goffers at Blackheath	26-1/2 x 18	IA	25.00
	19 x 13	IA	15.00
	13 x 9-1/2	IA	6.00
5. Henry Callender	24 x 16	AA	25.00
ABDULLAJEW			
6. Bengal Girls	20 x 16	AP	5.00
ABRAMS, HERBERT	American Contemporary		
7. Still Life	30 x 36	DAC	8.00
	15 x 18	DAC	6.00
	10 x 12	DAC	1.20
ACKERMANN, MAX	German	1887-	
8. Above the Towers	18 x 14	IA	10.00
9. Jubilieren--Tr.-Jubilation	25-1/2 x 20	AP	10.00
10. Triumph der Freude			
Tr.-Triumphant Joy	19-1/2 x 12-1/2	IA	10.00
ADAM, RICHARD BENNO	German	1873-1937	
11. Passenger Coach	12 x 18	PENN	1.00
ADAMS, JOHN OTIS	American	1851-1927	
12. Hunting in Autumn	7 x 9	AP	.50
ADAMS, JOHN QUINCY	American (Res. Vienna, Austria)		
		1874-1933	
13. Her First Recital	21 x 24	NYGS	7.50
	11 x 13	NYGS	3.00
ADLER, SAMUEL M.	American	1898-	
14. Yellow Bird	24 x 30	DAC	8.00
ADRION, JUCIEN	French	1889-	
15. Blue Waters	24 x 30	PENN	1.00
	11 x 14	DAC	2.80
16. On the Boulevard	25 x 31	CFA	12.00
	16 x 20	CFA	5.00
17. Sunny Day	19 x 23	CFA	12.00
AERTSEN, PIETER	Dutch	1508-1575	
18. The Cook	15 x 8	IA	3.00
AGAR, JOHN SAMUEL	English	1770-1835	
19. Bury Hunt	18 x 26	CAC	25.00
AGASSE, JACQUES LAURENT	Swiss	1767-1849	
20. Last Journey on the Road	11 x 16	CAC	12.00
AHLERS-HESTERMAN, FRIEDRICH (FRITZ)	German	1883-	

7

21. River Memories	27-1/2 x 32	ESH	10.00
AIGNER, EDUARD	German	1903-	
22. Coastline at Sete	18 x 24	ESH	12.00
ALAUX, GUSTAVE	French	1887-	
23. Departure of the			
Mayflower	22 x 15	CAC	10.00
ALBANI, FRANCESCO	Italian	1578-1660	
24. Danza di Amorini e			
Ratto di Proserpina--			
Tr.-Dance of Cupids			
Rape of Persephone	15 x 12	IA	3.00
25. Dance of Cupids--Detail			
of No. 24	11 x 15	IA	3.00
ALBERTI, ANTONIO	Italian		
26. Rio di S. Lorenzo	24 x 48	DAC	10.00
	9 x 17-1/2	DAC	2.00
ALBERTINELLI, MARIOTTO	Italian	1474-1515	
27. Visitation	15 x 10	IA	3.00
ALBO, AUGUST	Estonian	1893-1963	
28. Ballet	6 x 15	DAC	1.20
29. Boats Ashore	12 x 30	PENN	1.00
30. Boats Offshore	12 x 30	PENN	1.00
31. Dutch Interiors	24 x 40	DAC	8.00
	12 x 20	DAC	2.00
32. Emperor Ballet (2)	15 x 6	DAC	1.20 ea.
	8 x 6	DAC	.60 ea.
33. Free as the Wind	24 x 40	DAC	8.00
	12 x 18	DAC	2.00
34. From the Old West	24 x 20	PENN	1.00
35. Fruit Still Life	16 x 21	DAC	4.00
	10 x 14	DAC	1.40
	7 x 9	DAC	.80
36. Music Room	24 x 20	PENN	1.00
37. Once Upon a Time	24 x 30	DAC	8.00
38. Oriental Moonlight (2)	30 x 10	DAC	4.00 ea.
39. Sea in Sunlight	12 x 30	PENN	1.00
40. Seaman's Den	24 x 20	PENN	1.00
41. Strummin' Days	24 x 20	PENN	1.00
42. Strauss Waltz	26 x 42	DAC	8.00
	14 x 22	DAC	2.00
	10 x 14	DAC	1.00
43. Summer Respite	24 x 48	DAC	10.00
44. Swan Lake	24 x 40	DAC	8.00
	12 x 20	DAC	2.00
45. Les Sylphides	24 x 40	DAC	8.00
	12 x 20	DAC	2.00
ALBRIGHT, MALVIN MARR	American	1897-	
46. Peaceful Harbor	15-1/2 x 33	NYGS	10.00
ALDRICH, GEORGE AMES	American	1872-	
47. Winter's Glory	12 x 16	CAC	3.50
ALKEN, HENRY THOMAS	English	1784-1850	
48. Bachelor's Hall (6)	12 x 14-1/2	AA	5.00 ea.

49. Flowers of the Hunt: (6) Dandelion Jonquil Passion Flower Pink Rose Sunflower	14 x 18	CAC	42.00 ea.
50. Foxhunting (4)	8 x 26	AA	10.00 ea.
51. Foxhunting (4) Breaking Cover Drawing Cover Full Cry Tally Ho	11 x 16	CAC	30.00 ea.
52. Partridge Shooting (4)	10 x 12	AA	5.00 ea.
53. Rexworthy Billiard Parlor	12 x 21	CAC	10.00
54. Small Hunt and Coaches (6)	7 x 9	CFA	3.00 ea.
55. Sporting Tandems (2)	9 x 13	CFA	15.00 ea.

ALLEGRI, ANTONIO   See CORREGGIO

ALLINSON, ADRIAN PAUL	English	1890-	
56. Cotswald Cross Roads	15 x 22	RL	7.50
57. Cotswold Pattern	15 x 22	RL	7.50
58. Goat Farm	16 x 24	ESH	6.00

ALLORI, ALESSANDRO   See BRONZINO, ALESSANDRO

ALLORI, CRISTOFANO	Italian	1577-1621	
59. Judith	14 x 11	IA	3.00
ALMA-TADEMA, (SIR) LAURENCE	English	1836-1912	
60. Reading from Homer	14 x 29	CAC	7.50

ALQUIST   See SCHNARS-ALQUIST

ALT, JACOB	Austrian	1789-1872	
61. Traunsee	14 x 21	AR	10.00
ALT, RUDOLF VON	Austrian	1812-1905	
62. Landscape near Gastein	19 x 26-1/2	AR	15.00
ALTAMURA, SAVERIO	Italian	1826-1897	
63. Good Old Time!	16 x 11 oval	IA	3.00
ALTDORFER, ALBRECHT	German	1480-1538	
64. Landscape	8 x 6	CFA	4.00
65. Landscape with Church	8 x 5-1/2	CFA	1.90
66. Landscape with Village	11 x 7	CFA	4.00
67. Nativity 1523	17-1/2 x 14-1/2	AR	7.50
68. Susanna in the Bath	18 x 23	HNA	5.95
69. Virgin and Child in Glory	25-1/2 x 16-1/2	NYGS	20.00
AMADIO, GIOVANNI ANTONIO	Italian	1447-1522	
70. European Cities	30 x 12	DAC	4.00
	20 x 8	DAC	1.60
71. Gondolas (2)	15 x 40	DAC	8.00
	8-1/2 x 23-1/2	DAC	2.00
72. Paris--Corner Shops	15 x 40	DAC	8.00
	8-1/2 x 23-1/2	DAC	2.00
73. Paris--River Bridge	15 x 40	DAC	8.00

		8-1/2 x 23-1/2	DAC	2.00
74.	Paris--Street Cafês	15 x 40	DAC	8.00
		8-1/2 x 23-1/2	DAC	2.00
75.	Rome Eternal	15 x 40	DAC	8.00
		8-1/2 x 23-1/2	DAC	2.00

AMBRASETH, F.
76. Vers le Pacifique
    Tr. - Fair Weather

| Ahead | 25 x 34 | CAC | 12.50 |

AMBROGI, MICHELOZZO   See MELOZZO DA FORLI
AMICK, ROBERT WESLEY   American   1879-

77.	Bounding Main	27 x 36	NYGS	12.00
78.	The Craftsman	28 x 40	CFA	15.00
79.	Grand Canyon, Arizona	26-1/2 x 36	NYGS	12.00
80.	Indian Scout	22 x 35-1/2	NYGS	15.00
81.	Indian Weaver	22 x 28	CFA	7.50
82.	Man O'War	19-1/2 x 25-1/2	NYGS	7.50
83.	Overland Mail	26 x 40	NYGS	15.00
84.	Promised Land	27 x 36	NYGS	12.00
85.	Pueblo Indian	22 x 28	CFA	7.50
86.	Where the Sun Goes	18 x 30	CFA	7.50
		14 x 30	CFA	5.00
87.	Whirlaway	19-1/2 x 25-1/2	NYGS	7.50
		11 x 14	NYGS	3.00

AMIET, CUNO   Swiss   1868-

88.	Apple Pickers	21 x 16	CFA	10.00
89.	Breton Woman	14-1/2 x 17	CAC	10.00
90.	Haymaking	21 x 31	CAC	10.00
91.	Mountain Lake	24 x 27	CAC	12.00
92.	Roses	13 x 11	CAC	5.00
93.	Zinnias	16-1/2 x 20	CFA	6.00

AMIRY, T.

| 94. | Fantasy | 18 x 22-1/2 | ESH | 12.00 |

ANDERSON, HARRY   American   1906-

| 95. | In Time of Storm | 18 x 13-1/2 | IA | 5.00 |
| 96. | Master of Life, Health
    and Happiness | 15-1/2 x 22 | IA | 5.00 |
| 97. | What Happened to Your
    Hand? | 22 x 16 | IA | 5.00 |
| | | 16 x 22 | IA | 2.50 |

ANDERSON, HEATH

| 98. | Chinese Poppies | 22 x 28 | IA | 6.00 |

ANDERSON, ROLF

99.	Beagle	15 x 12	CFA	5.00
100.	Blond Cocker Spaniel	15 x 12	CFA	5.00
101.	Setter	15 x 12	CFA	5.00
102.	Wire-Haired Terrier	15 x 12	CFA	5.00

ANDRADE, MAGDA   Venezuelan (res. France)
    Contemporary

| 103. | Blue Harmony | 24 x 18-1/2 | RL | 10.00 |

ANDRE, ALBERT   French   1869-

| 104. | Bakery | 13 x 16 | CAC | 10.00 |

105.	Bookstalls	13 x 16	CAC	10.00
106.	Flower Vendor	13 x 16	CAC	10.00
107.	Hair Dresser	13 x 16	CAC	10.00
108.	News Vendor	13 x 16	CAC	10.00
109.	Stables	17 x 13	CAC	10.00
110.	Theatre	16 x 20	CAC	15.00

ANDREA DEL CASTAGNO See CASTAGNO, ANDREA DEL
ANDREA DEL SARTO See SARTO, ANDREA DEL
ANDREA DI CIONE See ORCAGNE
ANDREOTTI, E.

111.	The Concert	19 x 28	AA	9.00

ANDREWS, GEORGE HENRY English 1816-1898

112.	At Versailles	25 x 30	AA	10.00

ANDREWS, WALTER American 1906-

113.	Blue Gulf Stream	24 x 35-1/2	NYGS	12.00
114.	Breaking Surf	24 x 36	NYGS	12.00
		16 x 30	NYGS	6.00
115.	Canvas-Backs at Dusk	24 x 36	NYGS	12.00
116.	Dawn over the Marshes	24 x 30	NYGS	7.50
117.	Falcon Hunt	24 x 36	DAC	8.00
118.	Flight at Morn	24 x 30	NYGS	7.50
119.	Incoming Comers	24 x 36	NYGS	12.00
		16 x 30	NYGS	6.00
120.	Sunrise Flight	24 x 36	NYGS	12.00

ANGELICO, FRA. GIOVANNI DA FIESOLE (IL BEATO)

		Italian	1387-1455	
121.	Adoration of the Magi	16" circle	PENN	1.00
		11" circle	IA	3.00
122.	Angel Adoring	11 x 7	ESH	1.00
123.	Angel Musicians (2)	13 x 5	IA	3.00 ea.
124.	Annunciation (S. Marco)	16 x 20-1/2	AP	5.00
		15 x 20	ESH	6.00
		14 x 19	IA	7.50
		13 x 17	IA	3.00
		8-1/2 x 11	IA	1.75
125.	Angel--Detail of No. 124	24 x 18	AA	c. 7.50
		15 x 11	IA	3.00
		11 x 7	ESH	1.00
126.	Virgin--Detail of No. 124	15 x 11	IA	3.00
127.	Annunciation (S. Marco, vertical)	11 x 10	IA	3.00
128.	Annunciation (S. Marco, vertical with arched top)	13 x 11	IA	3.00
129.	Angel--Detail of No. 128	15 x 11	IA	3.00
130.	Annunciation (Cortona)	11 x 13	IA	3.00
131.	Annunciation and Adoration of the Magi	15 x 9	IA	3.00
132.	Christ as Pilgrim	11 x 15	IA	3.00

133. Christ Rising from the Tomb	11 x 15	IA	3.00
134. Communion of the Apostles	11 x 14	IA	3.00
135. Christ--Detail of No. 134	15 x 11	IA	3.00
136. Coronation of the Virgin (S. Croce)	15 x 11	IA	3.00
137. Angel Musicians (2)-- Details of No. 136	15 x 11	IA	3.00 ea.
138. Coronation of the Virgin (S. Marco)	13 x 12	IA	3.00
139. Christ and the Virgin-- Detail of No. 138	11 x 15	IA	3.00
140. Coronation of the Virgin (Uffizi)	15 x 11	IA	3.00
141. Crucifix and St. Dominic	15 x 11	IA	3.00
142. St. Dominic at the Foot of the Crucifix-- Detail of No. 141	15 x 11	IA	3.00
143. St. Dominic (Head)-- Detail of No. 141	15 x 11	IA	3.00
144. Crucifix--Detail of No. 141	15 x 11	IA	3.00
145. Crucifixion (S. Marco)	9 x 15	IA	3.00
146. St. Francis--Detail of No. 145	15 x 11	IA	3.00
147. St. Jerome--Detail of No. 145	15 x 11	IA	3.00
148. St. Marc--Detail of No. 145	15 x 11	IA	3.00
149. Crucifixion of the Saints Cosmas and Damian	11 x 14	IA	3.00
150. Deposition from the Cross	12 x 11	IA	3.00
151. Descent from the Cross	11 x 12	IA	3.00
152. Dormition of the Virgin	6 x 15	IA	3.00
153. Entombment	13 x 11	IA	3.00
154. Entry into Jerusalem	12 x 11	IA	3.00
155. Flight into Egypt	19 x 19	IA	7.50
	11 x 11	IA	3.00
156. Healing of Palladia	11 x 13	IA	3.00
157. Last Judgment	8 x 12	IA	3.00
158. Angels Dancing--Detail of No. 157	15 x 11	IA	3.00
159. Angels Dancing--Detail of No. 157	11 x 15	IA	3.00
160. The Damned--Detail of No. 157	10 x 15	IA	3.00
161. Lysias Delivered from the Devils	11 x 13	IA	3.00

162.	Madonna and Child with Angels	9 x 7	IA	3.00
163.	Madonna della Stella	16 x 11	IA	3.00
164.	Madonna and Child-- Detail of No. 163	15 x 11	IA	3.00
165.	Madonna of the Linaiuoli	15 x 8	IA	3.00
166.	The Maries	15 x 12	IA	3.00
167.	Marriage of the Virgin	6 x 15	IA	3.00
168.	Martyrdom of the Saints Cosmas and Damian into the Fire	11 x 14	IA	3.00
169.	Massacre of the Innocents	11 x 11	IA	3.00
170.	Nativity of Christ	13 x 11	IA	3.00
171.	Noli Me Tangere	13 x 11	IA	3.00
172.	Pieta	14 x 11	IA	3.00
173.	Presentation in the Temple	13 x 11	IA	3.00
174.	Resurrection of Christ	13 x 11	IA	3.00
175.	Angel--Detail of No. 174	15 x 11	IA	3.00
176.	Road to Calvary	12 x 11	IA	3.00
177.	St. Dominic (Detail from "Christ Mocked")	15-1/2 x 12	IA	3.50
		15 x 11	IA	3.00
178.	St. Laurence Distributing the Treasures of the Church	15 x 11	IA	3.00
179.	St. Laurence Receiving from Sixtus II the Treasures of the Church	15 x 11	IA	3.00
180.	St. Peter Martyr	10 x 13	IA	3.00
181.	St. Raymond of Cataluna	15 x 11 oval	IA	3.00
182.	St. Thomas of Aquinas	11 x 15	IA	3.00
183.	Sts. Cosmas and Damian before Lysias	11 x 15	IA	3.00
184.	Transfiguration	13 x 11	IA	3.00
185.	Virgin and Saints	10 x 10	IA	3.00
186.	Madonna and Child-- Detail of No. 185	15 x 11	IA	3.00
187.	Four Saints--Detail of No. 185	15 x 11	IA	3.00
188.	Four Saints--Detail of No. 185	15 x 11	IA	3.00
189.	Virgin Enthroned	14 x 12	CFA	2.50
190.	Visitation	9 x 11	IA	3.00
191.	Zacharias Writing the Name of John	11 x 15	IA	3.00
ANKER, ALBERT		Swiss	1831-1910	
192.	Blond Girl	16-1/2 x 13	NYGS	12.00
193.	First Smile	17 x 12	IA	4.50
194.	Girl Peeling Potatoes	16 x 12	CAC	4.00

195. Grandmother	17 x 12	CAC	4.00
196. Her Little Friend	17 x 12	CAC	4.00
197. Home Lesson	21 x 17	CAC	7.50
	16 x 12	CAC	4.00
198. Knitting Lesson	22 x 24	CFA	10.00
	18 x 20	CAC	7.50
199. Parish Clerk	22 x 17	IA	7.50
200. Pestalozzi and the Children	23 x 35	CFA	12.00
	12 x 16	CAC	4.00
201. Poultry Yard	22 x 17	CFA	7.50
	16 x 12	CAC	4.00
202. The Song	22 x 24	CAC	10.00
	18 x 20	CAC	7.50
203. School Boy	16 x 12	IA	4.00
204. School Girl	16 x 12	IA	4.00
205. Signing the Register	21 x 35	CAC	12.50
	11 x 18	CAC	4.00
206. Slumberland	17 x 22	CAC	4.00
207. Strawberry Girl	16 x 12	CAC	4.00
208. Sunday School Walk	21 x 35	IA	12.50
	11 x 18	IA	4.50
209. Tales of a Grandfather	12 x 18	CAC	4.00
210. Young Girl	15 x 12	CFA	4.00
211. Young Girl Knitting	16 x 12	CAC	4.00
212. The Winder	16 x 12	CAC	4.00
ANTONELLO DA MESSINA	Italian	1430-1479	
213. The Annunciate	15 x i1	IA	3.00
214. Crucifixion	15 x 11	IA	3.00
215. The Poet	13 x 10	IA	3.00
216. Young Man	12 x 9	IA	3.00
	7 x 6	NYGS	.50
ANTONIAZZO ROMANO	Italian	1430-1509	
217. Madonna and Child	15 x 10	IA	3.00
APOLINAR			
218. Mexican Panels--Nos. I and II	21 x 8 ea.	CFA	5.00 ea.
APPEL, KAREL	Dutch	1921-	
219. Bete du Soleil Tr. - Sun Animal	21 x 25-1/2	NYGS	12.00
220. Cry for Freedom	10 x 8	AP	1.50
APPLEYARD, J.			
221. Sunny Pastures	9 x 12	ESH	2.00
AQUILIO, MARCANTONIO	See ANTONIAZZO ROMANO		
ARALDI, ALESSANDRO	Italian	1460-1528	
222. Portrait of Barbara Pallavicino	15 x 11	IA	3.00
ARDON, MORDECAI	Israeli	1896-	
223. Story of a Candle	20 x 25-1/2	NYGS	12.00
ARENAL, LUIS	Mexican	1909-	
224. The Well	14-1/2 x 19-1/2	AP	5.00
	7 x 9	AP	.60
ARETINO See PARRI DI SPINELLI ARENTINO			

ARENTZ, JOSEPH	American		
225. Coast of Maine	22 x 32	AA	10.00
226. Land's End	24 x 36	AA	12.00
227. North Atlantic	27 x 39	AA	12.00
228. Sand Dunes	22 x 32	AA	10.00
229. South Atlantic	24 x 35	AA	12.00
ARENYS, RICARDO	Spanish		
230. Autumn Morn	23 x 46	NYGS	24.00
231. In the Pasture	16 x 40	NYGS	18.00
232. On the Range	16 x 40	NYGS	18.00
233. White Horses	31-1/2 x 24	NYGS	18.00
ARLEDGE			
234. Zebras	7 x 9	AP	.50
ARMOUR, H.			
235. Calf	12 x 9	ESH	2.00
236. White Kitten	12 x 9	ESH	2.00
ARNEGGER, ALWIN	Austrian	1883-1916	
237. Riviera Splendor	24 x 36	IA	12.00
ARP, JEAN (HANS)	German	1888-	
238. Design, Study in Relief	10-1/2 x 10	NYGS	8.00
ARTZ, DAVID ADOLF	Dutch	1837-1890	
239. The Sewing School	8 x 10	AP	.50
ASHLEY, JAMES F.			
240. Storm Clears	24 x 36	CAC	15.00
	16 x 24	CAC	6.00
241. Sunderland Hills	24 x 36	CAC	15.00
ASSYRIA			
242. Sculpture Relief-- Ashurnasirpal II (2) King in Chariot Hunting Lions	15 x 38	NYGS	15.00
Assyrian Chariots Overthrowing Enemy's Chariots	15 x 38	NYGS	15.00
ATAMIAN, CHARLES	Turkish (Res. France) 1872-		
243. Shrimping	19 x 23	RL	5.00
AUBERT, LOUIS	French	1720-1780	
244. Peep Show	11 x 8	AR	3.50
245. Pupils in Studio	13 x 9-1/2	AR	3.50
AUDUBON, JOHN JAMES	American	1785-1851	
246. Audubon Birds (4) Field Bunting Florida Jay Prothonatary Swamp Warbler Summer Redbird	11-1/2 x 15	PENN	2.98 set
247. Blue Grosbeak	16 x 13	NYGS	3.00
248. Blue Jay	16 x 13	NYGS	3.00
249. Carolina Parrot	30 x 21-1/2	NYGS	10.00
250. Carolina Turtle-Dove	21 x 17	NYGS	5.00
251. Common Crossbill	21 x 17	NYGS	5.00
252. Five Pair of Wood-			

	peckers	9 x 7	CFA	1.00
253.	Florida Jay	23 x 18	HNA	5.95
254.	Pileated Woodpecker	23 x 18	HNA	5.95
255.	Portrait of a Girl, c. 1830	23-1/2 x 17-1/2	NYGS	12.00
256.	Ruby-Throated Humming-bird	21 x 17	NYGS	5.00
257.	Scarlet Ibis	7 x 9	CFA	1.00
258.	Snowy Heron	10 x 8	NYGS	.50
259.	Wood Ibis	9 x 7	CFA	1.00
260.	Yellow-Breasted Chat	21 x 17	NYGS	5.00

AUSTRALIA
261. Aboriginal Paintings (5)   11 x 15   NYGS 2.00 ea.
      Fish in X-Ray Art
      Mimi Spirit Woman and A Cat Fish
      Spirit Man, Wili-Wilia, and the Mythical Kangaroo Man
      Spirit Men, Bradbatti and Kumail-Kumail
      Wet Season Seascape

AUSTRIAN, BEN		American	1906-	
262.	Pipe and Letter Rack	16 x 12	CFA	5.00
AVERCAMP, HENDRICK		Dutch	1585-1634	
263.	Ice Landscape	16 x 27-1/2	AP	15.00
AVERY, MILTON		American	Contemporary	
264.	Young Mother	24 x 18	AR	10.00
AVERY, RALPH		American	1906-	
265.	Homeward Bound	16 x 21	RL	10.00
266.	Umbrella Parade	20 x 28	RL	12.00
AVIGNON, SCHOOL OF		France	15th Century	
267.	Pieta of Villeneuve-les-Avignon	29 x 39	IA	24.00
		16-1/2 x 22-1/2	ESH	10.00
AYLING, GEORGE		English	1887-	
268.	Houses of Parliament	14 x 19-1/2	RL	3.50
269.	Natural Cornish Harbor	21 x 26	NYGS	7.50
270.	St. Paul's	14 x 19-1/2	RL	3.50
271.	Tower of London	14 x 19-1/2	RL	3.50
272.	Westminster Abbey	14 x 19-1/2	RL	3.50
AYLWARD, WILLIAM JAMES		American	1875-	
273.	Clipper Ship "Flying Cloud"	23-1/2 x 31-1/2	NYGS	10.00
274.	Landing of Columbus	28 x 40	CFA	15.00
275.	Landing of the Pilgrims	28 x 40	CFA	15.00
276.	U.S.S. Constitution	23-1/2 x 31-1/2	NYGS	10.00
AZTEC				
277.	Four Fortunes of the Maize (3)	7 x 21 (1)	AR	
		6 x 11-1/2 (2)	AR	12.00
				set of 3
278.	The Maize God	39 x 33	CFA	15.00
279.	Mayan Goddess	39 x 33	CFA	15.00

B

BABYLONIA			
280. A Bull	12 x 16	AR	7.50
281. A Dragon	12 x 16	AR	7.50
BACCICCIO, IL See GAULLI, GIOVANNI BATTISTA			
BACCIO See PAGHOLO, (FRA) BARTOLOMMEO DI			
BACH, FLORENCE JULIA	American	1887-	
282. Camellias	22 x 16	CFA	7.50
283. Fragrant Flowers	24 x 30	CAC	7.50
284. Gardenias	20 x 16	IA	3.50
285. Gems of the Garden	20 x 16	IA	3.50
286. Roses	22 x 16	CFA	7.50
	20 x 16	IA	3.50
287. White Mallows	16 x 20	CAC	7.50
BACHMANN, ALF	Dutch	1863-	
288. Autumn	23-1/2 x 31-1/2	ESH	10.00 (Pr.)
	12 x 16	ESH	3.00 (Pr.)
289. Bavarian Lake	19-1/2 x 27-1/2	ESH	8.00 (Pr.)
290. Bavarian Landscape in			
Autumn	19-1/2 x 11-1/2	IA	4.00
291. Bavarian Moorland	23-1/2 x 31-1/2	ESH	10.00 (Pr.)
	19-1/2 x 27-1/2	ESH	8.00 (Pr.)
	16 x 20	ESH	5.00
292. The Brook	23-1/2 x 31-1/2	ESH	10.00 (Pr.)
293. Chalet in Tyrol	19-1/2 x 11-1/2	IA	4.00
294. Church in Mountains	16 x 20	ESH	5.00
295. Dunes	21 x 31	CFA	7.50
296. Heatherland	19-1/2 x 27-1/2	ESH	8.00 (Pr.)
297. Landscape	19-1/2 x 27-1/2	ESH	8.00 (Pr.)
298. Spring	23-1/2 x 31-1/2	ESH	10.00 (Pr.)
299. Sunny Day	16 x 20	ESH	5.00
300. Sunny Landscape	16 x 20	ESH	5.00
301. Tyrol Mountains	19-1/2 x 27-1/2	ESH	8.00 (Pr.)
BACON, PEGGY	American	Contemporary	
302. Nobody's Pet	18 x 15	CAC	3.00
303. Nosegay	15 x 20	NYGS	5.00
304. Painting	8 x 10	MMA	.35
BALDASSARE, ESTENSE	Italian	1437-1504	
305. Portrait of a Family	29-1/2 x 24	NYGS	15.00
BALDOVINETTI, ALESSO (OR ALESSIO)			
	Italian	1425-1499	
306. Virgin Adoring the Child	15 x 10	IA	3.00
	10 x 8	ESH	1.00
BALDUNG (GRIEN), HANS	German	1485-1545	
307. Holy Family	18-1/2 x 14-1/2	NYGS	12.00
308. Allegory of the Vanity			
of all Earthly Things	19 x 12-1/2	CFA	3.50
BALESTRIERI, LIONELLO	Italian	1874-	
309. Beethoven's Sonata	19 x 44	CAC	15.00
	12 x 26	CAC	7.50
BAILEY, VERNON HOWE	American	1874-	

310. Magic City	20 x 24	NYGS	7.50
311. Metropolis	20 x 24	NYGS	7.50
BAILLE, HERVE	French	1896-	
312. Booksellers at Notre Dame	9-1/2 x 14	NYGS	3.00
313. Place de la Concorde	9-1/2 x 14	NYGS	3.00
314. Ballerinas (4)	14-1/2 x 11	PENN	1.00 set

Ballerinas in Dressing Room
Preparing for Rehearsal
Young Dancers Resting
Young Dancers Sitting

BARABINO, NICOLO	Italian	1832-1891	
315. Madonna and Child	15 x 8	IA	3.00
316. Detail of No. 315	20 x 27	IA	10.00
317. Detail of No. 315	15 x 11	IA	3.00
318. Madonna of the Olives	20 x 27	IA	10.00
	11 x 15	IA	3.00
BARGHEER, EDUARD	German	1901-	
319. Autumn Garden	13 x 19	NYGS	12.00
BARBARELLI, GIORGIO See GIORGIONE			
BARBIERI, GIOVANNI FRANCESCO See GUERCINO			
BARNABA DA MODENA	Italian	Ac. 1361-1385	
320. Virgin and Child		IA	15.00
BARNES, RENÉE	American	1886-	
321. Bunny Taxi	16 x 20	CFA	2.50
322. Humpty Dumpty	16 x 20	CFA	2.50
323. Nancy Lee's Playmates	16 x 20	CFA	2.50
324. Three Happy Pigs	16 x 20	CFA	2.50
BARNES			
325. Floral Rhapsody	24 x 30	CAC	7.50
BAROCCIO, IL (BAROCCI, FEDERICO)			
	Italian	1526-1612	
326. Frederick of Urbino as a Child	15 x 10	IA	3.00
327. Madonna of the Cherries	14 x 11	IA	3.00
328. Nativity	14 x 11	IA	3.00
BARRABAND (OR BARRABAN), JACQUES			
	French	1767/8-1809	
329. Le Grand Paradis	14 x 9	CFA	7.50
330. Le Paradis Emeraude	14 x 9	CFA	7.50
331. Le Paradis Rouge	14 x 9	CFA	7.50
332. Le Petit Paradis	14 x 9	CFA	7.50
BARRAUD, FRANCOIS (OR FRANCIS)			
	English	1856-1924	
333. Harbour of Barcelone	20 x 24	CAC	12.00
334. Our Daily Bread	21-1/2 x 22-1/2	NYGS	12.00
335. Village Philosopher	22 x 18	NYGS	10.00
BARRIVIERA, LINO BIANCHI	Italian	19th Century	
336. The Christ Head	28 x 22	DAC	4.00
	12 x 9	DAC	1.20
	10 x 8	DAC	.80
337. Fair in a Village	9 x 26	IA	10.00

338. Fair in a Village of			
the Lagune	9 x 26	IA	3.00
339. Out of Porta Faul at			
Viterbo	9 x 26	IA	3.00
BARTLETT, WILLIAM HENRY	English	1809-1894	
340. View from Hyde Park	20-1/2 x 28	AA	10.00
341. View of Mount Vernon	15-1/2 x 21	NYGS	5.00
342. Washington's Tomb,			
Mount Vernon	15-1/2 x 21	NYGS	5.00
BARTOLI, J.	American	Ac. 1796	
343. Madonna Ornas	14 x 9	CAC	6.00
BARTOLOMMEO DI FROSINO See FROSINO, BARTOLOMMEO DI			
BARTOLOMMEO, VENETO See VENETO, BARTOLOMMEO			
BARTOLOMMEO, FRA See PAGHOLO, BARTOLOMMEO DI (FRA)			
BASAITI (OR BAXAITI), MARCO Italian		d. 1521	
344. Christ and His Disciples	10 x 8	CFA	3.50
345. Christ Taking Leave of			
His Disciples	10 x 7	CAC	3.50
BASCHENIS, EVARISTO	Italian	1617-1677	
346. Unknown Beauty	27 x 35	CAC	12.00
BASSANO, FRANCESCO	Italian	1549-1592	
347. Rest During the Flight	23 x 31	CAC	12.00
BASSFORD, WALLACE	American	1900-	
348. Bride	9 x 12	NYGS	1.50
	6 x 7-1/2	NYGS	1.00
349. Bridegroom	9 x 12	NYGS	1.50
	6 x 7-1/2	NYGS	1.00
350. Mardi Gras	12 x 9	NYGS	1.50
	7-1/2 x 6	NYGS	1.00
351. Masquerade	12 x 9	NYGS	1.50
	7-1/2 x 6	NYGS	1.00
BASTIEN-LEPAGE, JULES	French	1848-1884	
352. Joan of Arc	9 x 10	NYGS	.50
BATEMAN, JAMES	English	1893-	
353. Haytime in the			
Cotswolds	18 x 23	RL	7.50
354. Richmond Park	15 x 26	CAC	12.00
BATONI, POMPEO	Italian	1708-1787	
355. The Holy Heart	15 x 12 oval	IA	3.00
356. Madonna and Child	15 x 11	IA	3.00
BAUMAN, LEILA T.			
357. U. S. Mail Boat	20 x 26	NYGS	15.00
BAZZI, GIOVANNI ANTONIO DE See SODOMA, IL			
BEAL, GIFFORD	American	1879-	
358. Circus Ponies	12 x 15	CAC	10.00
359. The Fisher	22 x 30	CFA	12.00
BEALL, CECIL CALVERT	American	1892-	
360. Geisha Girls (2)	30 x 10	DAC	4.00 ea.
	15 x 5	DAC	1.20 ea.
361. Oriental Beauties (4)	26 x 18	DAC	6.00 ea.
	14 x 11	DAC	2.00 ea.
	8 x 6	DAC	.60 ea.

362. Period Landmarks (8)   11 x 15   DAC   2.80 ea.
  363. Broadway and Liberty St., New York, 1830
  364. Capitol, Williamsburg, 1760
  365. Charleston, South Carolina, 1860
  366. Chinatown, San Francisco 1900
  367. French Quarter, New Orleans
  368. Philadelphia, Independence Square 1776
  369. Plantation Life
  370. Water Tower, Chicago, 1860
371. Siamese Dancers (4)   26 x 18   DAC   6.00 ea.
                                14 x 11   DAC   2.00 ea.
                                8 x 6   DAC   .60 ea.
BEAUNEVEU, ANDRÉ   French   Ac. 1360-1403
372. King Richard II   24 x 12   CAC   7.50
BECKER, FREDERICK   American   1888-
373. Still Life with Flowers   23 x 17   CAC   10.00
BECKERATH, WILLY VON   German   1868-1938
374. Brahms at the Piano   22 x 18   IA   3.00
                                11 x 9   IA   1.00
BECKMANN, MAX   German   1884-1950
375. Cabaret Girls   29-1/2 x 21-1/2 NYGS   18.00
376. Departure   8 x 10   MMA   .35
377. Dutch Landscape   27 x 22   CFA   12.00
378. Lillies   29 x 16   CFA   15.00
379. Rainbow, 1942   19-1/2 x 31-1/2 NYGS   18.00
380. Seascape (The Shore)   27-1/2 x 37   NYGS   24.00
381. Still Life with Candle   19 x 14   CFA   15.00
382. Still Life, Lillies   30 x 17   CAC   18.00
383. Tulips   29 x 14-1/2   NYGS   20.00
384. Winding Path in the
       Black Forest   33-1/2 x 19-1/2 NYGS   18.00
BEDA, FRANCESCO   Italian   1840-1900
385. Chess Game   24 x 36   IA   10.00
BEECHER, WILLIAM WARD   American
386. Mandolin   24 x 18   AA   7.50
387. Three B's   24 x 18   AA   10.00
388. Violin   24 x 18   AA   7.50
BEECROFT, HERBERT   American   1865-1962
389. The Lord Turned and
       Looked Upon Peter   22 x 17   IA   5.00
BEHAM (OR BÖHM), BARTHEL   German   1502-1540
390. Jacobea of Baden   17 x 12-1/2   CFA   5.00
BELL, ROBERT ANNING   English   1863-1933
391. Nurseryland   22 x 18   CAC   3.00
BELLECHOSE, HENRI   Belgian   Ac. 1415-1440
and MALOUEL, JEAN   Flemish   Ac. 1396-1419
392. Holy Communion and
       Martyrdom of St.
       Denis   17-1/2 x 22-1/2 ESH   10.00
BELLINI, GENTILE   Italian   1429-1507
393. Procession of the Cross   8 x 17   IA   3.00
394. Rescue of the Relics of

the Cross in the Canal	11 x 15	IA	3.00
BELLINI, GIOVANNI	Italian	c. 1430-1516	
395. Cristo in Pieta	15 x 11	IA	3.00
396. The Dead Christ	15 x 19	CAC	7.50
397. Entombment of Christ	9 x 15	IA	3.00
398. Madonna and Child in a Landscape	24 x 18-1/2	NYGS	7.50
399. Madonna of the Meadows	21-1/2 x 34	NYGS	18.00
400. Madonna of the Trees	13 x 10		
401. Pieta	11 x 15		
402. Portrait of Condottiere	20 x 14	CFA	7.50
403. Portrait of the Doge, Leonardo Loredano	17 x 12-1/2	NYGS	5.00
404. St. Francis in Ecstacy	25 x 28	NYGS	16.00
405. Souls in Purgatory	9 x 15	IA	3.00
406. Transfiguration	11 x 14	IA	3.00
407. Virgin and Child	13 x 10	IA	3.00
408. Virgin of the Red Cherubs	13 x 10	IA	3.00
BELLINI, JACOPO	Italian	1400-1470	
409. Madonna and Child	14 x 10	IA	3.00
410. Madonna and Child	15 x 10	IA	3.00
BELLOTTO, BERNARDO (CALLED CANALETTO)			
(See Also CANALE, ANTONIO	Italian	1720-1780	
411. The Gazzada	10 x 15	IA	3.00
412. Imperial Castle of Schlosshof in March-field	16-1/2 x 31-1/2	AJ	12.00
413. View of Munich	18 x 23	HNA	5.95
414. View of Pirna	18 x 30	CFA	15.00
415. View of Schoenbrunn Castle	18 x 31-1/2	AJ	12.00
BELLOWS, GEORGE WESLEY	American	1882-1925	
416. Ann in a Purple Wrap	25 x 20	PENN	1.00
417. Both Members of this Club	17 x 24	NYGS	10.00
418. Dempsey and Firpo	19 x 24	PENN	1.00
	15 x 21	NYGS	7.50
419. Gramercy Park	18 x 24	NYGS	10.00
420. Lady Jean	19 x 9	NYGS	5.00
	10-1/2 x 5	NYGS	.50
421. Sand Cart	21 x 31	CAC	12.00
	12-1/2 x 19	IA	5.00
	6-1/2 x 10	IA	.50
BELTRAFFIO, GIOVANNI ANTONIO			
	Italian	1467-1516	
422. Madonna and Child	14 x 11	IA	3.00
423. Narcissus	9 x 6	IA	1.50
BENALI			
424. Venice	23 x 31	CFA	15.00

BENCI, ANTONIO   See POLLAIUOLO, ANTONIO
BENCI, PIERO   See POLLAIUOLO, PIERO
BENDER, BILL
  425. Desert Foliage   24 x 36   DAC   8.00
                                    12 x 18   DAC   2.00
BENSA (OR BENJA), ERNESTO   Italian   Ac. 1897
  426. Staircase at the Bargello 24 x 15   CAC   10.00
BENEZIT, EMANUEL CHARLES LOUIS
                                    French   1887-
  427. Flowering Acaceas   20 x 25   CAC   7.50
BENNER, GERRIT   Dutch   1897-
  428. Chrysanthemum   24 x 19   CAC   7.50
  429. Zinnias   28 x 22   CAC   10.00
BENNETT, FRANK MOSS   English   1874-
  430. Hunt Breakfast   22 x 32   CFA   10.00
  431. Hunts and Coaches (6)   7 x 9   CAC   3.00
  432. Meet at the Lodge   22 x 32   CAC   10.00
  433. The Squire's Story   26 x 36   CFA   15.00
BENSON, FRANK WESTON   American   1862-1951
  434. A Rainy Day   25 x 30-1/2   NYGS   12.00
  435. My Daughters   15 x 21   CAC   7.50
  436. Still Life, 1925   25 x 31   NYGS   12.00
BENTON, THOMAS HART   American   1889-
  437. Cotton Pickers--
      Georgia   16 x 20   NYGS   7.50
  438. The Kentuckian   28 x 22   NYGS   10.00
  439. Louisiana Rice Fields   11 x 19   NYGS   5.00
  440. Music Lesson   17-1/2 x 21-1/2 NYGS   7.50
  441. Spring Tryout   18 x 24   NYGS   10.00
  442. Threshing Wheat   22 x 35-1/2   NYGS   15.00
BENVENUTO DI GIOVANNI DEL GUASTA   See GUASTA
BERCKHEYDEN, HIOB AUT BRECKBERG   See BRECKBURG, HIOB
BERELSMANN
  443. Low Tide   20 x 29   CAC   10.00
BERGHEM, CLAES   Dutch   1620-1683
  444. The Ford   11 x 17   CFA   4.00
BERLINGHIERI, BONAVENTURA Italian   1235-1274
  445. St. Francis   15 x 10   IA   3.00
BERMAN, EUGENE   American   1899-
  446. Giselle First Act
      Curtain   13 x 20   AR   12.00
  447. Hat Seller   25 x 19   CFA   12.00
  448. View in Perspective of
      a Perfect Sunset   18 x 23   HNA   5.95
BERNARDINO DI BETTO   See PINTURICCHIO
BERNATH, SANDOR   Hungarian (Res. U.S.)   1892-
  449. Schooner "Newport"   17 x 21   CAC   5.00
BERNDT, C.
  450. Autumn Flowers   24 x 31   CFA   12.00
  451. Gladiola   23 x 33   CFA   12.00
  452. Spring Blossoms   22 x 31   CFA   12.00
  453. Sunflowers   29 x 28   CFA   15.00

BERTELSMANN, WALTER	German	1877-	
454. Lowtide	20 x 29	CFA	10.00
BERTEN			
455. Magnolia	19 x 23	CAC	7.50
BERTI, RENE	Italian		
456. Steeplechasing	16 x 22	CFA	7.50
BERTRAND, PIERRE	French	1884-	
457. Le Balcon	17 x 22	RL	6.00
BESLER, BESIL	German	1561-1629	
458. Tulips (2)	21 x 18	AL	12.00 ea.
BESSE, RAYMOND	French	1871-	
459. Fishing Articles	16 x 22	CAC	10.00
BETANZOS			
460. Mexican Children (8)	10 x 8	DAC	1.00 ea.
BETZ, ANDREAS			
461. Fall at Lake Seeham	19 x 24	CFA	10.00
BEUCKELAER, JOACHIM	Flemish	1535-1574	
462. Fruit-Seller	10 x 15	IA	3.00
463. Poultry Market	11 x 15	IA	3.00
BEZOMBES, ROGER	French	1913-	
464. High Summer	19 x 24	CAC	10.00
465. Romantic Still Life	23 x 28	CAC	12.00
BIANCHI, LINO See BARRIVIERA, LINO BIANCHI			
BIANCHI, FRANCESCO See FERRARI, FRANCESCO BIANCHI			
BICCI, LORENZO DI, THE YOUNGER			
	Italian	1373-1452	
466. Saints Cosmas and			
Damian	10 x 4	IA	3.00
BIGI, FRANCESCO DI CRISTOFANO See FRANCIABIGIO, IL			
BIGORDI, BENEDETTO DOMENICO See GHIRLANDAIO,			
DOMENICO			
BILLE (OR BILLIE), JACQUES	French	1890-	
467. Anemonies	20 x 16	CAC	4.00
468. Larkspur	20 x 16	CAC	4.00
469. Still Life with Pitcher	18 x 24	CAC	7.50
470. Still Life with Plate	18 x 24	CAC	7.50
BINGHAM, GEORGE CALEB	American	1811-1879	
471. County Election	18 x 24	AA	12.00
472. Fishing on the Missis-			
sippi	18 x 22-1/2	PENN	1.00
			1.98 (Pr.)
473. Fur Traders Descending			
the Missouri	18 x 22	NYGS	12.00
474. Raftsmen Playing Cards	22-1/2 x 30	NYGS	15.00
	5-1/2 x 7-1/2	NYGS	.50
475. Shooting for the Beef	14 x 21	NYGS	7.50
476. Stump Speaking	18 x 24	AA	12.00
BINNING, B. C.			
477. Convoy at Rendezvous	16 x 29	CFA	15.00
BION, CYRIL W.	English		
478. Evening Glow in Ireland	14 x 18	CFA	7.50
479. Hills of Donegal	16 x 20	CFA	7.50

480. Northeast Ireland	16 x 20	CFA	7.50
481. Sunrise in Ireland	14 x 18	CFA	7.50
BIRCH, S. J. LAMORNA	English	1876-	
482. Cornwallis Pageantry	19 x 23	RL	7.50
483. Glorious Devon	18-1/2 x 25	RL	7.50
484. Old Quarry	20 x 30	RL	7.50
485. St. Ives at Low Tide	18 x 23	RL	7.50
486. The Tay in June	18 x 23	RL	7.50
BIRKMANN, JOHANN	Austrian	1876-	
487. Creek	16 x 20	ESH	5.00 (Pr.)
488. Sailing Boats	23-1/2 x 31-1/2	ESH	10.00 (Pr.)
	16 x 20	ESH	5.00 (Pr.)
BIRNEY, WILLIAM VERPLANCK	American	1858-1909	
489. Sleight of Hand	22 x 32	AA	10.00
BIRREN, JOSEPH P.	American	1865-1933	
490. Jonathan	16 x 16	CAC	6.00
BISHOP, RICHARD	American	1877-	
491. From a Blind	18 x 24	AA	15.00
BISSIÉRE, ROGER	French	1888-	
492. Peinture, 1951	8 x 10	ESH	1.00
493. Red, Black and Orange	30 x 12	ESH	15.00
494. Southern Cross	29-1/2 x 11	ESH	15.00
BITTNER, JOSEF			
495. June Flowers	22 x 16	NYGS	7.50
BLAIR, ROBERT N.	American	1912-	
496. Horses in the Rain	13-1/2 x 19	NYGS	5.00
BLAKE, LEO	American	1887-	
497. Berkshire Snows	20 x 24	AA	7.50
498. Mid-Winter	16 x 20	AA	5.00
499. Old Covered Bridge	16 x 20	AA	5.00
500. Winter in New England	20 x 24	AA	7.50
BLAKE, WILLIAM	English	1757-1827	
501. Pilgrimage to Canterbury	13 x 40	NYGS	18.00
	10 x 31	CAC	10.00
BLANCH, ARNOLD	American	Contemporary	
502. Floral Magic	16-1/2 x 11	NYGS	10.00
503. New England	13 x 20	CAC	5.00
504. Outdoor Circus	12 x 20	CAC	5.00
BLANCH, LUCILE	American	Contemporary	
505. Spring Flowers	20 x 14-1/2	NYGS	7.50
BLANCHARD, ANTOINE			
506. Paris of the Nineties (6)	12 x 18	DAC	2.00 ea.
	8 x 12	DAC	1.00 ea.
BLANCHARD, CAROL	American	Contemporary	
507. Angel	12 x 10	AA	4.00
508. Autumn	23 x 12	AA	10.00
509. Chimney Sweep	16 x 13	AA	7.50
510. Chris	12 x 10	AA	4.00
511. Hawking: Departure	16 x 12	AA	7.50
512. Hawking: Rendezvous	16 x 12	AA	7.50
513. Little Match Girl	16 x 13	AA	7.50
514. Spring	23 x 12	AA	10.00

515. Summer	23 x 12	AA	10.00
516. Winter	23 x 12	AA	10.00
BLAUE, WILHELM	German	1873-	
517. Map of the Americas	12 x 24	PENN	1.00
BLECHEN, KARL EDOUARD	German	1798-1840	
518. Capri	28 x 40	NYGS	20.00
BLENNER, CARL JOHN	American	1864-	
519. The Artist's Window	25 x 30	AA	7.50
520. Bowl of Phlox	25 x 30	AA	7.50
521. From My Garden	30 x 25	AA	7.50
522. Geraniums	20 x 24	AA	5.00
523. Gloucester Bouquet	30 x 25	AA	7.50
524. Harbor View--Phlox	28 x 22	AA	7.50
525. Mixed Glads	20 x 24	AA	5.00
526. Monhegan Harbor	26 x 36	CFA	7.50
527. Peonies	28 x 22	AA	7.50
528. Pink Gladioli	24 x 20	AA	5.00
529. Studio View--Phlox	20 x 24	AA	5.00
530. Summer Glory	20 x 16	IA	3.50
BLINKS, THOMAS	English	1860-1912	
531. Drop!	20 x 30	AA	20.00
532. The Rose	20 x 30	AA	20.00
533. Shamrock	20 x 30	AA	20.00
534. Steady!	19 x 30	AA	20.00
535. Thistle	21-1/2 x 30	AA	20.00
536. Twelfth of August	21-1/2 x 30	AA	20.00
537. Unity	20 x 30	AA	20.00
BLOOMSTER			
538. Fair Weather	25 x 30	CAC	7.50
BLONDIN, FERNAND	Swiss	1887-	
539. Place du Tertre	8 x 12	CFA	5.00
540. Porte St. Denis	8 x 12	CFA	5.00
541. Rue Chavalier le Barre	12 x 8	CFA	5.00
542. Rue Norvins	12 x 8	CFA	5.00
BLUME, PETER	American	1906-	
543. The Boat	16-1/2 x 20	NYGS	7.50
BOCCACCINO, BOCCACCIO, THE ELDER			
	Italian	1460-1529	
544. The Gypsye	10 x 7	IA	1.50
BOCCARDI, GIOVANNI (BOCCARDINO THE ELDER)			
	Italian	1460-1529	
545. The Trinity	15 x 11	IA	3.00
BOCCATI, GIOVANNI	Italian	1420-1480	
546. Virgin Enthroned with Angels	15 x 11	IA	3.00
547. Virgin Enthroned with Angel Musicians	15 x 11	IA	3.00
BOCCIONI, UMBERTO	Italian	1882-1916	
548. The City Rises	8 x 10	MMA	.35
549. States of Mind: The Farewells	18 x 23	HNA	5.95
BOCK, LUDWIG	German	1886-	

550. Still Life with Fruit	15 x 19		CAC	6.00
BODENHAUSEN, MATHILDE FREIIN VON				
	German		1870-	
551. Madonna	23 x 18		CAC	7.50
BOEHMER, HENRICH				
552. Sylvan Solitude	22 x 30-1/2		IA	10.00
BOERS, F. J. D.	German		1872-	
553. Espana (8)	14 x 10		DAC	1.00 ea.
BOGDANOVE, ABRAHAM J.	Russian (Res. U. S.)		1887-	
554. Monhegan Harbor	26 x 36		CFA	15.00
BOHROD, AARON	American		1907-	
555. America--Its History	22 x 32-1/2		NYGS	5.00
556. Landscape Near Chicago	15 x 20		CAC	7.50
557. St. James Park	17 x 22		CAC	7.50
BOHMER, GUNTER	German		1911-	
558. Merry-Go-Round	12 x 15		CAC	10.00
BOILLY, LOUIS LEOPOLD	French		1761-1845	
559. Arrival of the Mail Coach	8 x 14		IA	3.00
560. La Comparaison	14 x 11		CAC	12.00
561. La Comparaison Petits Pieds	14 x 11		CAC	12.00
562. Portrait of a Boy	7 x 5		IA	1.50
563. Le Prelude de Nina	14 x 11		CAC	12.00
564. The Storm	11 x 13		IA	3.00
565. La Vue Difficile	14 x 11		CAC	12.00
BOL, FERDINAND	Dutch		1616-1680	
566. Jacob's Dream	10 x 8		AR	4.00
BOLSTAD, E. MELVIN	American		1901-	
567. Arrival at the Inn	8 x 10		NYGS	1.50
568. Country Lawn Party	8 x 10		NYGS	1.50
569. County Fair	8 x 10		NYGS	1.50
570. The Express	6 x 8		NYGS	1.00
571. False Alarm	8 x 10		NYGS	1.50
572. Holiday Parade	20 x 25		NYGS	10.00
573. Horse Trolley	6 x 8		NYGS	1.00
574. Monday in the Country	16 x 20		NYGS	7.50
575. Morning Drive	6 x 8		NYGS	1.00
576. New-Fangled Engine	6 x 8		NYGS	1.00
577. Nine O'Clock Express	8 x 10		NYGS	1.50
578. Queen of Rails	6 x 8		NYGS	1.00
579. Rapid Transit	6 x 8		NYGS	1.00
580. Ride on Wagon	6 x 8		NYGS	1.00
581. School's Afire	11 x 14		NYGS	3.00
582. School's Out	8 x 10		NYGS	1.50
583. Shopping on Main Street	8 x 10		NYGS	1.50
584. Sunday Fire Drill	11 x 14		NYGS	3.00
585. Sunday in the Country	16 x 20		NYGS	7.50
586. Sunday Ride	6 x 8		NYGS	1.00
587. Sunday Visitors	20 x 25		NYGS	10.00
588. The Three-Alarmer	8 x 10		NYGS	1.50

BOLTRAFFIO   See BELTRAFFIO

BOMBOIS, CAMILLE	French	1883-	
589. Along the River	11 x 14	DAC	2.80
590. The Neighbor's Garden	24 x 18	NYGS	10.00
591. View of Clerval	18 x 23	HNA	5.95
BONAMICI, LOUIS	French		
592. Eventide	22 x 28	CAC	10.00
593. Fishermen of Martinique	20 x 26	CAC	10.00
BONFIGLI, BENEDETTO	Italian	1420-1496	
594. Archangel Gabriel	11 x 12	IA	3.00
595. Virgin Annunciate	11 x 12	IA	3.00
BONHEUR, ROSA	French	1822-1899	
596. Horse Fair	17 x 36	NYGS	18.00
	5 x 11	NYGS	.50
BONINGTON, RICHARD PARKES	English	1801-1828	
597. Coast of Picardy	14 x 18	CAC	8.50
598. La Place de Molards	20 x 25	CAC	12.00
BONNARD, PIERRE	French	1867-	
599. Cannes Harbour	21-1/2 x 18-1/2	ESH	10.00
600. Le Cannet	20 x 14	CAC	7.50
601. Chequered Table Cover	13 x 23-1/2	NYGS	10.00
602. Farm	17 x 22-1/2	ESH	10.00
603. Flowers	22 x 16	ESH	10.00
	10 x 8	ESH	1.00
604. Harbour of St. Tropez	16 x 20	AP	5.00
605. Nude at the Fireplace	18 x 23	HNA	5.95
606. Le Pont de Grenelle	18 x 22-1/2	ESH	10.00
607. Provencal Jug	22 x 18	AJ	10.00
608. Self-Portrait	10 x 8	MMA	.35
BOOTH, NINA MASON	American	1884-	
609. White Begonias	13 x 14	IA	3.00
610. Yellow Tulips	13 x 14	IA	3.00
BORCH, GERARD TER See TERBORCH, GERARD			
BORDI, MARIO	Italian	1896-	
611. Freedom of the Plains	20 x 30	IA	10.00
612. Rebel Herd	20 x 30	IA	10.00
BORDONE, PARIS PASCHALINUS	Italian	1500-1570/71	
613. Venetian Lovers	12 x 11	IA	3.00
BOREIN, EDWARD	American	1872-	
614. Steer Roping	12 x 18	AA	3.00
BORTHWICK, ALFRED EDWARD	Scotch	1871-	
615. The Presence	26 x 39-1/2	IA	15.00
	15 x 23-1/2	IA	7.50
	6-1/2 x 10	IA	10.00
		(H. C. Grav.)	
BOS, HENK			
616. Anemones with Eggs and Fruit	12 x 18	DAC	4.00
	8 x 12	DAC	1.00
617. Apples, Eggs and Biscuits	12 x 18	DAC	4.00
	8 x 12	DAC	1.00
618. Breakfast Time	12 x 18	PENN	1.00

619. Brown Jug and Canta-loupe	12 x 18	PENN	1.00
	8 x 8	DAC	.80
620. Cherries and Apples	8 x 8	DAC	.80
621. Copper and Apples	15-1/2 x 13-1/2	DAC	4.00
	8 x 7	DAC	.60
622. Chimney Lamp	13-1/2 x 15-1/2	DAC	4.00
	7 x 8	DAC	.60
623. Daily Bread	13-1/2 x 15-1/2	DAC	4.00
	7 x 8	DAC	.60
624. Earthenware and Peaches	13-1/2 x 15-1/2	DAC	4.00
	7 x 8	DAC	1.00
625. Eggs in Basket	13-1/2 x 15-1/2	DAC	4.00
	7 x 8	DAC	.60
626. Garden Bouquet	14 x 16	PENN	1.00
627. Grapes and Pear	8 x 8	DAC	.80
628. Green Grapes and Strawberries	12 x 18	PENN	1.00
629. Green Grapes and Zinnias	12 x 18	PENN	1.00
630. Harvest	14 x 16	PENN	1.00
	13-1/2 x 15-1/2	DAC	4.00
	7 x 8	DAC	.60
631. Lantern	15-1/2 x 13-1/2	DAC	4.00
632. Melon, Oranges and Green Pears	12 x 18	DAC	4.00
	8 x 12	DAC	1.00
633. Peaches, Grapes and Flowers	20 x 16	PENN	1.00
634. Pewter and Peaches	15-1/2 x 13-1/2	DAC	4.00
	8 x 7	DAC	.60
635. Pink Chrysanthemums with Purple Grapes	20 x 16	DAC	4.00
	12 x 10	DAC	1.20
636. Pitcher and Apples	16 x 14	PENN	1.00
637. Pitcher and Basket of Apples	20 x 16	PENN	1.00
638. Plums with Stein	13-1/2 x 15-1/2	DAC	4.00
	7 x 8	DAC	.60
639. Purple Grapes and Tomatoes	12 x 18	PENN	1.00
640. Purple Grapes, To-matoes and Peaches	12 x 18	DAC	4.00
	8 x 12	DAC	1.00
641. Red "Mums" with Fruit	12 x 18	DAC	4.00
	8 x 12	DAC	1.00
642. Red Roses with Fruit	12 x 18	DAC	4.00
	8 x 12	DAC	1.00
643. Roses and Basket of Eggs	20 x 16	PENN	1.00
644. Roses and Eggs	20 x 16	DAC	4.00

		12 x 10	DAC	1.20
645.	Still Life with Bread and Pears	14 x 16	PENN	1.00
646.	Still Life with Kettle	14 x 16	PENN	1.00
647.	Still Life with Pitcher	14 x 16	PENN	1.00
648.	Still Life with Plums	14 x 16	PENN	1.00
649.	Still Life with Pottery Jug	14 x 16	PENN	1.00
650.	Still Life with Storm Lantern	16 x 14	PENN	1.00
651.	Still Life with Straw- berries	14 x 16	PENN	1.00
652.	Still Life with Sun- flowers	16 x 14	PENN	1.00
653.	Still Life with Tange- rines	16 x 14	PENN	1.00
654.	Still Life with Tankard	14 x 16	PENN	1.00
655.	Strawberries, Green Grapes and Apples	12 x 18	DAC	4.00
		8 x 12	DAC	1.00
656.	Strawberries with Ewer	13-1/2 x 15-1/2	DAC	4.00
		7 x 8	DAC	.60
657.	Tangerines	15-1/2 x 13-1/2	DAC	4.00
		8 x 7	DAC	.60
658.	Tankard and Peaches	16 x 14	PENN	1.00
659.	Teakettle with Eggs	13-1/2 x 15-1/2	DAC	4.00
		7 x 8	DAC	.60
660.	Tomatoes with Ewer	13-1/2 x 15-1/2	DAC	4.00
661.	Tomatoes and Walnuts	8 x 8	DAC	.80
		6 x 6	DAC	.60
662.	Varied Bouquet with Fruit	20 x 16	DAC	4.00
		12 x 10	DAC	1.20
663.	Water Carafe with Fruit	13-1/2 x 15-1/2	DAC	4.00
664.	Water Jug and Pears	13-1/2 x 15-1/2	DAC	4.00
		7 x 8	DAC	.60
665.	White Chrysanthemums with Green Grapes	20 x 16	DAC	4.00
		12 x 10	DAC	1.20
666.	Yellow "Mums" with Fruit	12 x 18	DAC	4.00
		8 x 12	DAC	1.00
667.	Zinnias	14 x 16	PENN	1.00
		7 x 8	DAC	.60

BOSCH, HIERONYMUS VAN AEKEN   Flemish   1460-1516

668.	Adoration of the Magi	22 x 17-1/2	MMA	5.00
669.	Conjuror	18 x 22	ESH	10.00
670.	Garden of Delights Triptych	21 x 39-1/2	NYGS	15.00
		21 x 19-1/2 center		
		21 x 8-1/2 sides each		
671.	St. John at Patmos	23-1/2 x 18	NYGS	20.00

BOSS, EDOURD	Swiss	1873-	
672. Belpermoos	22 x 31	CAC	12.00
BOTKE, JESSIE ARMS	American	1883-	
673. Cranes	25 x 30	CFA	12.00
	17 x 20	CFA	5.00
674. Enchanted Pool	14 x 19	NYGS	3.00
675. Flamingoes	25 x 30	CFA	12.00
	17 x 20	CFA	5.00
676. Leadbeaters Cockatoos	18 x 22	CFA	7.50
677. Molucca Cockatoos	18 x 22	CFA	7.50
678. Nature's Dreamland	24 x 19	NYGS	7.50
679. Royal Cockatoos	25 x 30	CFA	12.00
	17 x 20	CFA	5.00
680. Tropical Beauty	25 x 30	CFA	12.00
	17 x 20	CFA	5.00
681. Tropical Pool	27 x 36	NYGS	15.00

BOTTICELLI, SANDRO (ALESSANDRO DI MARIANO DEL FILIPEPI)

	Italian	1444/7-1510	
682. Adoration of the Magi	19 x 28	NYGS	15.00
	17-1/2 x 23	AP	5.00
	16 x 24	PENN	1.00
	10 x 13	IA	3.00
683. Self-Portrait (Detail of No. 682)	15 x 9	IA	3.00
684. Angels--Detail of a Coronation of the Virgin	11 x 15	IA	3.00
685. Annunciation	14 x 11	IA	3.00
686. Birth of Venus	13 x 21	CAC	4.00
	9 x 15	IA	3.00
687. Venus (Detail of No. 686)	15 x 9	IA	3.00
688. Head of Venus (Detail of No. 686)	11 x 15	IA	3.00
689. Calumny of Apelles	10 x 15	IA	3.00
690. Detail of No. 689	15 x 11	IA	3.00
691. Gift Bearers	9 x 12	CFA	2.50
692. Judith	12 x 8	IA	3.00
693. Liberal Arts	9 x 12	CFA	2.50
694. Madonna and Child	18 x 12-1/2	IA	7.50
	15 x 10	IA	3.00
	13 x 9	IA	3.50
	10 x 7	IA	1.75
695. Madonna and Child with Angels (Nat.Gall.---U.S.)	30-1/2 x 20-1/2	NYGS	18.00
696. Madonna and Child with Angels (Uffizi)	15 x 11	IA	3.00
697. Madonna and Child with Angels (Borghese)	11" circle	IA	3.00
698. Madonna and Child with St. John	22 x 16	ESH	10.00
	14 x 10	IA	3.00

		15 x 11	IA	3.00
699.	Madonna of the Lilies	22" circle	NYGS	12.00
		6 x 6	NYGS	.50
700.	Madonna of the Magnificat	12" circle	IA	3.00
701.	Angels--Detail of No. 700	16 x 10	IA	3.00
702.	Head of Madonna--Detail of No. 700	15 x 11	IA	3.00
703.	Madonna of the Pomegranate	11" circle	IA	3.00
704.	Head of the Virgin--Detail of No. 703	15 x 11	IA	3.00
705.	Madonna of the Seraphim	16 x 9	IA	3.00
706.	Madonna with the Canopy	11" circle	IA	3.00
707.	Man with a Medal	15 x 11	IA	3.00
708.	Nativity	10 x 8	AP	.50
709.	Nuptial Allegory	8 x 10	ESH	1.00
710.	Pallas and the Centaur	16 x 12	IA	3.00
711.	Portrait of a Woman	15 x 10	IA	3.00
712.	Portrait of a Youth	15-1/2 x 12	NYGS	7.50
		8 x 6	NYGS	.50
713.	Primavera (Spring)	13-1/2 x 21	CAC	4.00
		10 x 15	IA	3.00
714.	The Graces--Detail of No. 713	15 x 11	IA	3.00
715.	The Flora--Detail of No. 713	15 x 11	IA	3.00
716.	Head of Flora--Detail of No. 713	15 x 11	IA	3.00
717.	Chloris--Detail of No. 713	15 x 11	IA	3.00
718.	Venus--Detail of No. 713	15 x 11	IA	3.00
719.	One of the Graces--Detail of No. 713	15 x 11	IA	3.00
720.	Salome with the Baptist's Head	7 x 10	IA	1.50
721.	Virgin of the Sea	15 x 11	IA	3.00
722.	Young Man	20 x 14	CFA	12.00

BOTTICINI, FRANCESCO   Italian   1446-1497

723.	Virgin Adoring the Child, and Angels	11" circle	IA	3.00

BOUCHER, FRANCOIS   French   1703-1770

724.	Autumn	16 x 20-1/2	NYGS	10.00
		13 x 16	CFA	12.00
		11 x 14	NYGS	3.00
		9 x 11	CFA	12.00
725.	The Breakfast	13 x 10-1/2	IA	3.00
726.	Cameos (4)	7 x 5	CFA	4.00 ea.
727.	Charms of the Country			

	Life	10 x 15	IA	3.00
728.	Diana's Rest	9 x 12	CFA	2.50
729.	Infant Saviour and the			
	Little St. John	13 x 11 oval	IA	3.00
730.	Madame Bergeret	30 x 22	NYGS	15.00
731.	Les Marchands des			
	Modes	12 x 16	CAC	3.00
732.	La Marquise de			
	Pompadour	16 x 12	CAC	3.00
733.	Musique	20-1/2 x 30	NYGS	12.00
734.	The Musette	11 x 14	IA	3.00
		10 x 13-1/2	IA	3.00
		8-1/2 x 11	IA	1.75
735.	The Nest	15 x 10	IA	3.00
		10 x 8	ESH	1.00
736.	Nude	13-1/2 x 8	AR	3.50
737.	Odalisque	10 x 11	CFA	2.50
738.	Renault and Armida	11 x 14	IA	3.00
739.	Repose of Diana After			
	the Bath	11 x 14	IA	3.00
740.	Reposing Girl with			
	Putto	10 x 12-1/2	AR	3.50
741.	Sleeping Shepherdess	28 x 25	NYGS	12.00
742.	Sleeping Shepherdess	10-1/2 x 14	IA	3.00
		8-1/2 x 11	IA	1.75
743.	Spring	16 x 20-1/2	NYGS	10.00
		13 x 16	CFA	12.00
		11 x 14	NYGS	3.00
		9 x 11	CFA	12.00
744.	Summer	16 x 20-1/2	NYGS	10.00
		13 x 16	CFA	12.00
		11 x 14	NYGS	3.00
		9 x 11	CFA	12.00
745.	Winter	16 x 20-1/2	NYGS	10.00
		13 x 16	CFA	12.00
		11 x 14	NYGS	3.00
		9 x 11	CFA	12.00
BOUDIN, EUGÈNE LOUIS		French	1824-1898	
746.	Beach at Trouville	18 x 23	HNA	5.95
747.	Church of the Salute and			
	the Dogana in Venice	8 x 15	IA	3.00
748.	Crinolines at Trouville	8 x 17	ESH	8.00
749.	Jetty at Deauville	18 x 23	HNA	5.95
		8 x 10	ESH	1.00
750.	Reefs at Antibes	10 x 14	IA	3.00
751.	Return of the Terre-			
	Neuvier	18 x 23	HNA	5.95
752.	Santa Maria della			
	Salute, Venice	18-1/2 x 28	RL	10.00
753.	View of Trouville	8 x 10	ESH	1.00
BOUGHTON, GEORGE H.		American	1833-1905	
754.	Pilgrims Going to Church	17-1/2 x 32	NYGS	10.00

BOUTS, DIRK (OR DIERICK DE LOUVAIN)
                              Dutch (Res. Belgium) 1420-1475

755. Adoration of Three Kings--Triptych (Three Kings Altar, called "The Pearl of Brabant")	18 x 36	IA	24.00
756. St. Christopher (Right Panel of No. 755)	23-1/2 x 10	IA	12.00

BOVÉ, ARMANDO MIRAVALLS   Spanish   1916-

757. Autumn Abundance	13 x 40	NYGS	18.00
758. Bountiful Harvest	13 x 39-1/2	NYGS	18.00
	7-1/2 x 24	NYGS	7.50
759. Dahlias with Fruit	31-1/2 x 9-1/2	NYGS	12.00
760. Fruit and Peonies	31-1/2 x 9-1/2	NYGS	12.00
761. Peonies	13 x 39	NYGS	15.00
762. Roses	13 x 39	NYGS	15.00
763. Still Life--Souvenirs	17 x 40	NYGS	18.00
764. Street Dancing, Seville	16-1/2 x 30	NYGS	10.00

BOWERS, H. N.

765. Meditation	20 x 16	CFA	10.00
766. Newsboy	20 x 16	CFA	10.00

BRACKMAN, ROBERT   American   1896-

767. Study--Morning interlude	20 x 15	NYGS	7.50

BRADBURY, BENNETT

768. Anchor Bay	24 x 36	DAC	8.00
	12 x 18	DAC	2.00
769. Coast Near Acapulco	12 x 18	DAC	2.00
770. Ebb Tide	24 x 36	DAC	8.00
	18 x 26	PENN	1.00
			1.98 (Pr.)
	12 x 18	DAC	2.00
771. Shelter Bay	24 x 36	DAC	8.00
	18 x 26	PENN	1.00
			1.98 (Pr.)
	12 x 18	DAC	2.00
772. Sierra Morn	24 x 36	DAC	8.00
	18 x 26	PENN	1.00
			1.98 (Pr.)
	12 x 18	DAC	2.00
773. Sunny Cove	24 x 36	DAC	8.00
	18 x 26	PENN	1.00
			1.98 (Pr.)
	12 x 18	DAC	2.00

BRADSHAW, PERCY V.   English

774. On Lake Maggiore	9 x 10	CAC	2.00
775. Street in Cassis	9 x 10	CAC	2.00
776. Welsh Estuary	9 x 10	CAC	2.00
777. Welsh Farm	9 x 10	CAC	2.00

BRAGA, V.

778. Necklace	24 x 30	AA	7.50

BRAMANTINO, IL   See SUARDI, BARTOLOMEO

BRANCUSI, CONSTANTIN	Roumanian	1876-	
779. Sculpture Group	10 x 8	MMA	.35
BRAQUE, GEORGES	French	1882-	
780. Anemones	14 x 28	CAC	16.00
781. Ballet (Male #1)	20 x 16	CFA	7.50
782. Ballet (Female #2)	20 x 16	CFA	7.50
783. Beach	15 x 30	CFA	15.00
784. Le Billard	17 x 24	PENN	1.00
785. Boats on Shore	17 x 23	ESH	10.00
786. La Carafe	8 x 10	ESH	1.00
787. Chrysanthemums	22 x 15	CAC	10.00
788. L'Estaque	8 x 10	ESH	1.00
789. Fish Bowl	17 x 18-1/2	NYGS	12.00
790. Le Grand Gueridon	30 x 12	ESH	15.00
791. Interior	20 x 26	CFA	15.00
	16-1/2 x 22-1/2	ESH	10.00
792. Le Jour	19 x 24	PENN	1.00
			1.98 (Pr.)
793. Jug and Ivy	16 x 21	ESH	10.00
794. Kitchen Table	8 x 10	AP	.50
795. Lemon and Peaches	9 x 28	CAC	12.00
796. Lemons	20 x 26	CAC	10.00
797. Lemons and Napkin Ring	14 x 40	AA	18.00
798. Lemons, Peaches and Compotier	9 x 28	AA	12.00
799. La Mandoline	20 x 27	CAC	15.00
800. Marble Table	24 x 14-1/2	PENN	1.00
801. Marine	19 x 28	CFA	15.00
802. Musician	8 x 10	AP	.50
803. Nature Morte	14-1/2 x 21	NYGS	7.50
804. Pedestal Table (High, Round)	30 x 12	CAC	15.00
805. Peonies	20 x 24	NYGS	10.00
	18 x 23	HNA	5.95
806. Pink Table	24 x 30	PENN	1.00
			1.98 (Pr.)
807. Pink Tablecloth	8 x 10	MMA	.35
808. Pitcher and Basket of Fruit	12 x 30	AR	10.00
809. Plums, Pears, Nuts and Knife	9 x 28	AA	12.00
810. Red Tablecloth	18 x 22-1/2	ESH	10.00
	8 x 10	ESH	1.00
811. Red Violin	17 x 22	CAC	12.00
812. Round Table	24-1/2 x 19	NYGS	12.00
813. Seascape	19 x 30	CFA	15.00
814. Ship in the Harbor of Le Havre	18 x 23	HNA	5.95
815. Still Life	18 x 22-1/2	ESH	10.00
	8 x 10	ESH	1.00
816. Still Life	14 x 7	CFA	7.50

817. Still Life, 1934	16 x 19	AR	7.50
818. Still Life Composition	11 x 14	DAC	2.80
819. Still Life, Fish	14 x 17	AP	7.50
820. Still Life, Grapes	20 x 28	CAC	16.00
821. Still Life in Black	11 x 19	CFA	5.00
822. Still Life: Le Jour	22 x 27-1/2	NYGS	16.00
823. Still Life, Lemons	16 x 22	AR	7.50
824. Still Life, Mandolin	8 x 10	AP	.50
825. Still Life on a Table	30 x 12	CFA	15.00
826. Still Life, Pipe	11 x 14	AR	5.00
827. Still Life, Playing Cards	19-1/2 x 25-1/2	AP	6.00
828. Still Life, the Table	17 x 27-1/2	NYGS	15.00
829. Still Life: Table	14-1/2 x 24	PENN	1.00
830. Still Life with Fish	15 x 18	PENN	1.00
831. Still Life with Fruit and Glass	15 x 18	CAC	10.00
832. Still Life with Glass and Lemon	9 x 12	CAC	5.00
833. Still Life with Lemons	12 x 32-1/2	IA	15.00
834. Still Life with Mandolin	21 x 30	CFA	15.00
	18 x 23	HNA	5.95
835. Still Life with Red Apples	17 x 26	CFA	12.00
836. Stranded Boat	8 x 10	ESH	1.00
837. The Studio	22 x 21	AA	12.00
838. Sugar Bowl with Fruit	9 x 30	AR	10.00
839. Le Tapis Vert	13 x 20	CAC	7.50
840. Tea Table	15 x 28	CFA	15.00
841. The Terrace	17-1/2 x 22	ESH	10.00
842. Violin and Pipe with the Word Polka	17 x 36	NYGS	15.00
843. The White Cloth	18 x 25	CAC	15.00
844. Wine Glass	18 x 28	CAC	15.00
845. Woman with Mandolin	19 x 14	MMA	4.00
	10 x 8	MMA	.35
BRASS, ITALICO (OR ITALO)	Italian	1870-1943	
846. Harlequin Sonata	22 x 28	CAC	10.00
BRAYER, YVES	French	1907-	
847. Chevaux en Camarque	18 x 24	PENN	1.00
848. La Maison Blanche	17 x 23	PENN	1.00
BREANSKI, ALFRED DE	English	1877-1957	
849. Cottage Flowers	16 x 10	CAC	2.00
850. Country Garden	16 x 10	CAC	2.00
851. Forest Blossoms	16 x 10	CAC	2.00
852. In the West Highlands-- Loch Awe	20 x 30	RL	12.50
853. September Morning-- Loch Achray	20 x 30	RL	12.50
854. Woodland Flowers	16 x 10	CAC	2.00
BRECKBERG, HIOB	Dutch	1628-1698	
855. Self-Portrait	15 x 13	IA	3.00
BRESSLER, EMILE	Swiss		

856. Flowers on a Grey			
Background	20 x 15	CAC	7.50
857. Landscape Near Geneva	20 x 25	CFA	10.00
BRETON, JULES	French	1827-1906	
858. Quiet Estuary	18 x 24	CAC	10.00
859. Shepherd's Star	26 x 20	CAC	7.50
	20 x 16	CAC	5.00
860. Song of the Lark	26 x 19-1/2	NYGS	12.00
	20 x 16	AP	3.00
	14-1/2 x 11	NYGS	3.00
	12 x 9	CAC	2.00
	10 x 8	NYGS	.50
BRETT, MOLLY			
861. All Aboard the Airliner	17 x 21	CAC	3.50
862. All the Fun of the Fair	17 x 21	CAC	3.50
863. Dragon Flies	15 x 12	CAC	2.00
864. Evensong	21 x 17	CAC	3.50
865. Goodnight Time	17 x 21	CAC	3.50
866. Helping Hand	12 x 15	CAC	2.00
867. Over the Heather	17 x 21	CAC	3.50
868. Play Time	17 x 21	CAC	3.50
869. Springtime on the Farm	17 x 21	CAC	3.50
870. Summer Sports	17 x 21	CAC	3.50
871. Teddy Bear Beach	17 x 21	CAC	3.50
872. Teddy Bear Camp	17 x 21	CAC	3.50
873. Toyland Holiday	17 x 20	CAC	3.00
874. Winter Games	17 x 20	CAC	3.00
875. Woodland Gardeners	17 x 21	CAC	3.50
876. Woodland Traffic	17 x 21	CAC	3.50
BREWER			
877. Rheims Cathedral	19 x 13	CAC	3.50
	15 x 10	CAC	2.50
BRIERLY			
878. Yacht America	19 x 26	CAC	12.00
BRIL, PAOLO	Flemish	1536-1626	
879. Landscape	10 x 15	IA	3.00
880. Landscape with Procris'			
Death	11 x 15	IA	3.00
BROMBERG, MANUEL A.	American		
881. Dr. Albert Einstein	20 x 16	CAC	5.00
BRONZINO, ALESSANDRO (OR AGNOLO OR ANGELO)			
	Italian	1503-1572	
882. Don Garcia de Medici,			
Son of Cosimo I	15 x 11	IA	3.00
883. Eleanor of Toledo with			
Her Son John	14 x 11	IA	3.00
884. Lucrezia Panciatichi	19 x 23	AA	10.00
885. Maria de Medici,			
Daughter of Cosimo I	15 x 11	IA	3.00
886. Portrait of a Young			
Man	37-1/2 x 29-1/2	NYGS	20.00
	8-1/2 x 6-1/2	NYGS	.50

887. Stefano Colonna	15 x 11	IA	3.00
888. Young Woman and her Little Boy	27-1/2 x 21	NYGS	12.00
BROOK, ALEXANDER	American	1898-	
889. Sentinels	12-1/2 x 19	NYGS	5.00
BROOKSHAW			
890. Still Life (6)	16 x 12	IA	6.00 ea.
Pears I			
Pears II			
Cherries III			
Cherries IV			
Peaches V			
Peaches VI			
BROSS			
891. Watchung Scene	20 x 24	CAC	15.00
BROUGHAM			
892. Early American Bouquet	18-1/2 x 23-1/2	PENN	1.00
BROWN, ELMORE J.	American	Ac. 1959	
893. Horses (6)	14 x 18	DAC	2.00 ea.
	8 x 10	DAC	.80 ea.
BROWN			
894. Harbinger of Spring	15 x 18	CAC	3.00
BROUWER, ADRIAEN	Flemish	1605-1638	
895. The Smoker	14 x 11	IA	3.00
BROWNSCOMBE, JENNIE A.			
896. New Scholar	16 x 21-1/2	AA	6.00
BRUEGHEL, JAN, THE ELDER (CALLED "DE VELOURS" OR "VELVET")	Flemish	1568-1625	
897. Bouquet of Flowers	22-1/2 x 16-1/2	ESH	10.00
	10 x 8	ESH	1.00
898. Flowers in a Blue Vase	23 x 18	HNA	.95
	20 x 16	CFA	10.00
899. Flowers in a Brown Vase	23 x 18	HNA	5.95
	20 x 16	CFA	10.00
900. May Day Frolic	16 x 22	NYGS	7.50
BRUEGHEL, PIETER, THE ELDER	Flemish	1525-1569	
901. The Blind Leading the Blind	10 x 17	IA	3.00
	9 x 12	CAC	2.50
902. The Census	18 x 25-1/2	DAC	6.00
903. Landscape with Country Dance	15 x 11	IA	3.00
904. Landscape with Fall of Icarus	16 x 25	AR	6.00
905. Misanthrope	9" circle	IA	3.00
906. Summer Harvesters	21-1/2 x 32	CAC	12.00
BRUEGHEL, PIETER, THE YOUNGER	Flemish	1564-1637/8	
907. Autumn	22 x 30	CFA	12.00
	21-1/2 x 29	NYGS	12.00
908. Carnival and Penitence	15 x 21	NYGS	7.50

909.	Children's Games			
	(Children at Play)	23-1/2 x 32	IA	18.00
910.	Corn Harvesters	22 x 30	CFA	12.00
911.	Hay Harvest	22 x 30	CFA	12.00
		16 x 22	AR	6.00
912.	Haymaking	24 x 30	PENN	1.00
913.	Landscape	13-1/2 x 25	PENN	1.00
914.	Landscape with Ice			
	Skaters	15 x 22	CFA	12.00
915.	Netherlands Proverbs	23 x 32	CFA	20.00
916.	Peasant Dance	31-1/2 x 45	IA	20.00
		20-1/2 x 30	IA	15.00
		16 x 23	AR	6.00
		15 x 22	IA	10.00
		11 x 14	IA	3.00
917.	Peasant Wedding	31-1/2 x 45	AJ	20.00
918.	Tower of Babel	15-1/2 x 21	NYGS	7.50
919.	Wedding Dance	31-1/2 x 45	AJ	20.00
		24 x 32	NYGS	15.00
		20-1/2 x 30	IA	15.00
		16-1/2 x 22	NYGS	7.50
		10 x 15	CFA	1.50
		7 x 9	NYGS	.50
920.	Merrymakers (4)--			
	Details of No. 919	8-1/2 x 6-1/2	NYGS	1.50 ea.
921.	Wedding Feast	31-1/2 x 45	IA	20.00
		20-1/2 x 30	IA	15.00
		16 x 23	AR	6.00
		15 x 21	IA	10.00
		11 x 14	IA	3.00
922.	Winter: Hunters in the			
	Snow	31-1/2 x 44	NYGS	24.00
		18 x 23	HNA	5.95
		22 x 30	IA	12.00
		15 x 21	AR	10.00
		11 x 14	IA	3.00
923.	Winter in Flanders	21 x 29-1/2	NYGS	15.00
		11 x 14	NYGS	3.00
BREUSTLE				
924.	Blueberry Hill	24 x 30	CAC	7.50
925.	Blue Horizon	24 x 30	CAC	7.50
		15 x 18	CAC	3.00
BRUSH				
926.	In the Garden	28 x 12	CAC	8.00
BRUSSEL				
927.	Flowerpiece	26 x 19	CAC	12.00
BRYANT, HAROLD				
928.	Challenge	24 x 32	CFA	10.00
		16 x 20	CFA	5.00
BUCHHOLZ, ROBERT				
929.	Autumn	21 x 29	CFA	10.00
BUCHOZ				

930. Bouquet, Frederick V	17 x 12	CAC	10.00
931. Bouquet, Louis XV	17 x 12	CAC	10.00
BUCHSER, FRANK	Swiss	1828-1890	
932. Plantation in Virginia	12 x 17	CAC	4.00
BUFFET, BERNARD	French	1928-	
933. Ave Maria	18 x 31-1/2	IA	15.00
934. Banks of the Marne	5 x 9	CFA	1.00
935. Banks of the Seine	5 x 9	CAC	1.00
936. Before Dinner	25-1/2 x 19-1/2	NYGS	12.00
937. Black Fishes	4 x 9	CFA	1.00
938. Le Bouquet	21 x 18	ESH	10.00
939. The Breakfast	25-1/2 x 19-1/2	NYGS	12.00
940. Brooklyn Bridge	15-1/2 x 39	NYGS	18.00
941. The Bullfighter	26 x 19	NYGS	15.00
942. Butterfly	8 x 10	ESH	1.00
943. Le Canal	22 x 36	CFA	18.00
	18 x 30	CAC	15.00
	17-1/2 x 30	ESH	15.00
944. Le Canal St. Martin	14 x 22-1/2	PENN	1.00
	13 x 22	CFA	10.00
945. Dallas	6 x 8	CFA	1.00
946. Fishermen's Harbor	26-1/2 x 36	NYGS	18.00
	19 x 26	CAC	20.00
947. Harbor	19-1/2 x 26	IA	20.00
948. Isola San Giorgio	22-1/2 x 30-1/2	ESH	15.00
949. Head of a Clown	22-1/2 x 18-1/2	ESH	15.00
	10 x 8	ESH	1.00
950. London, Tower Bridge	21-1/2 x 30	NYGS	18.00
	19 x 30	CAC	10.00
951. Man Resting	6 x 8	CFA	1.00
952. Matador	31 x 9-1/2	NYGS	12.00
953. New York Skyline	16 x 33	AP	15.00
	14 x 30	CAC	15.00
954. Orchid Still Life	19 x 25	CAC	12.00
955. Paris: La Cité	19 x 27	NYGS	20.00
	8 x 10	ESH	1.00
956. Piazetta San Marco	22-1/2 x 30	ESH	15.00
957. Place de la Concorde	18-1/2 x 30	ESH	15.00
958. Port Breton	5 x 9	CFA	1.00
959. Port of Beaulieu	8 x 10	ESH	1.00
960. Port of La Rochelle	22-1/2 x 37	ESH	18.00
	5 x 9	CFA	1.00
961. Rabbit and Red Casserole	7 x 7	CFA	1.00
962. The Station	5 x 9	CFA	1.00
963. Still Life	25 x 18	CAC	20.00
964. Still Life, the Lobster	20 x 27	CAC	15.00
965. Still Life, Melons and Pears	24 x 30	PENN	1.00
966. Still Life with White Plate	25-1/2 x 19	IA	20.00
967. Sunflowers	24 x 18	CFA	15.00

968. Toreador, 1958	31 x 9-1/2	NYGS	12.00
969. Venice	21 x 27	NYGS	20.00
970. Yacht, 1963	31-1/2 x 24	NYGS	18.00
BUFFMIRE, FRANK E.	American		
971. Deer Hunting	16-1/2 x 24	IA	7.50
972. Quail Shooting	16-1/2 x 24	IA	7.50
BUGJARDINI, GIULIANO	Italian	1475-1554	
973. Portrait entitled "The			
Nun by Leonardo"	15 x 11	IA	3.00
974. Portrait of Michelangelo	14 x 11	IA	3.00
BUKAC, JEAN			
975. Little Darlin's (6)	8 x 6	DAC	.40 ea.
Bless Mommy			
Bless Us			
Good Pickins			
Happy Birthday			
Post Haste			
School Days			
BULLER, AUDREY	American	1902-	
976. Comedy	12 x 20	NYGS	5.00
BUNDY, EDGAR			
977. Falling Leaves	28 x 40	CAC	15.00
978. Introduction	24 x 36	NYGS	10.00
979. Woodlands	22 x 28	CAC	10.00
BUONARROTI, MICHELANGELO	See MICHELANGELO		
BUONAVENTURA			
980. St. Mary Magdalen	21-1/2 x 15	AP	7.50
BURCHFIELD, CHARLES	American	1893-	
981. August Afternoon	13 x 19	NYGS	5.00
982. Ice Glare	18-1/2 x 15	NYGS	5.00
983. November Evening	24 x 15	PENN	1.00
984. Promenade	17-1/2 x 23-1/2	NYGS	12.00
	5-1/2 x 7-1/2	NYGS	.50
985. Sun and Rocks	21 x 30	NYGS	15.00
986. Sunflowers and Red			
Barn	16 x 20	CAC	10.00
BURGKMAIR, HANS	German	1473-1531	
987. Emperor Maximilian			
on Horse	17 x 11	AR	5.00
BURI			
988. Accordian Player	20 x 21	CAC	10.00
989. In an Alpine Inn	12 x 16	CAC	4.00
990. Politicians	20 x 25	CAC	10.00
BURKHARD			
991. Strandweg	12 x 16	CAC	2.00
BURLEIGH, C. H. H.	English		
992. Ludlow	18-1/2 x 22	RL	5.00
BURLIN, PAUL	American	Contemporary	
993. Street Scene	20 x 15	CAC	5.00
BURNAND			
994. Peter and John	11 x 18	CAC	3.00
BURRAUD			

995. Pytchley Hunt	17 x 28	CAC	25.00
BURRI, ALBERTO	Italian	1915-	
996. Sacco E Rosso	24 x 30	NYGS	15.00
BUSON, YOSA		1716-1783	
997. Autumnal Landscape	24 x 10-1/1	IA	12.00
BUTINONE, BERNARDINO JACOBI	Italian		
998. Christ Disputing with			
the Doctors	10 x 8-1/2	NYGS	12.00
BUTTERSACK			
999. In the Gloaming	23 x 30	CAC	10.00
1000. Last Ray of the Sun	12 x 21	CAC	5.00
BUXTON, R. H.	English	1871-	
1001. Check in the Valley	16 x 25	CAC	7.50
1002. Over Hill and Dale	16 x 25	CAC	7.50
BYRUM, RUTHVEN H.			
1003. Grandview	25-1/2 x 31	NYGS	7.50
1004. Heart of Smokies	25 x 30	CAC	10.00
1005. Indiana	25 x 30	AA	10.00
1006. New Found Gap	25 x 31	NYGS	7.50
1007. Peaceful Valley	28 x 33-1/2	NYGS	10.00
1008. Smokey Mountain Road	25 x 30	CAC	10.00
1009. Song of Blossoms	25 x 30	CAC	10.00
1010. Sycamore Bend	25 x 30	CAC	10.00
1011. Tennessee	25 x 30	AA	10.00

C

CADY, WALTER HARRISON	American	1877-	
1012. In Old Kentucky	15 x 18	CAC	4.00
CAGNACCI, GUIDO See CANLASSI, GUIDO			
CAHOON, RALPH			
1013. The Race	22 x 32	AA	12.00
1014. Sailor's Wedding Dance	22 x 32	AA	12.00
CALDER, ALEXANDER STERLING	American	1898-	
1015. Exhibition Poster	28 x 20	PENN	1.00
CALDERON, PHILIP HERMOGENES	French	1833-1898	
1016. Ruth and Naomi	26 x 21	IA	6.00
CALIARI, PAOLO See VERONESE, PAOLO			
CALLOT, HENRI EUGENE	French	1875-	
1017. Fishing Boats, Joinville	22 x 18-1/2	RL	5.00
1018. Harbor of Joinville	18 x 18	CAC	7.50
1019. Tuna Fleet	20 x 24	CAC	6.00
CALOGERO	Italian (Res. France)		
1020. Dolls (4)	16 x 12	DAC	2.80 ea.
	10 x 8	DAC	1.20 ea.
	8 x 6	DAC	.80 ea.
Doll at Carnival			
Doll with Clown			
Doll with Birdcage			
Doll with Fishbowl			
1021. L'Entr'acte	13 x 10	RL	5.00
1022. L'Ingenue	13 x 10	RL	5.00

1023.	Les Elegants	20 x 24	CAC	12.50
1024.	Party Girl	14 x 10	CFA	6.00
1025.	Portfolio (4)	16 x 12	PENN	1.98 set
1026.	Prim and Proper	14 x 10	CFA	6.00

CALVERT

1027.	Meet of the Vine			
	Hounds	17 x 28	CAC	25.00
1028.	Wynnstay Hunt	23 x 24	CAC	28.00

CAMERON, DAVID Y. (SIR)   Scotch   1865-1945

| 1029. | Heart of Perthshire | 20 x 17-1/2 | RL | 10.00 |

CAMPBELL

1030.	Blueroom Proofs	21 x 18	CAC	25.00
1031.	Blueroom Prints	21 x 18	CAC	10.00

CAMPIGLI, MASSIMO   Italian   1895-

| 1032. | Holiday | 19 x 24 | NYGS | 12.00 |

CAMPION

| 1033. | Sunny Day | 19 x 24 | CAC | 7.50 |

CANALETTO (CANALE, ANTONIO, CALLED CANALETTO)
See Also BELLOTTO, BERNARDO (CALLED CANALETTO)

Italian   1697-1768

1034.	Bacino from S. Giorgio			
	Maggiore	17-1/2 x 26	CAC	12.00
1035.	Bacino from the			
	Guidecca	17 x 26	NYGS	12.00
1036.	Basin of San Marco	18 x 23	HNA	5.95
1037.	Bucentaur at the			
	Piazetta	17 x 26	NYGS	12.00
1038.	Canal at Venice	12 x 20	PENN	1.00
1039.	Chiesa della Salute	18 x 13	CAC	6.00
1040.	Doge's Palace, Venice	22 x 36	NYGS	24.00
		12 x 20	PENN	1.00
1041.	Imperial Castle	18 x 31	CFA	12.00
1042.	Imperial Chalet	17 x 31	CFA	12.00
1043.	London from Richmond			
	House	18 x 20	CAC	15.00
1044.	Murano near Venice	11 x 16	AR	5.00
1045.	Piazza San Marco			
	(St. Mark's Square)	26-1/2 x 36	NYGS	18.00
		23 x 31	CFA	15.00
		18-1/2 x 24-1/2	PENN	1.00
				1.98 (Pr.)
1046.	Quay of the Piazetta	26-1/2 x 36	NYGS	18.00
1047.	Rialto	23 x 32	CFA	15.00
1048.	Santa Maria della			
	Salute	24 x 30	CFA	18.00
1049.	Stone Mason's Yard	10 x 13	CFA	1.50
1050.	Upper Grand Canal	8 x 14	CFA	1.50
1051.	Venice	25 x 35	CFA	18.00
1052.	Venice, Canal Grande	23 x 29	CFA	18.00
1053.	View of the Ducal Palace			
	and the Piazetta	9 x 15	IA	3.00
1054.	View of the Grand			

Canal in Venice	9 x 15	IA	3.00
1055. View of Venice, Church			
of the Salute	9 x 15	IA	3.00

CANDELL, VICTOR   1903-
| 0156. Night | 16 x 21 | CAC | 16.00 |

CANEDO, ALEXANDER   Mexican (Res. U.S.)   1902-
| 1057. Figure Study No. 1 | 17 x 21 | IA | 5.00 |
| 1058. Figure Study No. 2 | 17 x 21 | IA | 5.00 |

CANEVARI, GIOVANNI BATTISTA   Italian   1789-1876
| 1059. James Stuart, Son of | | | |
| Charles I | 15 x 10 | IA | 3.00 |

CANJURA
| 1060. Maternity | 23 x 12 | CFA | 12.00 |

CANLASSI, GUIDO (CALLED CAGNACCI)
	Italian	1600-1681	
1061. Cleopatra	27-1/2 x 24	AJ	12.00
1062. Sybil	13 x 11	IA	3.00

CANNERT
| 1063. Jonquils | 20 x 16 | CAC | 11.00 |

CAPELLE, JAN VAN DE   Dutch   1624-1679
| 1064. The Calm | 18 x 18 | CAC | 12.00 |

CAPULETTI, J.   Spanish   1924-
1065. The Artist's Palette	22 x 18-1/2	RL	10.00
1066. Art Student	18 x 14	CAC	5.00
1067. New Horizons	27 x 20	CAC	12.00
1068. Romeo and Juliet	18 x 21	CAC	10.00

CARAUD, JOSEPH   1821-1905
| 1069. Story Hour | 30 x 24 | IA | 10.00 |

CARAVAGGIO, MICHELANGELO MERISI DA
	Italian	1565-1609	
1070. Amor Sleeping	10 x 15	IA	3.00
1071. Basket of Fruit	11 x 14	IA	3.00
1072. Beheading of St. John			
the Baptist	10-1/2 x 15	IA	3.00
1073. Boy Bitten by a			
Lizard	14 x 11	IA	3.00
1074. Boy with a Basket of			
Fruit	12 x 11	IA	3.00
1075. Calling of St. Matthew	12 x 12	IA	3.00
1076. David Showing Goliath's			
Head	14 x 11	IA	3.00
1077. Deposition	15 x 10	IA	3.00
1078. Fall of St. Paul	15 x 11	IA	3.00
1079. Madonna and Child and			
St. Anne (Known as			
Madonna dei Pala			
Frenieri)	15 x 10-1/2	IA	3.00
1080. Martyrdom of St.			
Matthew	12 x 12	IA	3.00
1081. Martyrdom of St. Peter	14 x 11	IA	3.00
1082. Narcissus	13 x 11	IA	3.00
1083. The Pilgrims Madonna	15 x 11	IA	3.00

1084. Rest During the Flight into Egypt	11 x 14	IA	3.00
1085. St. John in the Desert	13 x 11	IA	3.00
1086. St. Matthew and the Angel	15 x 9	IA	3.00
1087. Still Life	18 x 23	HNA	5.95
1088. Still Life, Fruit	18 x 23	HNA	5.95
1089. Victorious Cupid	15 x 11	IA	3.00
CARDELLA, TONY	French	1898-	
1090. Calvi Corse	12 x 16	CAC	2.00
1091. Cassis	12 x 16	CAC	2.00
1092. Sanary sur Mer	12 x 16	CAC	2.00
1093. Saint Tropez	12 x 16	CAC	2.00
CARLSON, HARRY	American	1895-	
1094. Spring Time	20 x 24	CAC	15.00
CARMONTELLE			
1095. Family Mozart	12 x 8	CAC	10.00
1096. La Sonata	12 x 8	CAC	10.00
CAROLSFELD			
1097. Madonna	21 x 18	CAC	7.50
CARPACCIO, VITTORE	Italian	1486-1525	
1098. Angel Musician	15 x 11	IA	3.00
1099. Courtisans	15 x 10	IA	3.00
1100. Miracle of the Cross	10 x 11	IA	3.00
1101. Presentation in the Temple	15 x 11	IA	3.00
1102. St. George and the Dragon	6 x 15	IA	3.00
1103. St. Ursula's Dream	11 x 11	IA	3.00
CARPENTER, MARGARET			
1104. Bretagne	12 x 16	CAC	2.00
1105. Douarnrnez	12 x 16	CAC	2.00
1106. Sisters	28 x 28	AA	10.00
CARPIONI, GIULIO	Italian	1611-1674	
1107. Portrait	14 x 11	IA	3.00
CARRA, CARLO	Italian	1881-	
1108. Still Life, 1957	23-1/2 x 20	NYGS	12.00
CARRACCI, ANNIBALE	Italian	1560-1609	
1109. Beans-Eater	11 x 13	IA	3.00
CARRIER, JULES			
1110. Apple Blossoms	25 x 30	CFA	10.00
	16 x 20	CFA	5.00
1111. White and Gold	25 x 30	CFA	10.00
CARRIERA, ROSALBA	Italian	1675-1758	
1112. Portrait of a Princess of Este	14 x 11	IA	3.00
1113. Self-Portrait	14 x 11	IA	3.00
CARROLL, JOHN			
1114. Concert at Court	24 x 36	DAC	8.00
1115. Sleeping	15 x 20	NYGS	5.00
1116. Woodland Festival	24 x 36	DAC	8.00
CARRUCCI, JACOPO See PONTORMO, IL			
CARSON, FRANK	American	1881	

1117. Summer Holiday	19 x 23	CAC	7.50
CARY, WILLIAM			
1118. Boy	22-1/2 x 17-1/2	AA	12.00
1119. Courtship	16 x 30	AA	15.00
1120. Flowers	16 x 30	AA	15.00
1121. Fruit	16 x 30	AA	15.00
1122. Girl	22-1/2 x 17-1/2	AA	15.00
1123. Marriage	16 x 30	AA	15.00
CARZOU, JEAN		1907-	
1124. Fishing Boats	19 x 24	NYGS	12.00
1125. Honfleur	20 x 24	NYGS	12.00
CASANO, A.			
1126. Wayside Brook	24 x 48	DAC	8.00
CASCELLA, MICHELE	Italian	1882-	
1127. Autumn in Paris	27 x 36	IA	15.00
1128. Grand View of Portofino	26 x 48	IA	20.00
1129. Green Lantern, Carmel-			
by-the-Sea	24 x 36	IA	12.00
1130. Market in Portofino	27-1/2 x 36	IA	15.00
1131. Ocean Avenue, Carmel	24 x 36	IA	12.00
1132. Skiing in Cortina			
D'Ampezzo	27 x 36	IA	15.00
	16 x 21	IA	5.00
1133. Spring in the Abruzzi Hills	26 x 48	IA	20.00
1134. Sunday in Paris	26 x 48	IA	20.00
CASSATT, MARY	American (Res. France)		
		1845-1926	
1135. The Bath	18 x 23	HNA	5.95
1136. Boating Party	18 x 23	HNA	5.95
1137. In the Garden	24 x 19-1/2	PENN	1.00
1138. Little Sisters	18 x 22	NYGS	12.00
1139. The Loge	28 x 22	NYGS	15.00
1140. La Sortie du Bain	8 x 10	CAC	1.50
1141. Study for Banjo Lesson	16-1/2 x 16-1/2	PENN	1.00
CASSIOLI, AMOS	Italian	1832-1891	
1142. Battle of Legnano	13 x 22	IA	7.50
CASSINI			
1143. Cameos--Black (6)	14 x 9	CFA	10.00 ea.
CASTAGNO, ANDREA DAL	Italian	1410-1457	
1144. Portrait of Boccaccio	15 x 11	IA	3.00
1145. Portrait of Dante	15 x 11	IA	3.00
CASTAGNOLA, GABRIELE	Italian	1828-1883	
1146. Filippo Lippi and the			
Nun, Buti	15 x 11	IA	3.00
CASTELLO, VALERIO	Italian	1625-1659	
1147. Virgin of the Veil	11 x 15	IA	3.00
CATENA, VINCENZO DI BIAGIO	Italian	1470-1531	
1148. Judith	14 x 11	IA	3.00
1149. Portrait of a Man	18-1/2 x 14	CFA	3.50
1150. St. Christina	14 x 12	CAC	6.00
CATHELIN, BERNARD		1919-	
1151. Anemones on Blue	21 x 15	PENN	1.00

1152. Yellow Dahlias	28 x 19	NYGS	15.00
CAVALLINO, BERNARDO	Italian	1622-1654	
1153. Head of a Saint	14 x 11	IA	3.00
1154. St. George	14 x 11	IA	3.00

CAVAZZOLA, IL   See   MORANDO, PAOLO
CAVE PAINTING   See   PREHISTORIC ART
CERNY, CHARLES

1155. Marine Still Life	6-1/2 x 15	DAC	1.20
1156. Music Lover's Corner	16 x 20	CAC	9.00
1157. Poissons, 1637	13 x 16	CAC	4.00
1158. Poissons, 1638	13 x 16	CAC	4.00
1159. Quiet Haven	18 x 21	CAC	10.00
1160. Rhythm and Melody	16 x 20	CAC	9.00
1161. Ship Models (4)	8 x 10	DAC	.80 ea.
1162. Submarine Garden	13 x 16	CAC	4.00
1163. Wide World	16 x 20	CAC	9.00
1164. World of Silence	13 x 16	CAC	4.00

CERRITO

| 1165. La Reine de la Danse | 12 x 16 | CAC | 3.00 |

CESARE DA SESTO | Italian | 1477-1523 |

| 1166. Study, St. Jerome | 12-1/2 x 9-1/2 | AR | 4.00 |

CEYLON

| 1167. Female Figure with Hands in a Familiar Dance Pose--5th Century | 15 x 11 | NYGS | 2.00 |

CEZANNE, PAUL | French | 1839-1906 |

1168. L'Allée à Chantilly	26 x 21	NYGS	18.00
1169. Apple Basket	8 x 10	CAC	1.50
1170. Apples and Primroses	25 x 22	AA	15.00
1171. Baigneuses			
Tr. - The Bathers	11 x 20	CAC	5.00
	8 x 10	ESH	1.00
	6 x 9	NYGS	6.00
1172. Le Barrage Francois-Zola	20-1/2 x 28	NYGS	18.00
1173. Bathers in Front of a Tent	22 x 29-1/2	NYGS	20.00
1174. Bay of Marseilles Seen from L'Estaque	29 x 39-1/2	NYGS	18.00
	26 x 32	CAC	18.00
1175. The Blue Vase	23 x 18	HNA	5.95
	22-1/2 x 18	ESH	18.00
	20 x 16	AP	5.00
	10 x 8	ESH	1.00
1176. Boy in a Red Waistcoat	32 x 26	CAC	18.00
	31 x 25	NYGS	24.00
	20 x 16	AP	7.50
1177. Bridge at Maincy	17 x 21	PENN	1.00
1178. By the Riverside	26 x 32	CFA	20.00
	17-1/2 x 21-1/2	ESH	10.00
1179. Card Players (Two			

Figures--Louvre)	15 x 17	CAC	5.00
	11 x 13	IA	3.00
	8 x 10	ESH	1.00
1180. Chateau de Medan	22 x 27	NYGS	15.00
1181. Chestnut Trees at Jas de Bouffan	29 x 36	NYGS	15.00
	24 x 30	CAC	15.00
1182. Clos de Mathurins, Pontoise	8 x 10	ESH	1.00
1183. Country Landscape	23 x 32	CFA	18.00
1184. Dans la Vallée de L'Oise--Tr. - In the Valley of the Oise	24 x 30-1/2	AA	15.00
	18 x 22-1/2	IA	6.00
1185. Environs du Jas de Bouffan	16 x 22-1/2	ESH	10.00
1186. L'Estaque	25 x 35	CAC	20.00
	20 x 24	PENN	1.00
	17 x 22	CAC	10.00
	16 x 20	AP	5.00
	11 x 14	IA	3.00
	7 x 8	CFA	1.00
1187. Étude	15-1/2 x 10-1/2	NYGS	12.00
1188. Farm of Jas de Bouffan	20 x 25	PENN	1.00
1189. Faubourg au Printemps	18-1/2 x 22	NYGS	10.00
1190. Flowers	10 x 8	ESH	1.00
1191. Flowers and Fruit	22 x 16	CAC	10.00
1192. Flowers in a Delft Vase	10 x 8	ESH	1.00
1193. Flowers in a Jug	10 x 8	ESH	1.00
1194. Fruit and Jug	19 x 24	PENN	1.00
			1.98 (Pr.)
1195. Gardanne	16 x 19	AP	5.00
1196. The Gardener	10 x 8	ESH	1.00
1197. Grand Vase au Jardin	14 x 11	DAC	2.80
1198. Les Grandes Baigneuses	8 x 10	ESH	1.00
1199. The Great Pine	11 x 12	IA	3.00
1200. House of Père Lacroix	24 x 19	CAC	10.00
1201. House on the Bay	8 x 10	ESH	1.00
1201. House on the Hill	25 x 31	CFA	18.00
1202. Jas de Bouffan	10 x 12-1/2	NYGS	15.00
1203. Judgment of Paris	19-1/2 x 24	NYGS	15.00
1204. King's Retreat	25 x 31	CFA	18.00
1205. Kitchen Table	12 x 14	ESH	8.00
1206. Lac D'Annecy	20-1/2 x 26	NYGS	12.00
1207. Landscape	27 x 31	CFA	18.00
1208. Landscape at Aix	12 x 15	AR	3.00
1209. Landscape. Aix en Provence	23 x 19	CFA	15.00
1210. Landscape, Ile de France	8 x 10	ESH	1.00

1211. Landscape, L'Estaque	19-1/2 x 24	AA	7.50
1212. Landscape near Oise	18 x 22	CAC	10.00
1213. Landscape, Mte. Ste.-			
Victoire	25 x 30	CAC	20.00
	18 x 22-1/2	ESH	10.00
	8 x 10	ESH	1.00
1214. Landscape with Brook	17 x 23	PENN	1.00
			1.98 (Pr.)
1215. Landscape with Old			
House	26 x 31	CAC	18.00
1216. Landscape with a			
Viaduct, La Montagne			
Sainte-Victoire	25-1/2 x 32	NYGS	20.00
	18 x 22	NYGS	7.50
	6 x 7-1/2	NYGS	.50
1217. Lane of Chestnut			
Trees	18 x 12-1/2	NYGS	15.00
1218. Lane Through a Village	16 x 19	CAC	5.00
1219. Madame Cezanne	23 x 17	PENN	1.00
1220. Madame Cezanne in			
Red	15 x 11	IA	3.00
1221. La Maison du Pendu			
Tr.- House of the			
Hanged Man	20-1/2 x 25	AJ	12.00
	12 x 16	AA	3.00
1222. Mardi Gras	24 x 19	NYGS	10.00
	20 x 16	PENN	1.00
			1.98 (Pr.)
	10 x 8	ESH	1.00
1223. Marseilleveyre	8 x 10	ESH	1.00
1224. Mathurin's Meadow			
near Pontoise	8 x 10	ESH	1.00
1225. La Mer à L'Estaque	19 x 24	CAC	7.50
1226. Le Midi de France	24 x 30	PENN	1.00
			1.98 (Pr.)
1227. Milk Jug, Apples and			
Lemon	8 x 10	ESH	1.00
1228. Mill at Pontoise	26-1/2 x 33-1/2	IA	18.00
	17-1/2 x 22	ESH	10.00
	12 x 15	AP	5.00
	8 x 10	ESH	1.00
1229. La Montagne Sainte-			
Victoire	20 x 28	CFA	18.00
	17 x 22	CAC	10.00
	16 x 20	PENN	1.00
	14 x 19	NYGS	15.00
	8 x 10	ESH	1.00
	7 x 9	CFA	1.00
1230. La Montagne Sainte-			
Victoire au Deux			
Pins	18 x 23	HNA	5.95
1231. Nature Morte	14 x 20	CAC	5.00

1232.	Onions and Bottle	18 x 22	CAC	10. 00
1233.	Peasant in a Blue Blouse	22 x 18	ESH	10. 00
		10 x 8	ESH	1. 00
1234.	Le Pigeonnier de Bellevue--Tr. -Bird Tower at Bellevue	20 x 28	CFA	15. 00
		14 x 19	CAC	5. 00
1235.	Pines and Rocks	23 x 18-1/2	IA	5. 50
1236.	Pommes et Oranges Tr. - Apples and Oranges	20 x 24	PENN	1. 00
				1. 98 (Pr.)
		8 x 10	ESH	1. 00
1237.	Poplars	24 x 30	CAC	15. 00
		20 x 30	ESH	15. 00
		8 x 10	ESH	1. 00
1238.	Pot de Fleurs	20 x 24	PENN	1. 00
				1. 98 (Pr.)
		10 x 8	ESH	1. 00
1239.	Pot of Flowers with Pears	17-1/2 x 21	NYGS	12. 00
1240.	Pot of Geraniums and Fruit	25 x 31-1/2	AA	15. 00
1241.	Portrait of Ambroise Vollard	13 x 11	IA	3. 00
1242.	Quarry of Bibemus	25-1/2 x 21	NYGS	22. 00
1243.	Quays on the Seine	8 x 10	ESH	1. 00
1244.	Reefs at Antibes	10 x 14	IA	3. 00
1245.	Rocky Landscape	25 x 31-1/2	NYGS	22. 00
1246.	Roofs in Springtime in Suburb	24 x 30	PENN	1. 00
1247.	La Route Tournante Tr. - The Winding Lane	21-1/2 x 26	NYGS	15. 00
1248.	The Seine	22 x 27	CFA	15. 00
1249.	St. Faubourg in Springtime	18 x 22	CFA	10. 00
1250.	Self-Portrait	16 x 13	CAC	5. 00
1251.	Still Life	17-1/2 x 22-1/2	ESH	10. 00
		8 x 10	ESH	1. 00
1252.	Still Life with Apples	19 x 25	CFA	12. 00
1253.	Still Life with a Basket of Apples	18 x 23	HNA	5. 95
1254.	Still Life, Flowers	17 x 22	CAC	10. 00
1255.	Still Life #1651	14 x 20	CAC	5. 00
1256.	Still Life #17971	18 x 22	CAC	10. 00
1257.	Still Life with Chair, Bottle and Apples	18 x 23-1/2	NYGS	20. 00
1258.	Still Life with Ginger Jug	18 x 22	CAC	10. 00
1259.	Still Life with Jug	8 x 10	ESH	1. 00
1260.	Tree Before the House	22 x 18	ESH	10. 00

1261. Uncle Dominic	20 x 16-1/2	NYGS	10.00
	8 x 10	ESH	1.00
1262. Vase of Flowers			
(Nat'l Gallery)	28 x 23	NYGS	12.00
	10 x 8	ESH	1.00
1263. Vase of Flowers			
(Durand-Ruel)	20-1/2 x 16-1/2	NYGS	10.00
1264. Vase of Tulips	22-1/2 x 16	NYGS	10.00
1265. The Viaduct	8 x 10	ESH	1.00
1266. View of the Arc Valley	22 x 18	CFA	12.00
1267. Village Panorama	24 x 30	NYGS	15.00
CHABANIAN			
1268. Blue Horizon	22 x 30	CAC	10.00
1269. Moonlight on the			
Riviera	22 x 23	CAC	10.00
CHABAS, PAUL	French	1869-1937	
1270. September Morn	21 x 28	NYGS	12.00
	11 x 14	NYGS	3.00
CHABOR			
1271. Beauty of the Flowers			
#1	12 x 42	CFA	18.00
1272. Beauty of the Flowers			
#2	12 x 42	CFA	18.00
CHAFFOIS, LUCIEN	French	1925-	
1273. Les Roses et la Mer	20-1/2 x 25	NYGS	12.00
CHAGALL, MARC	French	1887-	
1274. L'Acrobate	25-1/2 x 16	PENN	1.00
1275. Artist and Model	28 x 20-1/2	AP	12.00
1276. Artist's Model	27 x 20	CFA	15.00
1277. The Big Circus	17 x 30	ESH	15.00
1278. Chambon sur Lac	23-1/2 x 17-1/2	PENN	1.00
1279. Le Cirque	24 x 19	NYGS	12.00
1280. Le Cirque	14 x 29	CAC	12.00
	11 x 20	CAC	5.00
1281. Le Cirque Bleu	10 x 8	ESH	1.00
1282. Clown on a White			
Horse	24 x 20	PENN	1.00
1283. The Cock	22-1/2 x 16	ESH	10.00
	10 x 8	ESH	1.00
1284. Les Deux Bouquets	28 x 21	NYGS	16.00
1285. Evening Enchantment	23-1/2 x 19-1/2	NYGS	12.00
1286. Flowers and Fruits	14 x 11	DAC	2.80
1287. Green Violinist	25-1/2 x 14-1/2	NYGS	15.00
1288. Gladioli	22-1/2 x 17	ESH	10.00
1289. I and My Village	28 x 22	MMA	12.00
	24 x 19	PENN	1.00
	7-1/2 x 6	NYGS	.50
1290. Lovers Above the			
Town	16 x 23	CFA	7.50
1291. Lovers in the Tree			
Tops	22 x 13	CAC	10.00
1292. Morning Mystery	23-1/2 x 19-1/2	NYGS	12.00

1293.	Newlyweds of the Eiffel Tower	18 x 24	PENN	1.00
		14 x 18	CAC	5.00
1294.	Plumes en Fleurs Tr. - Feathers in Bloom	24 x 18	PENN	1.00
		22 x 16	ESH	10.00
		10 x 8	ESH	1.00
1295.	Rabbi of Vitebsk	24 x 18-1/2	NYGS	12.00
		14 x 10-1/2	NYGS	3.00
1296.	Rabbi with Book	20 x 16	PENN	1.00
		14 x 11	CAC	3.00
1297.	Rabbi with Torah	24 x 18	NYGS	12.00
		14 x 10-1/2	NYGS	3.00
1298.	Red House	23 x 20	CFA	12.00
1299.	La Somnambule	26 x 20	CFA	15.00
1300.	Synagogue in Jerusalem	19 x 24	NYGS	10.00
1301.	Village Scene	8 x 10	ESH	1.00
1302.	Violinist	23-1/2 x 20	NYGS	10.00
1303.	Woman, Flowers and Bird	10 x 7-1/2	AP	1.50

CHAMBERS, C. BOSSERON

1304.	Christ at Five	20 x 16	IA	8.50
		15 x 12	IA	5.50
		12 x 9	IA	3.50
1305.	Confide in Me	20 x 16	IA	8.50
		15 x 12	IA	5.50
		12 x 9	IA	3.50
1306.	Crucifixion	20 x 16	IA	8.50
		15 x 12	IA	5.50
		12 x 9	IA	3.50
1307.	Divine Innocence	15 x 12	IA	5.50
		12 x 9	IA	3.50
1308.	Ecce Homo	15 x 12	IA	5.50
		12 x 9	IA	3.50
1309.	The Good Shepherd	20 x 16	IA	8.50
		15 x 12	IA	5.50
		12 x 9	IA	3.50
1310.	Heavenly Queen	20 x 16	IA	8.50
		15 x 12	IA	5.50
		12 x 9	IA	3.50
1311.	Holy Family	20 x 16	IA	8.50
		15 x 12	IA	5.50
		12 x 9	IA	3.50
1312.	Light of the World	20 x 16	IA	8.50
		15 x 12	IA	5.50
		12 x 9	IA	3.50
1313.	Little Flower	20 x 16	IA	8.50
		15 x 12	IA	5.50
		12 x 9	IA	3.50
1314.	Madonna and Child	15 x 12	IA	5.50
		12 x 9	IA	3.50

1315. Mary Most Holy	20 x 16	IA	8.50
	15 x 12	IA	5.50
	12 x 9	IA	3.50
1316. Miraculous Infant of Prague	20 x 16	IA	8.50
	15 x 12	IA	5.50
	12 x 9	IA	3.50
1317. Our Lady of Fatima	32 x 24	IA	18.00
	20 x 16	IA	8.50
	15 x 12	IA	5.50
	12 x 9	IA	3.50
1318. Sacred Heart of Jesus	32 x 24	IA	18.00
	20 x 16	IA	8.50
	15 x 12	IA	5.50
	12 x 9	IA	3.50
1319. Sacred Heart of Mary	20 x 16	IA	8.50
	15 x 12	IA	5.50
	12 x 9	IA	3.50
1320. St. Anthony	15 x 12	IA	5.50
	12 x 9	IA	3.50
1321. St. Francis	12 x 9	IA	3.50
1322. St. John	20 x 16	IA	8.50
	15 x 12	IA	5.50
	12 x 9	IA	3.50
1323. St. Joseph and Infant	20 x 16	IA	8.50
	15 x 12	IA	5.50
	12 x 9	IA	3.50
CHAMPION, THEO	German	1887-1952	
1324. Sunny Day	24 x 19	CAC	7.50
CHAPALLAZ			
1325. Cabanes pres Iserables	16 x 20	CAC	4.00
1326. Champery et les Dents du Midi	16 x 20	CAC	4.00
CHAPIN, JAMES	American	1887-	
1327. Boy with a Book	21 x 18	NYGS	7.50
1328. Motherhood	21-1/2 x 17-1/2	NYGS	10.00
1329. Picture Book	27 x 18	NYGS	10.00
	16-1/2 x 11	NYGS	4.00
CHAPMAN, CHARLES S.	American	1879-	
1330. Last Parable	14-1/2 x 18	IA	4.00
CHAPPEL			
1331. La Tango	28 x 22	CAC	7.50
CHAPUT, ROGER			
1332. Arlequin Flutiste	24 x 16	PENN	1.00
1333. Melancholie	24 x 16	PENN	1.00
CHARDIN, JEAN BAPTISTE SIMEON French		1699-1779	
1334. Attentive Nurse	18 x 23	HNA	5.95
1335. Attributes of the Arts	24-1/2 x 23	NYGS	15.00
1336. The Blessing (Saying Grace)	19-1/2 x 15	NYGS	10.00
	10 x 8	ESH	1.00
1337. Bowl of Plums	16 x 20-1/2	NYGS	10.00

1338. Child with a Top	11 x 12	IA	3.00
1339. The Designer	26 x 20	CAC	12.00
1340. Errand Woman	13 x 11	IA	3.00
1341. Girl with Battledore	10 x 8	ESH	1.00
1342. House of Cards	23 x 18	HNA	5.95
	10 x 8	ESH	1.00
1343. Kitchen Maid	23 x 18	HNA	5.95
	18 x 14-1/2	NYGS	10.00
1344. Laborious Mother	13 x 11	IA	3.00
1345. Music	18-1/2 x 30	ESH	12.00
1346. Soap Bubbles	21 x 16-1/2	NYGS	10.00
1347. Still Life with Flask			
(Glass Bottle)	22 x 18	NYGS	18.00
1348. Still Life with Tankard			
(Pewter Pitcher)	21-1/2 x 18	NYGS	18.00
1349. Young Governess	18 x 23	AA	7.50
1350. Youth with the Violin	11 x 12	IA	3.00
CHARLES			
1351. Bugle and Willow	20 x 16	PENN	1.00
1352. Guitar and Music			
Sheet	20 x 16	PENN	1.00
1353. Horse and Butterfly	16 x 20	PENN	1.00
1354. Rose and Recorder	16 x 20	PENN	1.00
CHAULEUR, JANE	French		
1355. Playmates	16 x 20	CAC	6.00
1356. Port of Croisic	16 x 22	CFA	10.00
	8 x 10	CFA	1.00
CHEN-CHI	Chinese	Contemporary	
1357. Artist's Home Town	14 x 18	CFA	6.00
1358. Bamboo	33 x 12	CAC	10.00
1359. Chrysanthemums	33 x 12	CAC	10.00
1360. Morning Traders	14 x 18	CFA	6.00
CHIRICO, GIORGIO DE	Italian	1888-	
1361. Combat	20 x 24	DAC	6.00
1362. Juan-les-Pins	28 x 21	NYGS	12.00
1363. Nostalgia of the Infinite	8 x 10	MMA	.35
1364. Toys of a Prince	8 x 10	MMA	.35
CHOULTZE, I. F.			
1365. Blanket of Snow	24 x 32	CFA	10.00
CHRISTUS, PETRUS	Flemish	c. 1410-1472	
1366. Legend of St. Eligius			
and Godeberta	28-1/2 x 25	IA	16.00
1367. Madonna and Donor	11 x 7	AR	4.00
1368. Portrait of a Girl	10-1/2 x 8	ESH	1.00
1369. Young Girl	11 x 9	CFA	4.00
CHRISTY, HOWARD CHANDLER	American	1873-	
1370. Summer Dreams	25 x 31	NYGS	10.00
	16-1/2 x 21	NYGS	5.00
	9 x 11-1/2	NYGS	1.00
CHU, CHARLES			
1371. Apple Blossoms (Two			
Birds)	22 x 14	AA	5.00

1372. Apple Blossoms (One Bird)	22 x 14	AA	5.00
1373. Blue Bird	22 x 14	AA	5.00
1374. Blue Birds	22 x 14	AA	5.00
1375. Bamboo Panel (Green Bird)	35 x 15	AA	7.50
1376. Bamboo Panel (Yellow Bird)	35 x 15	AA	7.50
1377. Chinese Female Figures (4 sheets, 2 per sheet)	10 x 12	AA	2.00 ea.
1378. Duck Panel (3 Ducks)	35 x 15	AA	7.50
1379. Duck Panel (Large Duck)	35 x 15	AA	7.50
1380. Mandarin Figures (2)	10 x 12	AA	2.00 ea.
1381. Pine Tree (Left)	15 x 35	AA	7.50
1382. Pine Tree (Right)	15 x 35	AA	7.50
1383. Pine Panel (Yellow Birds)	35 x 15	AA	7.50
1384. Pine Panel (Grey Bird)	35 x 15	AA	7.50
1385. Willows (Two Swallows)	22 x 14	AA	5.00
1386. Willows (One Swallow)	22 x 14	AA	5.00
CHUGTAI, M. ABDUR RAHMAN	India		
1387. Come Fill the Cup	30 x 24	NYGS	15.00
1388. For a Song	30 x 24	NYGS	15.00
CHURCH, FREDERICK EDWIN	American	1826-1900	
1389. Sunset	23-1/2 x 35-1/2	NYGS	15.00
CHURCHILL, WINSTON	English	1874-1965	
1390. Cap D'Ali	19 x 24	CAC	10.00
1391. Manton from LaPausa	17 x 27	CAC	10.00
CIARDI, GUGLIELMO	Italian	1842-1917	
1392. Seascape at San Giorgio	11 x 15	IA	3.00
CIGNANI, CARLO	Italian	1628-1719	
1393. Madonna and Child (of the Rosary)	15 x 11	IA	3.00
CIGNAROLI, VITTORIO AMEDEO	Italian	1747-1793	
1394. Landscape	17 x 20	IA	10.00
	11 x 13-1/2	IA	3.00
1395. Landscape with a Bridge	17 x 20	IA	10.00
	11 x 13	IA	3.00
CIKOVSKY, NICOLAI	American	1894-	
1396. From My Window	26 x 34-1/2	NYGS	12.00
1397. Outdoor Still Life	18 x 23	HNA	5.95
1398. Springtime in Virginia	16 x 21	NYGS	7.50
CIMABUE (GIOVANNI GUALYIERI)	Italian	1240-1302	
1399. Crucifix (Detail)	15 x 11	IA	3.00
1400. Madonna, Angels and St. Francis	11 x 11	IA	3.00
1401. St. Francis--Detail of No. 1400	15 x 10	IA	3.00

CIRINO, ANTONIO	Italian (Res. U.S.)	1889-	
1402. Home Town	25 x 30	AA	7.50
	16 x 20	AA	3.50
1403. Shady Village	25 x 30	AA	7.50
	16 x 20	AA	3.50
CISERI, ANTONIO	Italian	1821-1891	
1404. Ecce Homo	11 x 15	IA	3.00
1405. Transport to the Sepulcher	10 x 15	IA	3.00
CIUCURENCU, ALEXANDRU	Rumanian	1903-	
1406. Ciclamen	19 x 23-1/2	NYGS	10.00
CLAGHORN			
1407. At the Old Indian Queen	16 x 25	AA	5.00
1408. A Chance Passenger	21-1/2 x 35	AA	9.00
1409. Home for the Holidays	16 x 25	AA	5.00
1410. Independence Hall (Philadelphia)	20 x 30	AA	15.00
1411. Old Bruton Church (Williamsburg, Va.)	20 x 30	AA	15.00
CLAUDIO DI LORENA See GELLEE, CLAUDE			
CLAVE, ANTONI	Spanish	1913-	
1412. King Bacchus	26 x 19	NYGS	15.00
1413. The Musician	19-1/2 x 26	NYGS	12.00
1414. Still Life	17-1/2 x 23-1/2	NYGS	12.00
1415. Two Fish	17 x 22-1/2	ESH	10.00
1416. Twilight	22-1/2 x 31-1/2	NYGS	15.00
1417. Warrior on a Red Background	22-1/2 x 17-1/2	ESH	10.00
CLAVER, FERNAND	French	1913-	
1418. Place du Tertre	18 x 22	CAC	6.00
1419. Les Tuileries	18 x 22	CAC	6.00
CLEMENTZ, H.	German	1852-1930	
1420. Christ Among the Rich	15 x 19	CAC	5.00
1421. Christ and the Doctors	24-1/2 x 36	IA	12.00
1422. Christ Blessing the Children	28-1/2 x 38-1/2	IA	12.00
	19-1/2 x 27-1/2	IA	6.00
1423. Christ in the Temple	20 x 30	IA	5.00
CLEVE, JOOS VAN (THE YOUNGER) Flemish		1518-1554	
1424. Mater Dolorosa	14 x 9	IA	3.00
CLEVE, JOOS VAN (THE ELDER) Flemish		1485-1541	
1425. Joris W. Vezelier	24 x 18	NYGS	12.00
1426. Margarethe Boghe, Wife of Joris W. Vezelier	24 x 18	NYGS	12.00
1427. Rest During the Flight into Egypt	12 x 14	IA	3.00
CLOUET, FRANCOIS	French	1516-1572	
1428. Elizabeth of Austria	14-1/2 x 10-1/2	AP	5.00
CLOUET, JEAN	French	1485-1541	
1429. Diane de Poitiers	16 x 14-1/2	PENN	1.00
1430. Francis I	14 x 11	IA	3.00
1431. Henry II	12 x 9	AP	5.00

COBELLE, CHARLES	American		
1432. Italian Fantasy	16 x 42	CAC	15.00
1433. Parisian Fantasy	16 x 42	CAC	15.00
1434. Riviera Fantasy	16 x 42	CAC	15.00
1435. Venetian Fantasy	16 x 42	CAC	15.00
COBURN			
1436. White Sails	19 x 31	CFA	15.00
COCHRAN, ALLEN DEAN	American	1888-	
1437. Anemones and Tulips	20 x 16	CAC	3.50
1438. Grandeur of Summer	24 x 30	CAC	7.50
1439. Orchids	24 x 30	CAC	7.50
1440. Pansies	24 x 30	CAC	7.50
1441. Springtime	20 x 16	CAC	3.50
COGGESHALL, CLAVERT	American		
1442. Landscape	15 x 20	NYGS	5.00
COLANTONIO			
1443. St. Jerome	11 x 13	IA	3.00
COLEMAN, RALPH P.	American	1892-	
1444. The Saviour	20 x 16	IA	1.50
	14 x 11	IA	1.00
COLLETTI, JOSEPH	Italian (Res. U.S.) 1898-		
1445. Antique Landscape, Athens	16 x 22	PENN	1.00
1446. Antique Landscape, Capri	16 x 22	PENN	1.00
1447. Antique Landscape, Rome	16 x 22	PENN	1.00
1448. Antique Landscape, Venice	16 x 22	PENN	1.00
COLLINS			
1449. Sidewalk Cafe, Montmartre	24 x 40	DAC	8.00
	11 x 17-1/2	DAC	2.00
COMIOTTO			
1450. Carnations	20 x 16	CAC	4.00
COMPTON, E. T.	German-English	1849-1921	
1451. Alpine Stream	23 x 31	CFA	15.00
1452. Konigsee	24 x 34	CFA	12.00
CONINXLOO, EGIDE VAN	Flemish	1544-1607	
1453. Osea and the Prostitute	10 x 15	IA	3.00
CONSTABLE, JOHN	English	1776-1837	
1454. Bridge over the Stour	17-1/2 x 26-1/2	IA	15.00
1455. Cornfield	23-1/2 x 20	IA	15.00
	23 x 18	HNA	5.95
	21 x 17	IA	4.00
1456. Dedham Mill	17 x 25	CAC	15.00
1457. Flatford Mill	19 x 24	CAC	10.00
1458. Flatford Mill on the River Stour	9 x 7	CAC	1.00
1459. The Hay Wain	18 x 25-1/2	IA	7.50
	12-1/2 x 18	NYGS	5.00

1460. Hampstead Heath	21 x 27	NYGS	15.00
1460. Malvern Hall	21 x 31	AA	12.00
1461. Salisbury Cathedral	11 x 14	IA	3.00
1462. Salisbury Cathedral from the Bishop's Garden	15 x 20	CAC	10.00
1463. Salisbury Cathedral, View of	23-1/2 x 20	IA	15.00
	23 x 18	HNA	5.95
1464. View at Hampstead Heath	11 x 13	NYGS	3.00
1465. The White Horse	25 x 36	NYGS	18.00
	18 x 26	NYGS	10.00
	5-1/2 x 7-1/2	NYGS	1.50
1466. Wivenhoe Park, Essex	19-1/2 x 36	NYGS	15.00
CONTI, BERNARDINO DEI	Italian	1496-1522	
1467. Portrait of Francesco Sforza as a Child	15 x 10	IA	3.00
COOK, JOHN A.	American	1870-	
1468. Setting Sail	18 x 26	PENN	1.00
COOPER, GERALD (SIR)			
1469. Valley Farm	17 x 23	RL	6.00
COPLEY, JOHN SINGLETON	English (Res. U.S.)	1737-1815	
1470. Lady Frances Wentworth	28 x 23	AA	10.00
1471. Mrs. John Bacon	21-1/2 x 18	NYGS	12.00
1472. Paul Revere	26 x 21	NYGS	12.00
COPPING			
1473. The Hope of the World	27-1/2 x 20	IA	5.00
	11 x 8	IA	1.00
CORBIZZI, FILIPPO	Italian	1494-1515	
1474. Nativity	15 x 11	IA	3.00
1475. St. Catherine	15 x 10	IA	3.00
CORDOBA			
1476. After Lunch	6 x 8	CAC	2.00
1477. Country Home	6 x 8	CAC	2.00
1478. Farm	6 x 8	CAC	2.00
1479. Hill Town	6 x 8	CAC	2.00
1480. Late Supper	6 x 8	CAC	2.00
1481. Shore Dinner	6 x 8	CAC	2.00
1482. Tropical Breakfast	6 x 8	CAC	2.00
1483. Village	6 x 8	CAC	2.00
CORINA			
1484. At the Zoo (6)	14 x 11	DAC	1.20 ea.
CORINTH, LOVIS	German	1858-1925	
1485. Blue Lake	22 x 30	CFA	18.00
1486. Bouquet	22 x 27-1/2	NYGS	15.00
1487. Easter on Lake Walchen	22 x 29-1/2	NYGS	15.00
1488. Lake Walchen	21 x 30-1/2	ESH	12.00
1489. Pinks	15 x 18	NYGS	16.00

1490.	Road by the Sea	23 x 31	CAC	15.00
1491.	Tree at Walchen Lake	23 x 18	HNA	5.95
1492.	Tyrolese Landscape	22 x 29	CAC	15.00
1493.	View of the Valley of the Inn	21-1/2 x 29	NYGS	18.00
COROT,	JEAN BAPTISTE CAMILLE French		1796-1875	
1494.	The Artist's Studio	17 x 21	CAC	10.00
		18 x 23	HNA	5.95
1495.	La Bacchanale	28 x 22-1/2	PENN	1.00
1496.	Belfry at Douai	20 x 16	CAC	6.00
		10 x 8	ESH	1.00
1497.	Bridge at Mantes	8 x 10	ESH	1.00
1498.	Bridge at Narni	24 x 36	CAC	18.00
		16 x 23	CFA	12.00
1499.	Chateau-Thierry	15 x 22	CAC	7.50
1500.	Cottage in the Woods	18 x 24	PENN	1.00
1501.	The Colosseum	9 x 14	IA	3.00
1502.	Dance of the Nymphs	20 x 26	CAC	7.50
		16 x 20	CAC	5.00
		9 x 12	CAC	2.00
1503.	Dawn in the Glade	18 x 22	CAC	7.50
1504.	Farm at Recouvrieres	18 x 23	HNA	5.95
1505.	Florence, Seen from the Boboli Gardens	10 x 15	IA	3.00
1506.	Forest at Coubron	24 x 30	CAC	12.00
1507.	The Forum, Seen from the Palatinos	8 x 15	IA	3.00
1508.	Girl Reading by the Waterside	18 x 23	HNA	5.95
1509.	Girl with Red Bow	10 x 8	ESH	1.00
1510.	Gitana Playing the Mandolin	15 x 11	IA	3.00
1511.	Gypsy Girl at the Fountain	20 x 15	NYGS	7.50
1512.	Gypsy with Mandolin	27 x 20	CFA	7.50
1513.	Houses at Honfleur	17 x 25	CAC	12.00
1514.	Le Lac de Terni	24 x 36	CAC	15.00
1515.	The Lake	13 x 19	CFA	10.00
1516.	Landscape	11 x 17	AR	4.00
1517.	Landscape near Geneva	12-1/2 x 18	NYGS	5.00
1518.	Mlle. Octavie Sennegon	12 x 10	IA	3.00
1519.	Morning	11 x 12	IA	3.00
1520.	Morning: Dance of the Nymphs	11 x 14	IA	3.00
1521.	Mother and Child on the Beach	15 x 18	NYGS	8.00
1522.	Olevano Romano	8 x 13	IA	3.00
1523.	On the Way to Sevres	13 x 18	CFA	5.00
1524.	Pensive Girl	18 x 14-1/2	NYGS	16.00
1525.	Pont au Change, Paris	18 x 26	PENN	1.00

                                                            1.98 (Pr.)

1526.	Le Quai des Paquis,			
	Geneva	8 x 10	ESH	1.00
1527.	The Reader	17 x 13	CFA	10.00
1528.	Reading Girl	16 x 12	CAC	7.50
1529.	Residence and Factory			
	of M. Henry	18 x 23	HNA	5.95
1530.	Souvenir of Morte			
	Fontaine	11 x 14	IA	3.00
1531.	Spring	20 x 26	CAC	10.00
		16 x 20	CAC	5.00
		9 x 12	CAC	2.00
1532.	The Studio	21-1/2 x 18	ESH	10.00
1533.	Tivoli	9 x 12	CFA	2.50
1534.	Twilight on the Lake	16 x 18	CFA	12.00
1535.	View of Tivoli	15-1/2 x 22-1/2	ESH	10.00
		9 x 12	CAC	2.50
1536.	View near Volterra	22 x 30	NYGS	15.00
1537.	Villeneuve-les-Avignon	8 x 10	ESH	1.00
1538.	Wagon in the Dunes	19-1/2 x 25-1/2	NYGS	20.00
1539.	Woman with a Pearl	26 x 18	PENN	1.00
				1.98 (Pr.)
1540.	Wood-Gatherers	17 x 21	CAC	7.50

CORREGGIO, ANTONIO ALLEGRI DA   Italian   1494-1534

1541.	Antiope's Sleep	13 x 9	CFA	2.50
1542.	Danae with Cupids	11 x 14	IA	3.00
1543.	Deposition from the			
	Cross	11 x 13	IA	3.00
1544.	Education of Cupid	25 x 14	CAC	10.00
1545.	Madonna and Child	8 x 6	IA	1.50
1546.	Madonna della Scala	15 x 10	IA	3.00
1547.	Marriage of St.			
	Catherine	11 x 11	IA	3.00
1548.	Study of an Apostle	16 x 10	CFA	4.00
1549.	Virgin Adoring	13 x 11	IA	3.00
1550.	Virgin of the Bowl	15 x 10	IA	3.00
1551.	Virgin of St. Jerome	15 x 10	IA	3.00

CORRENS, ERICH   German   1822-1877

1552.	Southern Belle	28 x 22	IA	6.00
		20 x 16	IA	3.50
1553.	Detail of No. 1552	11 x 8-1/2	NYGS	1.50
1554.	Detail of No. 1552	12 x 9	IA	1.00
		11 x 8	CAC	1.50

COSGRAVE, JOHN O'HARA, JR.   American   1908-

1555.	Ships, American			
	Clipper (8)	12 x 16	DAC	1.60 ea.
1556.	The Challenge	18 x 24	PENN	1.00
				1.98 (Pr.)
1557.	Sovereign of the Seas	18 x 24	PENN	1.00
				1.98 (Pr.)

COSSA, FRANCESCO DEL   Italian   1439-1478

1558.	A Miracle of St. Vincent			
	Ferrer	11 x 15	IA	3.00

COSTIGAN, JOHN EDWARD	American	1888-	
1559. Fishermen Three	16 x 20	NYGS	7.50
COTAN, JUAN SANCHEZ Y	Spanish	1561-1627	
1560. Still Life	22 x 28	NYGS	12.00
COTMAN, JOHN SELL	English	1782-1842	
1561. Dieppe Harbor	11 x 21	NYGS	20.00
COTTAVOZ, ANDRÉ		1922-	
1562. Boats in Cannes Harbor	16 x 22	ESH	10.00
COUNIS, SALOMON GUILLAUME	French (Res. Italy)	1785-1859	
1563. Paolina Buonaparte (La Bella Greca)	23 x 19	AA	10.00
	11 x 8-1/2	IA	1.50
COURBET, GUSTAVE	French	1819-1877	
1564. Chateau de Chillon	21 x 27	NYGS	12.00
	12 x 14	NYGS	3.00
1565. Dreaming Gypsy	11 x 13	IA	3.00
1566. Fishing Boats on the Beach at Deauville	17 x 22-1/2	ESH	10.00
	8 x 10	ESH	1.00
1567. Ladies by the Seine	7 x 8	CFA	1.00
1568. Ladies by the Water-side	8 x 11	CFA	2.50
1569. Landscape at Etretat	18 x 23	HNA	5.95
1570. The Proudhon Family	22-1/2 x 17	ESH	10.00
1571. Still Life with Apples and Pomegranate	17 x 23-1/2	NYGS	15.00
1572. The Stone-Breakers	12 x 19-1/2	AP	5.00
1573. The Trellis	24 x 29	CAC	15.00
COURTEAU			
1574. Notre Dame	24 x 48	IA	10.00
COUSE	American	1866-1936	
1575. Corn Ceremony	20 x 26	CAC	6.00
	15 x 17	CAC	3.00
1576. Indian Love Affair	20 x 26	CAC	7.50
1577. Treasure Jar	20 x 26	CAC	6.00
	15 x 17	CAC	3.00
COVARRUBIAS, MIGUEL	Mexican	1902-1957	
1578. America	25 x 36	CAC	10.00
1579. Diego Rivera	15-1/2 x 11	NYGS	4.00
1580. Flower Fiesta	28 x 22-1/2	NYGS	12.00
COX, JOHN ROGERS	American	1915-	
1581. Gray and Gold	15 x 21	NYGS	7.50
COYPEL, CHARLES ANTOINE	French	1694-1752	
1582. Democritus	13 x 11	IA	3.00
COZENS, JOHN ROBERT	English	1752-1799	
1583. The Lake and Town of Nemi	14-1/2 x 20-1/2	NYGS	20.00
CRANACH, LUKAS (THE ELDER)	German	1472-1553	
1584. Betrothal of St. Catherine	22 x 15	CAC	10.00
1585. Madonna of the Arbour	27-1/2 x 20	AJ	15.00

1586. Martin Luther	8 x 6	IA	1.50
1587. Stag Hunt	22-1/2 x 32	NYGS	18.00

CRANACH, LUKAS (THE YOUNGER)   German   1515-1586

1588. Portrait of a Lady	28 x 22	CAC	15.00
	20 x 15	AJ	7.50
1589. Portrait of a Man	20 x 15	AJ	7.50

CRANDALL

1590. Coast Cottage	20 x 24	CAC	10.00

CRANE, BRUCE   American

1591. Winter Idyl	15 x 14	CAC	3.00

CREDI, LORENZO DI   Italian   1456-1537

1592. Portrait of a Girl	18 x 11	NYGS	12.00

CRESPI, GIOVANNI MARIA (LOSPAGNUOLO)   Italian   1665-1747

1593. Confirmation	15 x 11	IA	3.00
1594. Familiar Scene	15 x 11	IA	3.00
1595. Miracle of St. Francis	15 x 9	IA	3.00

CRIVELLI, CARLO   Italian   1430/35-1495

1596. Annunciation	22-1/2 x 16	NYGS	10.00
1597. Madonna Enthroned	15 x 5	IA	3.00
1598. Virgin Enthroned with Child	15 x 7	IA	3.00

CROSONI

1599. Chalets in Switzerland	24 x 48	DAC	10.00
	9 x 17-1/2	DAC	2.00

CROPSEY, JASPER F.   American   1823-1900

1600. Mountain Glimpse	25 x 38	AA	12.00
1601. Mountain Lakes	24 x 35-1/2	NYGS	15.00
1602. Susquehanna River	26 x 47-1/2	AA	15.00
1603. Woodland Stream	24 x 35-1/2	NYGS	15.00

CROSS

1604. Cypresses at Cagnes	24 x 30	CAC	15.00

CUNDALL, CHARLES   English   1890-

1605. Oast Cottage	20 x 24	CFA	10.00

CURR, TOM

1606. Follow Me	27-1/2 x 20	IA	5.00
	11 x 8	IA	1.00
1607. The Healer	19 x 26	CAC	5.00

CURRADI, FRANCESCO (IL CAVALIER CURRADO)

	Italian	1570-1661	
1608. Narcissus	11 x 12	IA	3.00

CURRAN, CHARLES C.   American   1861-1942

1609. Children Catching Minnows	12 x 21	CAC	7.50
1610. Dewdrops and Roses	14 x 11	CAC	3.00

CURRIER AND IVES

CURRIER, NATHANIEL	American	1813-1888	
IVES, JAMES MERRITT	American	1824-1895	
1611. Across the Continent	17-1/2 x 27	NYGS	12.00
1612. American Scene, Morning	16 x 24	CAC	10.00
1613. Grist Mill	24 x 32	CAC	10.00
1614. Rocky Mountains	17-1/2 x 25-1/2	NYGS	12.00

		9-1/2 x 14-1/2	NYGS	1.50
1615.	Winter Scene, Evening	16 x 24	CAC	7.50
1616.	Portfolio (6)	8-1/2 x 11-1/2	PENN	1.00 set

A Disputed Heat
Home to Thanksgiving
Across the Continent
Old Homestead in Winter
Whale Fishery
Clipper Ship Dreadnaught off Tuskar Light

| 1617. | Portfolio (8) | 7 x 5 | DAC | .20 ea. |

American Farm Scenes
Drive through the Highlands
Cottage by the Cliff
Retrieving
Chance for Both Barrels
American Country Life
Western River Scenery
Snowy Morning

| 1618. | Portfolio (12) | 9-1/2 x 14-1/2 | NYGS | 15.00 set |
| | | | or | 1.50 ea. |

American Hunting Scenes
Central Park, Winter
The Road, Winter
Rocky Mountains
Midnight Race on the Mississippi
Clipper Ship "Dreadnaught"
Great Ocean Yacht Race
Woodcock Shooting
Trotting Cracks at the Forge
Peytona and Fashion
American National Game of Baseball
"Lightning Express" Trains

CURRY,	JOHN STEUART	American	1897-1946	
1619.	Flying Codonas	18 x 15	NYGS	5.00
1620.	Line Storm	15-1/2 x 24	NYGS	10.00
		6 x 10	NYGS	.50
1621.	Spring Bouquet	16-1/2 x 21-1/2	NYGS	7.50
1622.	Wisconsin Landscape	18 x 35	CFA	15.00
		12 x 24	PENN	1.00
CURTIS,	LELAND	American	1897-	
1623.	Crest of the Sierras	22 x 28	CFA	7.50
1624.	Sentinels of the West	28 x 40	CAC	15.00
CUYP,	AELBERT	Dutch	1620-1691	
1625.	Horsemen and Herdsmen			
	with Cattle	25 x 35-1/2	NYGS	18.00
1626.	Landscape	7-1/2 x 12	CFA	3.00
1627.	The Maas at Dordrecht	21 x 31	NYGS	16.00
1628.	View of a Town	7 x 12	AR	3.00
CYDNEY		American	Contemporary	
1629.	Between the Acts	20 x 16	NYGS	7.50
		14 x 11	NYGS	3.00
		8 x 6	NYGS	1.00

1630. Curtain Call	20 x 16	NYGS	7.50
	14 x 11	NYGS	3.00
	8 x 6	NYGS	1.00
1631. Future Ballerina	16 x 20	NYGS	7.50
1632. Her First Bouquet	17 x 10	NYGS	4.00
	10 x 6	NYGS	1.25
1633. Little Ballerina	14 x 11	NYGS	3.00
	8 x 6	NYGS	1.00
1634. Little Starlet	14 x 11	NYGS	3.00
	8 x 6	NYGS	1.00
1635. Stage Visitor	17 x 10	NYGS	4.00
	10 x 6	NYGS	1.25
1635. Starlet on Stage	17 x 10	NYGS	4.00
	10 x 6	NYGS	1.25
1636. Stealing the Show	14 x 11	NYGS	3.00
	8 x 6	NYGS	1.00
1637. Whispering	14 x 11	NYGS	3.00
	8 x 6	NYGS	1.00

D

DA COSTA, MILTON	Brazilian	1915-	
1638. Against a Blue Background	21 x 29-1/2	NYGS	15.00
DADDI, BERNARDO	Italian	c. 1280-1348	
1639. Crucifixion	16 x 9	IA	3.00
1640. Nativity of the Virgin	15 x 11	IA	3.00
1641. St. Catherine	7 x 9	NYGS	.50
1642. The Virgin (Uffizi)	16 x 9	IA	3.00
1643. The Virgin (Rome)	15 x 11	IA	3.00
1644. The Virgin of Succour	15 x 9	IA	3.00
DAFFINGER, MORITZ MICHAEL	Austrian	1790-1849	
1645. Alpine Rose	14 x 10	CFA	2.50
1646. Basket with Fruit	24 x 28	IA	12.00
1647. Bluebells	14 x 10	CFA	2.50
1648. Bluebells (Glocken-blume)	14 x 10	CFA	2.50
1649. Daphine Flower	14 x 10	CFA	2.50
1650. Devil's Eye	14 x 10	CFA	2.50
1651. Dwarf Alpine Roses	14 x 10	CFA	2.50
1652. Dwarf Box-Tree	14 x 10	CFA	2.50
1653. Field Flowers	14 x 10	CFA	2.50
1654. Forest Cyclamen	14 x 10	CFA	2.50
1655. Forget-Me-Nots	14 x 10	CFA	2.50
1656. Hedge-Rose	14 x 10	CFA	2.50
1657. Lady's Slipper	14 x 10	CFA	2.50
1658. Little Love Flowers	14 x 10	CFA	2.50
1659. Lung Weed	14 x 10	CFA	2.50
1660. Marsh Marigolds	14 x 10	CFA	2.50
1661. Meadow Anemones	14 x 10	CFA	2.50
1662. Ox Eye	14 x 10	CFA	2.50
1663. Primroses	14 x 10	CFA	2.50

1664. Purple Gentian	14 x 10	CFA	2.50
1665. Red Lilies	14 x 10	CFA	2.50
1666. Rose of France	14 x 10	CFA	2.50
1667. Snow Rose	14 x 10	CFA	2.50

DA FORLI, MELOZZO   See   MELOZZO DA FORLI

DALBY, DAVID   English

1668. Melton Hunt	24 x 37	AA	15.00

DALI, SALVADOR   Spanish   1904-

1669. Bacchanale	6 x 7	CFA	1.00
1670. Christ of St. John of			
the Cross	36 x 20-1/2	NYGS	25.00
	28 x 16	NYGS	12.00
	14 x 8	NYGS	3.00
1671. Columbus Discovers			
America	28 x 21	NYGS	15.00
1672. Composition, 1942	22 x 15-1/2	NYGS	12.00
1673. Crucifixion	28 x 17-1/2	NYGS	12.00
	14 x 8-1/2	NYGS	3.00
1674. Gala and the Angelus			
of Millet	8 x 10	MMA	.35
1675. Inventions of Monsters	8 x 10	AP	.75
1676. Madonna of Port			
Lligat	28 x 21	NYGS	12.00
	14 x 10-1/2	NYGS	3.00
1677. Nature Morte Vivante	21-1/2 x 28	NYGS	12.00
1678. Persistence of			
Memory	8 x 10	AP	.50
1679. Sacrament of the Last			
Supper	19 x 30	NYGS	12.00
	15 x 24	PENN	1.00
	8-1/2 x 14	NYGS	3.00
	7-1/2 x 12	IA	.50

DALLIN, CYRUS EDWIN   American   1861-1944

1680. Appeal to the Great			
Spirit	17 x 14	CAC	5.00
	12 x 9	CAC	2.00

DANCHIN, LEON

1681. Black Cockers	15 x 18	IA	12.00
1682. Gordon Setter	16 x 20	IA	12.00
1683. Irish Setters	16 x 19	IA	12.00
1684. Irish Setter with Teal	19 x 26	IA	15.00
1685. Sketches of Setters	10-1/2 x 14-1/2	IA	10.00
1686. Three Setters	11 x 16	IA	7.50

DANHAUSER, JOSEF   Austrian   1805-1845

1687. Reading the Will	21 x 26	IA	12.00

DANTE, JESUS

1688. Cristo-Misericordia	28 x 18	IA	10.00
	14 x 9	IA	2.50

DARANIYAGALA, JUSTIN   Ceylonese   1903-

1689. The Fish	26 x 18-1/2	NYGS	12.00

DARCHE, THERESE
1690. Boulevard des

Capucines	11 x 14	IA	2.50
1691. Boulevard de la Madeleine	11 x 14	IA	2.50
1692. Cafe de la Paix, Opera	11 x 14	IA	2.50
1693. Champs Elysees	11 x 14	IA	2.50
1694. Marche St. Medard	20 x 16	IA	4.00
1695. Notre Dame Vue des Quais	16 x 20	IA	4.00
1696. Place du Chatelet	11 x 14	IA	2.50
1697. Place du Tertre	20 x 16	IA	4.00
1698. Place du Tertre, Paris	11 x 14	IA	2.50
1699. Quai aux Fleurs	20 x 16	IA	4.00
1700. Rue du Haut Pave	20 x 16	IA	4.00
1701. Rue de Rivoli	16 x 20	IA	4.00
1702. Square St. Julien le Pauvre	16 x 20	IA	4.00

DA SESTO, CESARE   See CESARE DA SESTO
DAUBIGNY, CHARLES FRANCOIS   French   1817-1878

1703. Banks of the Oise	8 x 14	CFA	2.50
1704. Boats on the Oise	8 x 15	IA	3.00

DAUMIER, HONORÉ   French   1808-1879

1705. L'Amateur	13 x 10	NYGS	4.00
1706. The Barrel Organ	9 x 7	CFA	1.00
1707. The Burden	9 x 7	CFA	1.00
1708. The Collector	16 x 13	CFA	10.00
	10 x 8	ESH	1.00
1709. Court Scene Interior	20 x 24	NYGS	10.00
1710. Legal Studies (16)		AA	35.00 set
			(H.C.)
1711. Notre Dame de Paris	22 x 16	PENN	1.00
			1.98 (Pr.)
1712. On the Barricades	22 x 17-1/2	AP	7.50
1713. Print Collector	16 x 12	CFA	10.00
	10 x 8	ESH	1.00
1714. La Soupe	7 x 10-1/2	NYGS	4.00
1715. Third Class Carriage	16 x 22	NYGS	7.50
	5-1/2 x 7-1/2	NYGS	.50
1716. Three Lawyers	15-1/2 x 12-1/2	NYGS	7.50
1717. Uprising	22 x 28-1/2	NYGS	15.00

DAVID, GERARD JANSZ   Dutch   1460-1523

1718. Adoration of the Kings	22-1/2 x 22-1/2	NYGS	18.00
1719. Arrest of the Judge Sisamne	13 x 11	IA	3.00
1720. Madonna with the Soup	13 x 11	IA	3.00
1721. Rest on the Flight into Egypt	18 x 18	NYGS	7.50
1722. Transfiguration	15 x 11	IA	3.00

DAVID, JACQUES-LOUIS   French   1748-1825

1723. Napoleon in his Study	28 x 17	NYGS	12.00
	14 x 8-1/2	NYGS	3.00
1724. Portrait of M.			

Seriziat	14 x 11	IA	3.00
1725. Portrait of Madame Seriziat and her Son	14 x 11	IA	3.00
DAVIES, ARTHUR BOWEN	American	1862-1928	
1726. Italian Landscape, the Apennines	28 x 43	NYGS	18.00
1727. Dearest Dolls	19 x 31	PENN	1.00
DAVIES, KEN			
1728. Black Board	20 x 26	CFA	10.00
1729. Blotter	16 x 24	CFA	10.00
1730. Bookcase	19 x 39	CFA	15.00
1731. End of Day	15 x 21	CFA	7.50
1732. George Washington	11 x 8	CFA	3.00
1733. Marine Collection	26 x 35	CFA	15.00
1734. Martha Washington	11 x 8	CFA	3.00
1735. Old Red Mill	15 x 21	CFA	7.50
1736. Red Accent	12 x 10	CFA	3.00
1737. Yellow Accent	12 x 10	CFA	3.00
DA VINCI See LEONARDO DA VINCI			
DAVIS, GLADYS ROCKMORE	American		
1738. Deborah and Nietzsche	16-1/2 x 22	NYGS	6.00
	5-1/2 x 7	NYGS	.50
1739. Music Lesson	16-1/2 x 22	NYGS	7.50
DAVIS, H. W. B.	English	1833-1914	
1740. Mother and Son	15-1/2 x 21	IA	4.00
DAVIS, STARK	American	1885-	
1741. Pheasants	24 x 24	CFA	10.00
DAVIS, STUART	American	1894-	
1742. Summer Landscape	18 x 27	MMA	6.50
1743. Visa	8 x 10	MMA	.35
DAWSON, MONTAGUE	English		
1744. Days of Adventure	20 x 30	RL	10.00
1745. Eight Bells	20 x 30	RL	10.00
1746. Fine Weather and a Fair Wind	20 x 30	RL	10.00
1747. Golden West	16-1/2 x 33	RL	10.00
1748. Neck and Neck	17 x 25	RL	7.50
1749. Ocean Racers	25 x 19	RL	7.50
1750. Racing Wings	20 x 30	RL	10.00
1751. Royal Racer	25 x 19	RL	7.50
1752. Summer Breezes	17 x 30	RL	10.00
1753. Winning Tack	17 x 25	RL	10.00
DAWSON, MURIEL			
1754. All on a Summer's Day	20 x 18	CAC	3.50
1755. Blue Butterfly	21 x 17	CAC	3.50
1756. Crossing the Stream	21 x 17	CAC	3.50
1757. Dragon Flies	15 x 12	CAC	3.50
1758. Fairy Boat	21 x 17	CAC	3.00
1759. Feeding the Calf	17 x 22	CAC	3.00

1760. Feeding the Donkey	17 x 22	CAC	3.00
1761. Feeding the Chickens	21 x 17	CAC	3.00
1762. Feeding the Lamb	21 x 17	CAC	3.00
1763. Finding the Leveret	15 x 12	CAC	2.00
1764. First Aconite	17 x 21	CAC	3.00
1765. Fun on the Beach	17 x 21	CAC	3.00
1766. Fun on the Gate	18 x 21	CAC	3.50
1767. Fun with the Chicks	21 x 17	CAC	3.50
1768. Gathering Apples	21 x 17	CAC	3.00
1769. Goose Girl	20 x 17	CAC	3.00
1770. Happy Childhood	12 x 15	CAC	2.00
1771. Happy Springtime	17 x 21	CAC	3.50
1772. Many Friends	17 x 21	CAC	3.00
1773. On the Cliff Top	21 x 17	CAC	3.50
1774. Picking Mushrooms	21 x 17	CAC	3.00
1775. Rabbits	17 x 21	CAC	3.50
1776. See Saw	21 x 17	CAC	3.50
1777. Squirrel's Breakfast	17 x 20	CAC	3.00
1778. Rainbow	15 x 12	CAC	2.00
1779. Three Scotties	17 x 20	CAC	3.00
1780. Tinker Tailor	21 x 17	CAC	3.50

DE CHIRICO, GIORGIO   See   CHIRICO, GIORGIO DE
DEARMAN

1781. Seasons (4)	10 x 12	AA	5.00 ea.

DEGAS, EDGAR HILAIRE GERMAIN   French   1834-1917

1782. L'Absinthe	24 x 18	PENN	1.00
1783. After the Bath	7 x 5	CFA	1.00
1784. Arabesque	22-1/2 x 12-1/2	ESH	10.00
	10 x 8	ESH	1.00
1785. At the Racecourse	18 x 23	HNA	5.95
1786. Ballerina	15 x 12	AA	6.00
1787. À L'Opera	18 x 22	NYGS	16.00
1788. Ballet	18 x 24	CFA	12.00
1789. Ballet Class	27-1/2 x 26	NYGS	15.00
1790. Ballet Dancer	8 x 5	CFA	1.00
1791. A Ballet Dancer: Fourth Position	19 x 24	NYGS	18.00
1792. Ballet Encore	16 x 20	PENN	1.00
1793. A Ballet Girl	15 x 12	AA	6.00
1794. Ballet Girls on Stage	22 x 15-1/2	NYGS	7.50
1795. Before the Ballet (Detail)	11 x 14	NYGS	3.00
1796. Before the Race	13 x 31	ESH	15.00
1797. Behind the Curtain	22-1/2 x 16-1/2	NYGS	10.00
1798. Café Concert	26 x 21	HNA	5.95
	10 x 8	ESH	1.00
1799. Carriage at the Races	14 x 21	ESH	10.00
1800. Classe de Danse	27 x 24	NYGS	12.00
	20 x 15	NYGS	4.00
1801. Curtain Call	8 x 10	ESH	1.00
1802. Dance Green Room	18 x 23	HNA	5.95
1803. The Dancer	15 x 10	CFA	5.00

1804. Dancer, Study No. One	16 x 10	NYGS	3.00
1805. Dancer, Study No. Two	16 x 10	NYGS	3.00
1806. Dancer Adjusting Costume	13 x 9	CFA	5.00
1807. Dancer at the Practice Bar	31 x 19	CAC	15.00
	8 x 5	CFA	1.00
1808. Dancer in her Dressing Room	31 x 13	IA	15.00
1809. Dancer on Stage	22-1/2 x 15-1/2	ESH	10.00
	10 x 8	ESH	1.00
1810. Dancer Leaning Forward	8 x 5	CFA	1.00
1811. Dancer Posing	10 x 8	ESH	1.00
1812. Dancer Posing for the Photographer	23 x 18	HNA	5.95
1813. Dancer Seated Lacing her Buskin	24-1/2 x 19-1/2	ESH	10.00
	10 x 8	ESH	1.00
1814. Dancer Standing	8 x 5	CFA	1.00
1815. Dancer Tying Her Slipper	22-1/2 x 17	ESH	10.00
1816. Dancer with Arms Behind Head	7 x 6	CFA	1.00
1817. Dancer with a Bouquet Curtsying	18 x 23	HNA	5.95
	18 x 20	PENN	1.00
1818. Dancer with Fan	15 x 10	CFA	5.00
1819. Dancer with Hand on Back	8 x 5	CFA	1.00
1820. The Dancers	23 x 18	HNA	5.95
	13-1/2 x 13-1/2	AR	3.00
1821. Dancers (Pink and Green)	24 x 22	NYGS	12.00
1822. Dancers Adjusting their Slippers	10-1/2 x 30	ESH	15.00
	9 x 27	PENN	1.00
1823. Dancers at the Practice Bar	31 x 25-1/2	NYGS	15.00
	7 x 6	NYGS	.50
1824. Dancers in Blue	22-1/2 x 21	ESH	10.00
	8 x 10	ESH	1.00
1825. Dancers in the Wings	17 x 13	NYGS	5.00
1826. Dancers on a Red Bench	19 x 21-1/2	PENN	1.00
1827. Dancers Preparing for the Ballet	28 x 23	NYGS	12.00
1828. Dancing Class	26 x 21	HNA	5.95
	24 x 20	PENN	1.00
	22-1/2 x 15-1/2	ESH	10.00
	10 x 8	ESH	1.00

1829.	Dancing Lesson	27 x 24	NYGS	12.00
		20 x 15	NYGS	4.00
1830.	Dancing Recital	15 x 20	NYGS	7.50
1831.	Dancing Studio	13 x 9	CFA	5.00
1832.	Danseuse au Bouquet	16 x 20	NYGS	7.50
		11 x 14	NYGS	3.00
		6 x 7	NYGS	.50
1833.	Danseuse de Dos	16 x 10-1/2	NYGS	5.00
1834.	Danseuses	9 x 12	NYGS	4.00
		8 x 10-1/2	NYGS	4.00
1835.	Danseuses Saluant	16 x 10-1/2	NYGS	5.00
1836.	Danseuses sur un Banquette	20 x 29	AR	12.00
1837.	Ecole de Danse	15 x 20	NYGS	7.50
		11 x 14	NYGS	3.00
1838.	L'Entree des Masques	19 x 25-1/2	AA	12.00
1839.	Femme à l'Ombrelle	11 x 8	NYGS	7.5u
1840.	Fin d'Arabesque	8 x 10	ESH	1.00
1841.	Four Dancers	19-1/2 x 23-1/2	PENN	1.00
		11 x 14	NYGS	3.00
1842.	Le Foyer de la Danse à l'Opera	18 x 23	HNA	5.95
		12-1/2 x 18	NYGS	6.00
		8 x 10	ESH	1.00
1843.	Girl at Ironing Board	20 x 16	PENN	1.00
1844.	Girl Looking through Opera Glasses	9 x 5	CFA	1.00
1845.	Green Dancers	8 x 10	ESH	1.00
1846.	Group of Dancers	8 x 10	ESH	1.00
1847.	Harlequin	8 x 10	ESH	1.00
1848.	Head of a Woman	12 x 10	NYGS	12.00
1849.	Ironers	21 x 22	CFA	7.50
185u.	Jeune Femme en Costume de Ville	10 x 8	NYGS	4.00
1851.	Jockeys	17 x 21-1/2	NYGS	20.00
1852.	Jockeys at Training	16 x 19	NYGS	16.00
1853.	Jockeys in the Rain	18-1/2 x 25	NYGS	15.00
1854.	Laundresses	21 x 24	PENN	1.00
1855.	Landscape	6 x 12	CFA	5.00
1856.	Little Harlequin	10 x 8	ESH	1.00
1857.	Mademoiselle Valpincon	19 x 28	NYGS	12.00
1858.	Master of Ballet Moraine	10 x 8	ESH	1.00
1859.	Millinery Shop	14 x 15-1/2	AJ	6.00
1860.	Petit Rat	10 x 7-1/2	NYGS	4.00
1861.	Pink and Green	23-1/2 x 21-1/2	NYGS	12.00
1862.	Race Horses	19 x 22	PENN	1.00
				1.98 (Pr.)
		18 x 23	HNA	5.95
1863.	Red Ballet Skirts	24 x 18	NYGS	12.00
1864.	La Repasseuse	26 x 21	NYGS	15.00
1865.	Seashore with Dunes	5-1/2 x 12	AJ	2.50

1866.	Seated Dancer	20 x 26	PENN	1.00
		10 x 8	ESH	1.00
1867.	Scène de Ballet	18 x 24	NYGS	12.00
1868.	Portfolio (8)	c. 10 x 12	PENN	1.98 set
	Dancing Class			
	Ballerina on Stage			
	Taking the Bow			
	Before the Ballet			
	Ballet Study			
	Two Dancers on Stage			
	Dancer with Bouquet			
	Rehearsal			
1869.	Study for "The Dancing			
	Class"	24 x 20	PENN	1.00
		10 x 8	ESH	1.00
1870.	Study in Half-Length	24 x 18	CAC	15.00
1871.	Three Dancers	25 x 19	CAC	10.00
		10 x 8	ESH	1.00
1872.	Le Tub	6 x 9	CAC	1.00
1873.	Two Dancers on Stage	24 x 19	PENN	1.00
		24 x 18	NYGS	7.50
1874.	Violinist Seated	15 x 11-1/2	NYGS	10.00
1875.	Washer Woman Carrying			
	Washing	6 x 8	CFA	1.00
1876.	Woman with Chrys-			
	anthemums	28 x 35-1/2	NYGS	18.00
		17 x 21-1/2	NYGS	7.50
		7-1/2 x 8	NYGS	.50
1877.	Woman Washing in			
	Her Bath	6 x 9	CFA	1.00
1878.	Yellow Harlequin	23 x 12	CAC	15.00
DE GRAZIA		American		
1879.	Mariachi in Blue	24 x 8	AA	5.00
1880.	Mariachi in Red	24 x 8	AA	5.00
1881.	Navajo Family	15 x 32	AA	12.00
DEHN, ADOLF ARTHUR		American	1895-	
1882.	Caribbean Fantasy	17 x 11	NYGS	10.00
1883.	Love, Labor and			
	Leisure	22 x 33	IA	12.00
1884.	Minnesota Farm	13-1/2 x 20	NYGS	7.50
1885.	Minnesota in August	12-1/2 x 18-1/2	NYGS	5.00
DE HOOCH, PIETER See HOOCH, PIETER DE				
DE JONGH See JONGH, TINUS DE				
DELACROIX, EUGENE		French	1798-1863	
1886.	Basket of Flowers in			
	Park	15 x 20	CFA	7.50
1887.	Etude de Cavalier	26 x 20	CAC	12.00
1888.	Flower Piece	23 x 29	AR	15.00
1889.	Hamlet	8 x 10	CAC	4.00
1890.	Head of a Lion	7 x 7-1/2	AR	5.00
1891.	Odalisque	9 x 12	CFA	2.50
DE LA TOUR See LATOUR, MAURICE QUENTIN DE				

DELDEVEZ
  1892. Spanish Afternoon   18 x 24   CAC   15.00
DELLA PORTA, FRA BARTOLOMMEO (BACCIO) See
        PAGHOLO, BARTOLOMMEO DI
DE LOO
  1893. Bayou Scenes (4)   10 x 24   DAC   2.80 ea.
                        5 x 12   DAC   .80 ea.
DELLA ROBBIA, ANDREA See ROBBIA, ANDREA DELLA
DELLA ROBBIA, LUCA See ROBBIA, LUCA DELLA
DEL PACCHIA See PACCHIA, GIROLAMO DEL
DEL SARTO, ANDREA See SARTO, ANDREA DEL
DEMAN, ALBERT   French   Contemporary
  1894. The Stream of Life   17 x 26   RL   10.00
DEMUTH, CHARLES   American   1883-1935
  1895. Acrobats   8 x 10   MMA   .35
  1896. Calla Lilies   13 x 19   CAC   5.00
  1897. Flower Study No. 1 18 x 12   CAC   5.00
  1898. Flower Study No. 4 18 x 12   CAC   5.00
DENIS, MAURICE   French   1870-
  1899. Sketches of Birds   11 x 15   ESH   8.00
DENISE
  1900. Portraits of Young
        Women (6)   14 x 11   DAC   1.20 ea.
                        8 x 6   DAC   .60 ea.
          Breath of Spring
          Garden Walk
          Gentle Breezes
          The Letter
          Little Sailor
          Springtime in Paris
DE PISIS See PISIS, FILIPO DE
DE POSTELS, ROBERT N.   American   1908-
  1901. The Happy Hours   16 x 34   NYGS   10.00
                    10-1/2 x 22   NYGS   5.00
DE POTVIN
  1902. Porte de la Tournelle 24 x 48   IA   10.00
DE PREDIS, AMBROGIO See PREDIS, GIOVANNI AMBROGIO DE
DERAIN, ANDRE   French   1880-1954
  1903. Ballet   18 x 23   CAC   15.00
  1904. Barges on the Thames 18 x 23   CAC   15.00
  1905. Blackfriars   19-1/2 x 24   NYGS   15.00
  1906. Blue Oak   16 x 20   NYGS   5.00
  1907. Boats in Harbour   8 x 10   ESH   1.00
  1908. Classical Landscape 8 x 10   ESH   1.00
  1909. Fishing Harbour   18 x 23   HNA   5.95
  1910. Flowers in a Vase   22-1/2 x 28-1/2 NYGS   12.00
                    6 x 7   NYGS   .50
  1911. Fruit Bowl   21 x 30   NYGS   15.00
  1912. Gravelines   20-1/2 x 31   NYGS   15.00
  1913. Great Pine   23 x 28   NYGS   18.00
  1914. Harbour   16 x 20   CFA   7.50
  1915. Harlequin   23-1/2 x 20   PENN   1.00

		23 x 18	HNA	5.95
1916.	Hyde Park	14 x 21	CFA	7.50
1917.	Landscape	23 x 30	ESH	15.00
1918.	London	6 x 8	CFA	1.00
1919.	London Bridge	24 x 30	MMA	6.50
		17 x 26	CFA	7.50
		8 x 10	MMA	.35
1920.	Nude	18 x 14	CFA	5.00
1921.	Old Bridge	25 x 31	NYGS	15.00
1922.	Pool of London	15 x 23	NYGS	12.00
1923.	Port of Collioure	15-1/2 x 20	AP	7.50
1924.	Red Landscape	8 x 10	ESH	1.00
1925.	Southern Landscape	8 x 10	ESH	1.00
1926.	The Tree	8 x 10	ESH	1.00

DE RIBERA   See RIBERA
DEROY, LEBRETON

1927.	View of Los Angeles	12 x 16	CFA	10.00

DESCHAMPS, GABRIEL   French   1919-

1928.	Dejeuner Provençal	23 x 28	RL	12.50
1929.	Little Boats, St. Jean	23 x 28	RL	12.50
1930.	Port de Cannes	28 x 22-1/2	RL	12.50
1931.	Le Rade de Villefranche	28 x 22-1/2	RL	12.50
1932.	Sailing Days	20-1/2 x 25	RL	12.50

DESIDERIO DA SETTIGNANO   Italian   1428-1464

1933.	St. John	15 x 11	IA	3.00

DESMOULINS

1934.	Fruits and Flowers	24 x 30	DAC	6.00

DESMAREST, S.

1935.	Flower Gatherers	12 x 16	DAC	2.00
		8 x 10	DAC	.80
1936.	Fountain	12 x 16	DAC	2.00
		8 x 10	DAC	.80
1937.	Little Women	12 x 16	DAC	2.00
		8 x 10	DAC	.80
1938.	Youthful Strollers	12 x 16	DAC	2.00
		8 x 10	DAC	.80

DESNOYERS, FRANCOIS   French   1894-

1939.	Bridge at Albi	8 x 10	ESH	1.00
1940.	Fishermen's Festival at Sete	17-1/2 x 22	ESH	10.00
1941.	Harbour of Algier	24 x 30	CAC	15.00
1942.	Pont du Diable	8 x 10	ESH	1.00
1943.	Poppies and Corn-flowers	22 x 18	CAC	10.00
1944.	Venice, 1930	13 x 22	CAC	10.00
1945.	Wild Flowers	22-1/2 x 18-1/2	ESH	10.00

DESOTO, MINNIE B. HALL   American

1946.	Christ the King	20 x 16	IA	5.00

DESSAU

1947.	Jesus, the Children Are Calling	25-1/2 x 19	IA	5.00
		11 x 8	IA	1.00

DE STAEL
   1948. Bottles   10 x 8   ESH   1.00

DE STAEL			
1948. Bottles	10 x 8	ESH	1.00
1949. Footballers	22 x 18	ESH	10.00
1950. Jazz Players	22-1/2 x 16	ESH	10.00
DETLEFSON, PAUL			
1951. Memories	24 x 40	DAC	8.00
	12 x 18	DAC	2.00
1952. Old Mill Stream	24 x 40	DAC	8.00
	12 x 18	DAC	2.00
1953. Red Caboose	24 x 30	DAC	8.00
1954. School's Out	24 x 40	DAC	8.00
	12 x 18	DAC	2.00
DEVE, EUGENE	French	1826-1887	
1955. The Calm	8 x 10	ESH	1.00
DEVIS, ARTHUR WILLIAM	English	1763-1822	
1956. Master Simpson			
(Friends)	30-1/2 x 25	IA	12.00
	24 x 19	IA	10.00
	18 x 14-1/2	IA	5.00
	14 x 11	IA	3.00
(Detail)	11-1/2 x 9	IA	1.50
	10 x 8	IA	1.00
DE ZURBURAN See ZURBURAN, FRANCISCO DE			
DIAZ, R.			
1957. Clown au Chapeau	21 x 15	IA	6.00
1958. Clown au Cheveux			
Rouges	18-1/2 x 15	IA	6.00
1959. Clown avec Marguerite	23-1/2 x 12	IA	6.00
DIAZ DE LA PENA, NARCISSE VIRGILE			
	French	1809-1876	
1960. Fontainebleau Woods	9 x 15	IA	3.00
1961. Three Little Girls	24 x 16	CFA	12.00
DICKINSON, PRESTON	American	1891-1930	
1962. Harlem River	13 x 19	NYGS	5.00
1963. Still Life	14-1/2 x 20-1/2	NYGS	10.00
DIDIER-POUGET, WILLIAM	French	1864-	
1964. Enchanted Valley	19 x 30	RL	7.50
DIETZ, ELMAR GEORG	German	1902-	
1965. Coast of Marinella	22 x 12	CFA	8.50
1966. Gondola	22 x 12	CFA	8.50
DILL, OTTO	German	1884-	
1967. Summer Day in Rome	26-1/2 x 21-1/2	ESH	10.00
DISNEY, WALT	American	1900-	
1968. Bambi Meets His			
Forest Friends	20 x 24	NYGS	4.00
	15 x 18	NYGS	2.00
	10 x 12	NYGS	1.00
1969. Forest Secrets	20 x 24	NYGS	4.00
	15 x 18	NYGS	2.00
	10 x 12	NYGS	1.00
1970. Good Friends All	20 x 24	NYGS	4.00
	15 x 18	NYGS	2.00

	10 x 12	NYGS	1.00
1971. Snow White's Last			
Call for Dinner	20 x 24	NYGS	4.00
	15 x 18	NYGS	2.00
	10 x 12	NYGS	1.00
DIX, OTTO	German	1891-	
1972. Bernina	23 x 26	CAC	10.00
1973. Mountain and Stream	23 x 26	CFA	10.00
1974. Sunrise in Hegau	28 x 24-1/2	ESH	12.00
DIXON, MAYNARD	American	1875-	
1975. Home on the Desert	18 x 20	NYGS	7.50
DOEVE			
1976. Flower Subjects (4)	9 x 8	DAC	.80 ea.
DOLCI, CARLO	Italian	1616-1686	
1977. Ecce Homo	10 x 7	IA	1.50
1978. The Eternal Father			
1979. The Magdalene	10 x 14 (Lozenge)	IA	3.00
1980. Madonna and Child	15 x 11	IA	3.00
1981. Madonna del Dito	15 x 12	IA	3.00
1982. Madonna of the	14 x 11	IA	3.00
Veil			
1983. Portrait of Arnolfo	14 x 11	IA	3.00
de'Bardi	14 x 11	IA	3.00
1984. St. Agnes	14 x 11	IA	3.00
1985. St. Apollonia	13 x 11	IA	3.00
1986. St. Rosa	13 x 9	IA	3.00
1987. Virgin and Child	14 x 11	IA	3.00
DOMENICHINO	Italian	1581-1641	
1988. Chase of Diana	11 x 15	IA	3.00
1989. Cumaean Sibyl	15 x 11	IA	3.00
1990. Landscape with Venus,			
Amor and Satyrs	10 x 13 oval	IA	3.00
DOMENICO DI BARTOLO	Italian	1400-1449	
1991. Madonna and Child	15 x 8	IA	3.00
DOMENICO VENEZIANO See	VENEZIANO, DOMENICO DI		
BARTOLOMMEO			
DONATELLO (DOMENICO DI NICOLO DI BETTO DEI SARDI)			
	Italian	1382-1466	
1992. Nicolo da Uzzano	15 x 11	IA	3.00
1993. St. George	15 x 11	IA	3.00
DONGEN, CORNELIUS (OR KEES) VAN			
	Dutch	1877-	
1994. "Bar du Soleil" à			
Deauville	18-1/2 x 22	ESH	10.00
1995. Beach at Deauville	18 x 22	CAC	10.00
1996. Bois de Boulogne	19 x 23	CAC	15.00
1997. Flower Basket	23 x 18	NYGS	10.00
1998. Tulips	19 x 36	NYGS	15.00
	12-1/2 x 23-1/2	NYGS	7.50
DORING, ANTON			
1999. Garden Glory	20 x 15-1/2	NYGS	7.50
DOSAMANTES, FRANCISCO	Mexican	1911-	

2000. The Kiln	25 x 19-1/2	NYGS	15.00
DOSSI, DOSSO (GIOVANNI LUTERI) Italian		1479-1542	
2001. Circe and Her Lovers			
in a Landscape	23 x 31-1/2	NYGS	16.00
DOU, GERARD	Dutch	1613-1675	
2002. Hydropic Woman	14 x 11	IA	3.00
2003. School Master	14 x 11	IA	3.00
DOVE, ARTHUR C.	American	1880-1817	
2004. Abstract, Flour Mill	25-1/2 x 16	NYGS	10.00
2005. Mars, Orange and			
Green	13-1/2 x 20	NYGS	10.00
DOVASTON			
2006. And So the Story Goes	20 x 30	CAC	7.50
2007. Auld Lang Syne	22 x 30	CAC	7.50
DROLLING, MARTIN (THE ELDER) French		1752-1817	
2008. Interior of a Kitchen	11 x 14	IA	3.00
DROUAIS, FRANCOIS-HUBERT French		1727-1775	
2009. Duc d'Orleans	32 x 12-1/2	AL	12.00
2010. The Duke of Berry and			
the Count of Provence			
as Boys	11 x 15	IA	3.00
2011. Group Portrait	30 x 25	AA	12.00
2012. Mlle. de Charlois	32 x 12-1/2	AL	12.00
DRUMMOND			
2013. Bourbon Street	15 x 40	DAC	8.00
2014. New Orleans (2)	10 x 24	DAC	2.80 ea.
	5 x 12	DAC	.80 ea.
DUBOIS, P. H.			
2015. Art Class	10 x 14	CAC	10.00
2016. Lakeside Road	16 x 20	NYGS	7.50
2017. Paris Cafe Morning	20 x 16	CAC	5.00
2018. Sunday by the Sea	16 x 20	NYGS	7.50
DUCCIO DI BUONINSEGNA Italian		1255-1319	
2019. Calling of the Apostles,			
Peter and Andrew	16 x 17	NYGS	10.00
2020. La Madonna dei			
Francescani (The			
Virgin Adored)	9 x 7	IA	1.50
2021. The Maries at the			
Tomb	11 x 12	IA	3.00
2022. The Virgin	15 x 11	IA	3.00
DUCHAMP, MARCEL (DUCHAMP-VILLON)			
	French	1888-	
2023. Nude Descending a			
Staircase No. 2	30 x 18	NYGS	18.00
DUFY, JEAN	French	1888-	
2024. Bois de Boulogne	18 x 23	CFA	12.00
	11 x 14	DAC	2.80
2025. Champs Elysees	18 x 22	DAC	5.00
	11 x 14	DAC	2.80
2026. Circus Band	23-1/2 x 18	NYGS	10.00
	14 x 11	NYGS	3.00

2027. Guitar Clown	23-1/2 x 18	NYGS	10.00
	14 x 11	NYGS	3.00
2028. Le Fiacre	18-1/2 x 24	AA	12.00
2029. Jockeys	18-1/2 x 24	PENN	1.00
2030. Mannequins at the Races			
Races	16 x 24	PENN	1.00
2031. Mediterranean Scene	18 x 24	PENN	1.00
2032. Normandy Tree	16 x 20	PENN	1.00
2033. Paris: Ile de la Cité	23 x 18	NYGS	15.00
2034. Paris: La Seine	23 x 18	NYGS	15.00
2035. Regatta	11-1/2 x 27-1/2	PENN	1.00
2036. Le Rond Point	18 x 22	DAC	5.00
	11 x 14	DAC	2.80
2037. St. Jeannet	20 x 24	PENN	1.00
2038. San Giorgio Maggiore	20 x 24	PENN	1.00
2039. Springtime in Paris	18-1/2 x 35-1/2	NYGS	15.00
2040. The Phaeton--			
Detail of No. 2039	14 x 6	NYGS	4.00
2041. Sunday Afternoon	19 x 24	NYGS	10.00
2042. The Three-Quarter			
Coach	14 x 18	NYGS	4.00
2043. View of Paris	17 x 23	CFA	15.00
DUFY, RAOUL	French	1877-1953	
2044. Anemones	22-1/2 x 16-1/2	ESH	10.00
	16 x 12	NYGS	4.00
	10 x 8	ESH	1.00
2045. Ascot	11-1/2 x 30	CFA	10.00
2046. Baccarat Party	16 x 20	PENN	1.00
2047. The Beach	8 x 10	ESH	1.00
2048. Beach Promenade	18 x 24	NYGS	12.00
2049. Before the Start	6 x 9	CFA	1.00
2050. Blue Mozart	6 x 8	CFA	1.00
2051. Boating, 1935	24 x 30	ESH	15.00
	11 x 14	DAC	2.80
2052. Bouquet	24 x 18-1/2	NYGS	12.00
2053. Bullfight	20 x 24	AR	12.00
2054. The Cage	23 x 18	HNA	5.95
	18-1/2 x 14	CFA	7.50
2055. Cargo Noir	19 x 24	CAC	15.00
2056. Carnival at Nice	20 x 24	AR	12.00
2057. Casino in Nice	20 x 24	NYGS	12.00
2058. Chateau and Horses	23 x 28	NYGS	12.00
2059. Circus	18 x 24	CAC	10.00
2060. Circus Band	24 x 18	CAC	10.00
	14 x 11	CAC	3.00
2061. The Concert	18 x 23	HNA	5.95
	8 x 10	ESH	1.00
2062. Le Concerte Orange	18 x 22-1/2	ESH	10.00
2063. The Cornfield	21 x 26	NYGS	15.00
2064. Deauville	14 x 32	CFA	15.00
	18 x 23	HNA	5.95
2065. Deauville, 1935	17-1/2 x 25-1/2	NYGS	12.00

2066.	Decor for the Ballet "Palm Beach"	18 x 22-1/2	ESH	10.00
2067.	Flowers	10 x 8	ESH	1.00
2068.	Gladioli	24 x 18-1/2	NYGS	12.00
2069.	Haymakers	14 x 18	CFA	7.50
2070.	Homage to Mozart	25-1/2 x 20	NYGS	15.00
2071.	Honfleur Harbor	18 x 24	NYGS	12.00
2072.	Horas du Pin	21-1/2 x 28	NYGS	12.00
2073.	Joinville	11-1/2 x 29	NYGS	12.00
2074.	The Lawn	7 x 9	CFA	1.00
2075.	Lilies	14 x 12	CFA	5.00
2076.	Marseilles, the Old Port	18-1/2 x 24	NYGS	12.00
2077.	Monte Carlo	19 x 23	AR	15.00
2078.	Open Window in Nice	24 x 20	CAC	7.50
2079.	Paddock	20 x 24	CFA	15.00
2080.	Paddock at Chantilly	13 x 18	CAC	7.50
2081.	Paddock at Deauville	12 x 30	AR	10.00
		13 x 18	CAC	7.50
		10-1/2 x 26	PENN	1.00
2082.	Paddock at Longchamp	7 x 9	CFA	1.00
2083.	Piazetta	18 x 24	AA	12.00
2084.	Polo	18 x 24	NYGS	12.00
2085.	Port of Honfleur	20 x 24	CFA	15.00
2086.	Race at Epsom	7 x 9	CAC	4.00
2087.	Racecourse at Deauville	17 x 22-1/2	ESH	10.00
2088.	Races	14 x 19	CAC	5.00
2089.	Races at Deauville	20 x 26	CAC	15.00
2090.	Races at Goodwood	18 x 23	HNA	5.95
2091.	Red Violin	17 x 22	CFA	12.00
		6 x 8	CFA	1.00
2092.	Regatta, 1938	11-1/2 x 29	NYGS	12.00
2093.	Regatta at Deauville	18-1/2 x 23	ESH	10.00
2094.	Regatta at Henley	19-1/2 x 26	NYGS	12.00
2095.	Regates on Thames	20 x 24	CFA	15.00
2096.	Roses	17 x 22-1/2	ESH	10.00
2097.	Rowing at Henley	19 x 25	CAC	15.00
2098.	Sailboats at Le Havre	14 x 17	CAC	4.00
2099.	Sailboats at Normandy	12-1/2 x 30-1/2	ESH	15.00
2100.	St. Jean	15 x 19	CAC	12.00
2101.	The Sea at Le Havre	8 x 10	ESH	1.00
2102.	Self-Portrait of the Artist with His Model	16-1/2 x 21-1/2	NYGS	7.50
2103.	The Stands at St. Cloud	6 x 9	CFA	1.00
2104.	The Steamer	16 x 12	CAC	4.00
2105.	Syracuse	18-1/2 x 25	NYGS	15.00
2106.	Toledo	6 x 8	CFA	1.00
2107.	Track No. 1	13 x 18	AR	6.00
2108.	Track No. 2	13 x 18	AR	6.00

2109. Tulipes	19 x 25	AA	12.00
2110. Vase of Anemones	23 x 18	HNA	5.95
2111. Vernissage	19 x 26	CFA	15.00
2112. Village Garden	19-1/2 x 26-1/2	NYGS	12.00
2113. Yacht Basin	8 x 10	ESH	1.00
2114. Yachts at Deauville	14 x 18	CAC	7.50
DUNBAR, P.	English		
2115. Off San Francisco	24 x 30	NYGS	7.50
DUPLESSIS, JOSEPH S.	French	1725-1802	
2116. Benjamin Franklin	22 x 18	NYGS	12.00
DURAND, ASHER BROWN	American	1796-1886	
2117. Catskill Mountains	16-1/2 x 24	NYGS	10.00
2118. Monument Mountain	24 x 35-1/2	NYGS	15.00
2119. Sunday Morning	24-1/2 x 35-1/2	NYGS	15.00
	17-1/2 x 26	NYGS	7.50
DURER, ALBRECHT	German	1471-1528	
2120. Adoration of the Magi	11 x 13	IA	3.00
2121. The All Holy	22 x 20	IA	18.00
2122. The Apostles Paul and Mark	27 x 10	CFA	10.00
2123. The Apostles John and Peter	27 x 10	CFA	10.00
2124. The Castle Court, Innsbruck	14 x 10	CFA	5.00
2125. Celandine	11 x 6	CFA	4.00
2126. Christ on the Cross	12-1/2 x 8-1/2	AR	3.50
2127. Columbine	14 x 11	CFA	4.00
2128. Courtyard of Innsbruck	14 x 10	CFA	5.00
2129. Covered Bridge, Nurnberg	16 x 13	CFA	4.00
2130. Head of an Apostle	11-1/2 x 9-1/2	AR	3.00
2131. Interior of Castle Innsbruck	13 x 10	CFA	5.00
2132. Impenitent Thief	12 x 6	CFA	3.50
2133. Iris	20 x 12	AR	7.50
2134. Large Group of Plants	16 x 12	CFA	5.00
2135. Lavender	10 x 8	CFA	4.00
2136. Little House by a Pond	7 x 9	CFA	4.00
2137. Little Owl	7 x 5	CFA	3.00
2138. Madonna of the Iris	10 x 8	ESH	1.00
2139. Madonna Surrounded by Animals	12 x 10	CFA	4.00
2140. A Mounted Knight	16 x 13	CFA	5.00
2141. Nurnberg from the West	6-1/2 x 14	AR	4.00
2142. Nurnberg Wife in Ball Dress	12 x 8	CFA	4.00
2143. Nurnberg Wife in Church Dress	12 x 8	CFA	4.00
2144. Nurnberg Wife in House Dress	12 x 8	CFA	4.00
2145. Pansies	11 x 6	CFA	4.00

2146. Peonies	15 x 12	CFA	7.50
2147. Penitent Thief	12-1/2 x 6-1/2	AR	3.50
2148. Portrait of the Artist at Age 13	11 x 7	AR	3.00
2149. Portrait of the Artist's Father	20 x 16	AR	12.00
	14 x 11	IA	3.00
	13 x 10	AR	1.50
2150. Portrait of the Artist's Wife, Agnes, Drawn as St. Anne	15-1/2 x 11-1/2	AR	5.00
2151. Portrait of Emperor Maximilian I	21 x 19	NYGS	10.00
	15 x 12	CAC	5.00
2152. Portrait of Ulrich Varnbuhler	16 x 13	CFA	5.00
2153. Praying Hands (Hands of a Praying Apostle)	17 x 12	IA	2.50
	11 x 8	IA	1.00
	10-1/2 x 7-1/2	IA	1.50
2154. The Quay at Antwerp	8 x 11	CFA	3.00
2155. Reunion of the Saints	22 x 20	AR	15.00
2156. St. Jerome	16 x 11	CFA	5.00
2157. St. John's Church in Nurnberg	11 x 17	CFA	7.50
2158. Self-Portrait	23 x 18	HNA	5.95
	18 x 14	CAC	7.50
	18 x 14	CAC	10.00
	14 x 11	IA	3.00
	11 x 8	CFA	2.50
2159. Squirrels	9 x 8-1/2	NYGS	3.00
2160. Study of a Dead Roller	11 x 8	AR	3.50
2161. Sunset	18 x 14	AR	7.50
2162. Three Linden Trees	14 x 9	CAC	5.00
2163. Three Riders Attacked by Death	12 x 17-1/2	AR	5.00
2164. View of Trient	9-1/2 x 14	AR	3.50
2165. Virgin and Child	10 x 8	ESH	1.00
2166. Wing of a Roller	8 x 8	AR	3.50
2167. Young Field Hare	10 x 9	CFA	2.50
	9-1/2 x 8	NYGS	7.50
DURRIE, GEORGE HARVEY	American	1820-1863	
2168. Home to Thanksgiving	14-1/2 x 24-1/2	NYGS	7.50
DUVAL			
2169. Chartres	8 x 10	ESH	1.00
DYCK, (SIR) ANTHONY See VAN DYCK			
DYF, MARCEL	French	1899-	
2170. Autumn's Bounty	19 x 16	IA	5.00
2171. By the Towpath	20-1/2 x 25	RL	12.50
2172. Flowers from My Garden	20 x 16	IA	5.00

2173. Girl with a Birdcage	18-1/2 x 15	IA	5.00
2174. Girl with a Mandolin	18-1/2 x 15	IA	5.00
2175. Peonies in a Stone Vase	24 x 20	RL	12.50
2176. Portrait of Claudine	24 x 20	RL	10.00
2177. Reverie	24 x 20	RL	12.50
2178. The Sonnet	21-1/2 x 18	RL	15.00
2179. Springtime Symphony	20 x 16	IA	5.00
2180. Summer's Offering	19 x 16	IA	5.00
2181. Terrace in Summer	26 x 21-1/2	RL	12.50

DZIGURSKI, ALEX

2182. Golden Sunset	24 x 40	AA	12.00
2183. Imperia, Italy	16 x 20	IA	3.00
2184. Mediterranean Coast	24 x 36	AA	12.00
2185. Pacific Breakers	24 x 40	AA	12.00
2186. Positano, Italy	16 x 20	IA	3.00
2187. Rock-Bound Coast	24 x 48	AA	15.00

E

EAKINS, THOMAS — American — 1844-1916

2188. The Actress	10 x 7	NYGS	.50
2189. The Biglen Brothers Racing	18 x 23	HNA	5.95
2190. The Concert Singer	10 x 7	NYGS	.50
2191. John Biglen in a Single Scull	24 x 15-1/2	NYGS	12.00
	9 x 6	NYGS	.50
2192. Max Schmitt in a Single Scull	20-1/2 x 30	NYGS	5.00
2193. Pushing for Rail	14 x 21-1/2	NYGS	7.50
2194. Sailing	12-1/2 x 18-1/2	NYGS	5.00
2195. Turning Stake Boat	17 x 25	PENN	1.00
2196. William Rush Carving	7 x 10	NYGS	.50
2197. Will Schuster and Black Man Shooting	19 x 26	NYGS	15.00
	7 x 9-1/2	NYGS	.50

EARL (OR EARLE), MAUDE — English — ac. 1884-1934

2198. Golden Retriever	25 x 30	AA	10.00

EARL (OR EARLE), RALPH — American — 1751-1801

2199. William Carpenter	23-1/2 x 17-1/2	NYGS	12.00
2200. Winter Window Box	18 x 30-1/2	PENN	1.00

EBBINGHAUS, KARL — German — 1872-1950

2201. Sacred Heart of Jesus	39-1/2 x 27-1/2	IA	10.00
	29 x 21-1/2	IA	5.00
2202. Sacred Heart of Mary	39-1/2 x 29	IA	7.50
	29 x 21	IA	5.00

EBERHARDT   See   MEYER-EBERHARDT

EDWARDS, MAGDALENE

2203. Iris	17-1/2 x 17	NYGS	3.00
2204. Orchid	17-1/2 x 17	NYGS	3.00

EDZARD, DIETZ — German (Res. France) — 1893-

2205. Angelica	20 x 16	AA	7.50
2206. At the Lodge	16 x 12	CFA	3.00
2207. At the Opera	27 x 22	CFA	12.00
	16 x 12	CFA	3.00
2208. La Chanteuse	16 x 12	CFA	3.00
2209. Christine	20 x 16	AA	7.50
2210. Le Debut	16 x 12	CFA	3.00
2211. Flowers and Music (2)	17 x 9	ESH	6.00 ea.
2212. Flowers and Music with Piano	18 x 23	HNA	5.95
2213. Flowers and Music with Violin	18 x 23	HNA	5.95
2214. Le Grand Ballet	18 x 26	DAC	6.00
2215. On the Banks of the Seine	18-1/2 x 23	ESH	10.00
2216. Les Parisiennes	17 x 21	CAC	15.00
2217. Place de la Concorde	28-1/2 x 23-1/2	NYGS	15.00
EGYPT			
2218. King Tutankhamen, Golden Effigy of	21-1/2 x 19	NYGS	10.00
2219. Lady Tent-Shenat, Painted Wooden Stele of	10 x 8	ESH	1.00
2220. Tomb Decoration	8 x 10	ESH	1.00
EHEMANN			
2221. Algiers	12 x 20	ESH	4.00 (Pr.)
2222. Flower Market	12 x 20	ESH	4.00 (Pr.)
2223. Mallorca	12 x 20	ESH	4.00 (Pr.)
2224. Marrakesch	12 x 20	ESH	4.00 (Pr.)
2225. Sailing Harbour	12 x 20	ESH	4.00 (Pr.)
2226. Sunflowers	19-1/2 x 27-1/2	ESH	8.00 (Pr.)
EICHHORN, ALFRED	Austrian	1909-	
2227. The Isle	17 x 26	CFA	12.00
EICHINGER, E.	German	1929-	
2228. The Connoisseur	10 x 12	RL	2.50
EICHSTAEDT, RUDOLPH	German	1857-1926	
2229. Christ in Emmaus	18-1/2 x 26-1/2	IA	7.50
EILSHEMIUS, LOUIS MICHEL	American	1864-	
2230. Village near Delaware Watergap	18-1/2 x 27-1/2	PENN	1.00
EISENDIECK, SUZANNE	German	1908-	
2231. Nicole	22 x 18	DAC	4.00
2232. Nicole et Nicolette	22 x 26	DAC	6.00
2233. Sunday at Sannois	20 x 24	CAC	12.00
ELDER, JOHN A.	American	1833-1895	
2234. Jackson, General T. J.	30 x 22	NYGS	12.00
	20 x 14-1/2	NYGS	6.00
	14 x 10	NYGS	3.00
	8 x 6	NYGS	1.00
2235. Lee, General Robert E.	30 x 22	NYGS	12.00
	20 x 14-1/2	NYGS	6.00

		14 x 10	NYGS	3.00
		8 x 6	NYGS	1.00
ELFORD, VICTOR		English		
2236. Henley Royal Regatta		18 x 27	RL	7.50
EL GRECO See GRECO, EL				
ELLINGER, DAVID Y.		American	Ac. 1947	
2237. Country Auction		22 x 27	CAC	18.00
ELLIS				
2238. Fragrant June		24 x 20	NYGS	7.50
2239. July Splendor		24 x 20	NYGS	7.50
ELMIGER, FREDERICK				
2240. Autos, Early (6)		9 x 11	DAC	.80 ea.
		6 x 8	DAC	.40 ea.

Buick Touring Car, 1910
Chevrolet Roadster, 1913
Ford Touring Car, 1911
Nash Rambler Runabout, 1902
Oldsmobile Runabout, 1901
Packard Limousine, 1908

2241. Musical Instruments				
(6)		11 x 5-1/2	DAC	.80 ea.
2242. Regalia, Period (8)		14 x 5	DAC	.80 ea.
2243. Soldiers, Continental				
(4)		20 x 7	DAC	1.60 ea.
		14 x 5	DAC	.80 ea.

American Dragoon
Continental Army Private
Colonel of Artillery
Washington's Bodyguard

| 2244. Transportation (8) | | 14 x 5 | DAC | .80 ea. |

Christmas Shopping
Fire!
Gypsy Caravan
Journey's End
On the Erie Canal
Parting Guests
Shore Leave
Sunday Picnic

2245. Treasure Maps (4)		11 x 14	DAC	2.00 ea.
EMBLER, E.				
2246. Late Summer Day		20 x 40	DAC	8.00
		9 x 17-1/2	DAC	2.00
EMERY, LESLIE		American		
2247. Children of Erin				
(Donegal)		28-1/2 x 19	IA	10.00
2248. Child Song		28-1/2 x 14	IA	7.50
2249. Golf Clowns (8)		12-1/2 x 10	IA	2.00 ea.

Case of Mistaken Identity
Hand Niblick
Midsummer Nightmare
Club House Activity
Golf Shark

A Little Help, Please
Nineteenth Hole
Perplexed

2250. The Phoenix	21-1/2 x 16	IA	7.50
2251. Tender Burden	24-1/2 x 18	IA	6.00
2252. This Is My Love	19 x 24	IA	7.50
ENDE, HANS	German	1864-1918	
2253. Twilight	18 x 24	CFA	7.50
ENNESS, A. W.	English	1876-1948	
2254. Bluebell Wood	18 x 28	RL	7.50
2255. Evening Solitude	18-1/2 x 22-1/2	RL	6.00
ENSOR, JAMES	Belgian	1860-1949	
2256. Carnival	20-1/2 x 28	NYGS	12.00
	7 x 9	NYGS	.50
2257. Skeletons Fighting for Body of a Hanged Man	8 x 10	MMA	.35
2258. Tribulations of St. Anthony	8 x 10	MMA	.35
ENSTROM, IRENE	American	Ac. 1960	
2259. Grace	16 x 21	IA	3.00
	10 x 13-1/2	IA	2.00
ERBSLOH, ADOLF	German	1881-1947	
2260. In the Alps	12 x 16	ESH	4.00
ERNI, HANS	Swiss	1909-	
2261. Two Horses	18 x 23	HNA	5.95
ERNST, MAX	German	1891-	
2262. Flying Geese	18 x 23-1/2	PENN	1.00
2263. The Nymph Echo	8 x 10	MMA	.35
2264. Petrified City	19 x 23	NYGS	18.00
ESTÈVE, MAURICE	French	1904-	
2265. Composition, 1956	18-1/2 x 22-1/2	ESH	10.00
ESCHBACH, PAUL	French	1881-	
2266. Off Concarneau	20 x 24	CAC	6.00
2267. Winter Sunshine	23 x 28	CAC	12.00
ETRUSCAN ART			
2268. Amphora with Black Figures	15 x 11	NYGS	4.00
2269. Black, Figured Amphora	15 x 11	NYGS	4.00
2270. Dancer	41 x 33	CFA	25.00
	10 x 8	ESH	1.00
2271. Dancer (Poster)	29 x 23	CFA	15.00
2272. Flute Player	23 x 18	HNA	5.95
	22-1/2 x 18	ESH	10.00
2273. Fresco with Horses	9 x 32-1/2	NYGS	12.00
2274. Lyre Player	22-1/2 x 18	ESH	10.00
2275. Musicians	15 x 30-1/2	NYGS	12.00
2276. The Offering	17 x 22-1/2	ESH	10.00
2277. Pair of Winged Horses	15 x 11	NYGS	4.00
2278. Pipe Player	10 x 8	ESH	1.00
2279. Red-Figured Crater	15 x 11	NYGS	4.00

2280. Red-Figured Vase	15 x 11	NYGS	4.00
EURICH, RICHARD	English	1903-	
2281. Continental Harbour	19-1/2 x 25	RL	6.00
EUSTACHIO, FRA	Italian	1473-1555	
2282. King David Adoring	9 x 8	IA	1.50
EVE, JEAN	French	1900-	
2283. St. Remy	11 x 14	DAC	.80
2284. Winter in St. Remy	11 x 14	DAC	2.80
EVERGOOD, PHILIP	American	1901-1963	
2285. Child and Sparrow	21 x 15	AA	6.00

EYCK, HUBERT VAN See VAN EYCK
EYCK, JAN VAN   See VAN EYCK

F

FABRIANO, GENTILE See GENTILE DA FABRIANO			
FAED, JOHN	Scotch	1819-1902	
2286. Washington on the			
Field of Trenton	26 x 20	CAC	10.00
	20 x 16	CAC	5.00
FALICK, MURRAY			
2287. Pistols, Early			
American (6)	5 x 8	IA	1.50 ea.
Flintlock (3)			
Percussion (2)			
Single Shot (1)			
FANTIN-LATOUR, HENRI (IGNACE HENRI JEAN THEODORE)			
	French	1836-1904	
2288. Bouquet de Julienne			
et Fruits	19 x 18	IA	6.00
2289. Chrysanthemums	23 x 18	HNA	5.95
2290. Flowers and Fruit	28 x 24	CFA	15.00
	23 x 18	PENN	1.00
2291. Portrait of Sonia	23 x 18	HNA	5.95
2292. Roses and Blue Jug	11 x 13	IA	3.00
2293. Still Life	22 x 27	NYGS	16.00
2294. Still Life--Corner of			
a Table	16 x 20	CFA	7.50
2295. Summer Bouquet	11 x 14	DAC	2.80
FATTORI, GIOVANNI	Italian	1825-1908	
2296. Repose	9 x 19	IA	3.00
FAUSETT, DEAN (WILLIAM DEAN) American		1913-	
2297. Ancient Maple	25 x 30	AA	12.00
2298. Autumn in Vermont	16 x 20	AA	3.50
2299. Big Elms	16 x 20	NYGS	7.50
2300. Colorado Ranch	16 x 24	CFA	6.00
2301. Country Road	18 x 24	NYGS	15.00
2302. Derby View, Vermont	21-1/2 x 36	AA	3.50
2303. Haying Time	16 x 20	NYGS	7.50
2304. The Lake	18 x 24	NYGS	15.00
2305. Midsummer	24 x 36	AA	12.00
2306. River Village	23-1/2 x 36	IA	12.00

2307.	Road to the Hills	25 x 30	AA	3.50
2308.	Vermont Pastorale	16 x 20	AA	3.50

FAUST, CARL   German   1874-1935

2309.	Apple Blossoms	19-1/2 x 27-1/2	ESH	8.00 (Pr.)
2310.	Beer-Drinking Monk	9 x 12	ESH	2.00 (Pr.)
2311.	Cloister Cellar	16 x 20	ESH	5.00 (Pr.)
2312.	Greek Fishing Boats	19-1/2 x 27-1/2	ESH	8.00 (Pr.)
2313.	Sunny Forest	23-1/2 x 19-1/2	ESH	8.00 (Pr.)

FAWSETT

2314.	Ducks (6)	12 x 16	CFA	6.00 ea.

FEDDEN, MARY   English   Contemporary

2315.	Breton Musicians	18 x 25	RL	7.50

FEININGER, LYONEL   American   1871-1956

2316.	Barefoot Church in Halle	24-1/2 x 31	NYGS	18.00
2317.	Before the Rain	17 x 31	CFA	18.00
2318.	Big Cutters	15 x 28	ESH	12.00
2319.	Blue Coast	16 x 30	NYGS	15.00
2320.	Blue Marine	18 x 32	NYGS	15.00
2321.	Cathedral of Halle	20-1/2 x 17	PENN	1.00
2322.	The Church	24 x 19	PENN	1.00
				1.98 (Pr.)
2323.	The Church	18 x 14-1/2	NYGS	10.00
2324.	Church in Erfurt	31 x 24-1/2	IA	18.00
2325.	Church of the Minorites	19-1/2 x 16-1/2	IA	4.00
2326.	Gelmoroda	27-1/2 x 22	IA	18.00
2327.	Gelmoroda XII	23 x 18	HNA	5.95
2328.	Gelmoroda, 1926	27-1/2 x 22	NYGS	18.00
2329.	Market Place in Halle (Day of Devotion)	30 x 24	IA	18.00
2330.	Mouth of River Rega	18-1/2 x 28-1/2	ESH	12.00
2331.	Mouth of River Rega III	18-1/2 x 30-1/2	IA	12.00
2332.	Orange Sails	16-1/2 x 28	IA	15.00
2333.	Pyramid of Sails	18 x 29	NYGS	18.00
2334.	Sight of a Village	21 x 23-1/2	PENN	1.00
2335.	Steamer "Odin II"	21-1/2 x 32	MMA	15.00
		8 x 10	MMA	.35
2336.	Stormy Arrival	10 x 16	IA	8.00
2337.	Topsail Schooner	20 x 26	AR	12.00
2338.	Two Yachts	9-1/2 x 14	IA	8.00
2339.	Village Street	22 x 28	NYGS	15.00

FERRANDIZ CASTELLS, JUAN   Spanish

2340.	Adoration	21 x 15	NYGS	7.50
		14 x 10	NYGS	3.00
2341.	Holy Night	21 x 15	NYGS	7.50
		14 x 10	NYGS	3.00

FERRARI, FRANCESCO BIANCHI   Italian   1460-1510

2342.	Christ in the Gethsemane Garden (Detail)	14 x 11	IA	3.00

FERRARI, GAUDENZIO	Italian	1487-1546	
2343. Adoration of the Magi	9 x 22	AR	4.00
FERRUZZI. ROBERTO	Italian	1854-1934	
2344. Madonnina (Madonna			
of the Street)	26 x 20	IA	10.00
	20-1/2 x 16	NYGS	4.00
	15 x 10	IA	3.00
	10 x 7-1/2	NYGS	.50
2345. Detail of No. 2344	15 x 20	IA	7.50
	11 x 15	IA	3.00
FETI, DOMENICO	Italian	1487-1946	
2346. Prodigal Son	15 x 11	IA	3.00
FEUCHTMAYER, JOSEPH			
2347. Honey Taster	15 x 9	CFA	5.00
FEUERBORN, JOSEPH			
2348. Cablecar to Chinatown	40 x 20	IA	15.00
2349. Golden Candles	40 x 20	IA	15.00
2350. Hong Kong	20 x 40	IA	15.00
2351. Matador I	36 x 12	IA	12.00
2352. Matador II	36 x 12	IA	12.00
2353. Opening Night	20 x 40	IA	15.00
2354. Still Life	20 x 40	IA	15.00
FIENE, ERNEST	German	1894-	
2355. Clown in Front of a			
Mirror	20 x 16-1/2	PENN	1.00
2356. New England Farm	16 x 21	NYGS	7.50
FIESOLE, GIOVANNI DA See	ANGELICO, FRA		
FIGURA, HANS	Austrian	1898-	
2357. Amsterdam Flower			
Market	10 x 13	CFA	15.00
2358. Au Bacchus D'Or	9 x 8	CFA	12.00
2359. Au Pont Neuf, Paris	10 x 13	CFA	20.00
2360. Booksellers, Paris	9 x 8	CFA	12.00
2361. Bookstalls by Notre			
Dame, Paris	13 x 11	CFA	22.00
2362. Bookstalls by the			
Seine	13 x 11	CFA	22.00
2363. Broadway	16 x 9	CFA	24.00
2364. Brooklyn Dock	12 x 15	CFA	24.00
2365. Flower Vendors by the			
Seine	9 x 8	CFA	12.00
2366. Flower Vendors, Paris	10 x 9	CFA	15.00
2367. Graben Street, Vienna	9 x 8	CFA	12.00
2368. Les Halles, Paris	12 x 11	CFA	20.00
2369. Helsingfors Harbour	12 x 9	CFA	15.00
2370. Kartner Street, Vienna	9 x 8	CFA	12.00
2371. Kitzbuehel, Tyrol	8 x 12	CFA	15.00
2372. Lepic Street, Paris	11 x 9	CFA	20.00
2373. Malmoe City Hall,			
Averige	10 x 13	CFA	20.00
2374. Mount Zugspitze	13 x 16	CFA	27.00
2375. New York Telephone			

	Building	13 x 8	CFA	24.00
2376.	Oberammergau, Seide	13 x 16	CFA	27.00
2377.	Paris, Arc de			
	Triomphe	9 x 8	CFA	12.00
2378.	Paris Opera House	10 x 13	CFA	20.00
2379.	Pont Alexandra III	10 x 13	CFA	20.00
2380.	Quai Montebello	10 x 13	CFA	20.00
2381.	Quimper, Market			
	Street	12 x 9	CFA	20.00
2382.	Sacre Coeur	9 x 8	CFA	12.00
2383.	St. Etienne du Mont	13 x 10	CFA	20.00
2384.	St. Peter's, Rome	9 x 8	CFA	12.00
2385.	Slussen Circus--View			
	of Stockholm	10 x 12	CFA	15.00
2386.	Stadhaus in Stockholm	10 x 12	CFA	15.00
2387.	South Street	14 x 11	CFA	24.00
2388.	Stockholm Roodarholman	12 x 9	CFA	17.50
2389.	Street Scene	10 x 5	CFA	12.00
2390.	Street Scene, Paris	11 x 7	CFA	5.00
2391.	Tyrolean Scene	8 x 11	CFA	15.00
2392.	Vatican Garden, Rome	9 x 8	CFA	12.00
2393.	Vienna Market	9 x 8	CFA	12.00
2394.	Vienna--Stall Burgasse	9 x 9	CFA	12.00
2395.	Vienna Street Scene	9 x 8	CFA	12.00
2396.	Vienna University	6 x 7	CFA	10.00
2397.	Windmill in Haarlem	15 x 11	CFA	20.00
2398.	Windmill near Shiedam	15 x 14	CFA	24.00
FILDES, SAMUEL LUKE		English	1844-1927	
2399.	The Doctor	17-1/2 x 26	NYGS	10.00
		12 x 17	CAC	7.50
2400.	Her Majesty, Queen			
	Elizabeth II	20 x 15	CAC	7.50
FILIPEPI, ALESSANDRO See BOTTICELLI				
FINI, LEONOR		Brazilian (Res. France)		
2401.	Livia	31 x 10	NYGS	12.00
2402.	Losange	28 x 18	NYGS	15.00
2403.	Melita	31 x 10	NYGS	12.00
2404.	Two Sisters	25 x 20	CFA	15.00
FINTZ				
2405.	Houses	20 x 24	DAC	6.00
FIORENZO DI LORENZO		Italian	1440-1522/5	
2406.	Crucifixion and Saints	15 x 10	IA	3.00
2407.	Miracoli di S.			
	Bernardino	15 x 11	IA	3.00
2408.	Miracoli di S.			
	Bernardino (7)	15 x 10	IA	3.00 ea.
FIORI, FEDERICO See BAROCCIO, IL				
FIRLE, WALTHER		German	1859-	
2409.	The Fairy Tale	18 x 24	NYGS	7.50
		11 x 14	NYGS	3.00
2410.	Sunday Devotion	22 x 31	CAC	12.00
FISHER				

2411. Glass Bowl	20 x 16	CAC	3.50
2412. Springtime Symphony	20 x 16	CAC	3.50

FLANDRIN, JULES

2413. Christ Mourning the City	20 x 16	IA	6.00
		(H. C. Grav.)	
	20 x 16	IA	4.00
	15 x 12	IA	3.00
2414. Pearl Diver	17 x 21	CAC	10.00

FLEGEL, GEORG   German   1563-1638

2415. Centaurs and Straw- berries	8 x 10	ESH	1.00
2416. Iris, Convolvulus and Cherries	10 x 8	ESH	1.00
2417. Iris and Insects	8 x 10	ESH	1.00
2418. Iris, Liserons and Cherries	8 x 10	ESH	1.00
2419. Still Life with Parrot	8 x 10	ESH	1.00

FLINT, (SIR) WILLIAM RUSSELL   English   1880-

2420. Golden Sands, Bam- burgh	16-1/2 x 22	NYGS	7.50
2421. Wet Sands, Bamburgh	16-1/2 x 22	NYGS	7.50

FLOWERS, PETER   English   1916-

2422. Old Watermill at Storrington	16 x 24	RL	6.00

FONTANESI, ANTONIO   Italian   1818-1882

2423. Santa Trinita Bridge at Florence	10 x 15	IA	3.00

FORAIN, JEAN LOUIS   French   1852-1931

2424. Court Scene: Interior	20 x 24	NYGS	10.00

FORBES, A. STANHOPE   Irish   1857-1947

2425. Young Anglers	18-1/2 x 23	RL	5.00

FORD, LAUREN   American   1891-

2426. Choir Practice	16 x 21	NYGS	7.50
2427. Guardian Angel	26 x 19-1/2	IA	7.50
	12 x 9	IA	1.00

FOREIN

2428. Steer Roping	12 x 18	CAC	3.00

FOSTER

2429. Connecticut Hills	21 x 24	CAC	10.00

FOSTER, DERYCK

2430. Royal Dragon	20 x 30	IA	10.00

FOUJITA, TSUGOHARU   Japanese (Res. France)   1886-

2431. Café	24 x 20	PENN	1.00
			1.98 (Pr.)
2432. Demoiselles	11 x 14	DAC	2.80
2433. French Window	14 x 11	DAC	2.80
2434. Girl with Kitten	26 x 20	DAC	6.00
	14 x 11	DAC	2.80
2435. Holiday	16 x 36	CFA	18.00
2436. In the Kitchen	24 x 20	PENN	1.00
2437. Little Cavalier	25-1/2 x 18-1/2	PENN	1.00

2438.	Place Vendome	14 x 11	DAC	2.80
2439.	Quai aux Fleurs	24 x 40	PENN	1.00
				1.98 (Pr.)

FOUQUES, R. H.   German (Res. France)
| 2440. | Cape Finisterre | 19-1/2 x 25 | RL | 7.50 |

FOUQUET, JEAN   French   c. 1420-1481
2441.	Angel Announcing to the Virgin Her Death	7 x 5	IA	1.50
2442.	Annunciation	7 x 5	IA	1.50
2443.	Birth of the Baptist	7 x 5	IA	1.50
2444.	Chancellor of France	12 x 9	CFA	2.50
2445.	Death of the Virgin	7 x 5	IA	1.50
2446.	Etienne Chevalier Adoring the Madonna	7 x 5	IA	1.50
2447.	Guillaume Juvenal des Ursins	14 x 11	IA	3.00
2448.	Madonna and Child, with Angels	7 x 5	IA	1.50
2449.	Marriage of the Virgin	7 x 5	IA	1.50
2450.	Sainte Marguerite	8 x 10	ESH	1.00
2451.	Visitation	7 x 5	IA	1.50

FRA ANGELICO See ANGELICO, FRA
FRA BARTOLOMMEO   See PAGHOLO, (FRA) BARTOLOMMEO DI
FRAGONARD, JEAN-HONORE   French   1732-1806
2452.	Arbor with Two Children	10 x 13	NYGS	3.00
2453.	La Baiser à la Derobe	9 x 12	IA	10.00
			(H. C. Grav.)	
2454.	Dame Langoreuse	12 x 9	IA	10.00
			(H. C. Grav.)	
2455.	Education, First of All	18 x 23	HNA	5.95
		11 x 13	IA	3.00
2456.	L'Escarpolette (The Swing)	18-1/2 x 14-1/2	NYGS	7.50
2457.	Farmer's Family	15 x 18	CAC	7.50
2458.	Frist Step	9 x 10	CAC	7.50
2459.	A Game of Horse and Rider	24 x 18	NYGS	10.00
		16 x 12	DAC	2.00
2460.	A Game of Hot Cockles	24 x 18	NYGS	10.00
2461.	Girl at Her Studies	10 x 8	ESH	1.00
2462.	Girl Reading	22-1/2 x 18	ESH	10.00
2463.	Girl with a Marmot	10 x 8	CFA	4.00
2464.	Good Mother	11 x 9	CAC	1.50
2465.	Infant Cheri	9 x 10	CAC	7.50
2466.	Inspiration	14 x 11	IA	3.00
2467.	Lady Carving Her Name	8 x 10	CAC	1.00
2468.	The Letter	23 x 18	ESH	10.00
		21 x 17	CAC	10.00
		10 x 8	ESH	1.00

2469.	Love Letter	30 x 24	NYGS	10.00
2470.	Love Unto Death	18 x 12	AR	4.00
2471.	Music Lesson	11 x 12	IA	3.00
		8 x 10	ESH	1.00
2472.	Oath of Love	11 x 9	CAC	1.50
2473.	Park at Villa D'Este	18 x 13	CFA	4.00
2474.	Park Landscape	11 x 14	CFA	4.00
2475.	Portrait of Constance Lowendahl, Countess of Turpin de Crissé	13 x 10 oval	IA	3.00
2476.	La Reverence	8 x 10-1/2	NYGS	4.00

FRANCA, OZZ

2477.	Boats in Harbor (2)	40 x 15	DAC	8.00 ea.
		22 x 8-1/2	DAC	2.00 ea.
2478.	Skylines (2)	15 x 40	DAC	8.00 ea.
		8-1/2 x 22	DAC	2.00 ea.

FRANCESCHINI, BALDASSARE See VOLTERRANO, IL

FRANCESCHINI, MARC ANTONIO Italian   1648-1729

2479.	Cupid	15 x 11	IA	3.00

FRANCESCO DI GENTILE   Italian   15th Century

2480.	Madonna of the Butterfly	15 x 11	IA	3.00

FRANCESCO DI GIORGIO MARTINI   Italian   1439-1502

2481.	Annunciation	15 x 10	IA	3.00
2482.	Madonna and Child with Two Saints	15 x 9	IA	3.00
2483.	Peace and War	15 x 10	IA	3.00

FRANCIA, IL (RAIBOLINI, FRANCESCO)   Italian   1450-1508

2484.	Madonna, Child and Saints	8 x 6	NYGS	.50
2485.	Madonna and Child with Infant St. John	22 x 17	AA	7.50
2486.	Madonna and Child with St. Francis and St. Jerome	24 x 18	AA	7.50
2487.	Portrait of Evangelista Scappi	13 x 11	IA	3.00
2488.	St. Stephen	15 x 11	IA	3.00

FRANCIABIGIO, IL (BIGI, FRANCESCO DI CRISTOFANO)
                                Italian   1482-1525

2489.	Venus	15 x 6	IA	3.00

FRANCK, FREDERICK   Dutch (Res.U.S.)   1909-

2490.	Downtown Rhythms	14 x 20	NYGS	7.50
2491.	From Manhattan Bridge	14-1/2 x 20	NYGS	7.50
2492.	Manhattan Nocturne	15-1/2 x 21	NYGS	10.00

FRANCIS, DOROTHY

2493.	Korean Boy	23 x 16	AA	6.00
2494.	Korean Girl	23 x 16	AA	6.00
2495.	Mexican Boy	26 x 20	AA	7.50
2496.	Mexican Brother and Sister	23 x 33	AA	12.00
2497.	Mexican Girl	26 x 20	AA	7.50

2498. Topsy	21-1/2 x 16	AA	6.00
2499. Turvy	21-1/2 x 16	AA	6.00
FRANKE			
2500. Ripe Sheaves	21 x 35-1/2	NYGS	12.00
FRANKL, FRANZ			
2501. Meadow Stream	25 x 33	CFA	12.00
2502. Pine Cove	25 x 33	CFA	15.00
2503. Winding Brook	26 x 33	CFA	12.00
FRAZIER, KENNETH	American	1867-1949	
2504. End of the Trail	13 x 16	CAC	4.00
	9 x 12	CAC	2.00
FREEMAN, JANE	English	1883-	
2505. Chums	24 x 19-1/2	IA	10.00
	14 x 11	IA	2.00
	10 x 8	IA	1.00
2506. Peasant Man at Prayer	17 x 12	CAC	1.50
FREITAG, CLEMENS			
2507. Quiet Waters	24 x 32	IA	12.00
2508. When the Leaves Begin to Fall	24 x 32	IA	12.00
FRIEDRICH, CASPAR	German	1774-1840	
2509. Summer Landscape	24 x 35	CFA	18.00
2510. Tree in a Landscape	18 x 23	HNA	5.95
FRIESZ, EMILE OTHON	French	1879-	
2511. Port de Dieppe	23-1/2 x 20	PENN	1.00
2512. Port of Toulon	18 x 23	PENN	1.00
2513. Still Life with Brigantine	20-1/2 x 25-1/2	NYGS	10.00
FRÖLICHER, OTTO	Swiss	1840-1890	
2514. Park Landscape	18-1/2 x 24-1/2	ESH	7.50
FROMHOLD, MARTIN			
2515. Summer Bouquet	22 x 16	NYGS	7.50
FROMMHOLD, ERNST	German	1879-1955	
2516. Clearance in a Wood	23-1/2 x 31-1/2	IA	12.00
2517. Down to the Valley	18 x 23-1/2	IA	6.00
2518. Spring	18 x 23	CFA	6.00
2519. Sunny Forest Road	18 x 23-1/2	IA	6.00
2520. Wagon Trail	18 x 24	CAC	7.50
2521. Woodland Stream	24 x 32	CAC	10.00
FROOT			
2522. When Evening Comes	24 x 30	CAC	10.00
FROSINO, BARTOLOMMEO DI	Italian	1366-1440	
2523. St. Aegidius	12 x 11	IA	3.00
FUGEL, GEBHARD	German	1863-	
2524. Last Supper	23 x 19-1/2	IA	10.00
	17 x 30	IA	5.00
	9-1/2 x 17	IA	2.00
FUJITA See FOUJITA			
FUNK			
2525. Green Meadows	22 x 28	CAC	6.00
FUSARO			
2526. Little Boats at Meze	18 x 22-1/2	ESH	10.00

G

GADDI, TADDEO (ANGELO DI TADDEO)

Italian   1300-1366

2527. Coronation of the Virgin	15 x 10	IA	3.00
	12 x 6	CFA	1.50
GAINSBOROUGH, (SIR) THOMAS	English	1727-1788	
2528. The Artist's Daughter	17 x 14	PENN	1.00
2529. Blue Boy	30-1/2 x 22	NYGS	12.00
	26 x 20	PENN	1.00
			1.98 (Pr.)
	24 x 16	CFA	10.00
	18 x 13	NYGS	5.00
	14 x 10	NYGS	3.00
	12 x 9	NYGS	1.50
2530. Count Rumford	28 x 22-1/2	NYGS	10.00
	11-1/2 x 9-1/2	NYGS	1.50
2531. Duchess of Devon- shire	28 x 21	CAC	30.00
			(Grav.)
2532. Hon. Mrs. Graham	28 x 22	CAC	30.00
			(Grav.)
	28 x 22	CAC	12.00
	20 x 16	CAC	7.50
2533. Margaret	20 x 16	AA	6.00
2534. The Painter's Daughters	23 x 21-1/2	NYGS	18.00
2535. Portrait of Mrs. Siddons	17 x 13	CAC	5.00
2536. View near King's Bromley-on-Trent	25-1/2 x 35-1/2	NYGS	15.00
2537. View of Dedham	18 x 23	HNA	5.95
GAIR, FRANCIS			
2538. Looking Toward Chanctonbury Ring	18 x 25	CAC	7.50
2539. Italian Landscape	18 x 25	CAC	7.50
GALEMA, ARJEN	Dutch		
2540. Last Supper (After DaVinci)	24 x 40	DAC	4.00
	14 x 28	DAC	2.80
	12 x 20	DAC	1.20
	8 x 15	DAC	.60
	8 x 10	DAC	.48
GALL, DELLA	American		
2541. Chatou	18 x 22	CAC	7.50
2543. Jeune Femme	18 x 14	CAC	5.00
2544. Jeune Femme à la Toilette	18 x 14	CAC	5.00
2545. Jeune Femme and Bouquet	18 x 14	CAC	5.00
2546. River Seine	18 x 22	CAC	10.00

GAMBLE
| 2547. Blossom Time | 16 x 20 | CAC | 6.00 |
| 2548. California Poppies | 20 x 30 | CAC | 10.00 |

GAND, GIUSTO DI   See   GIUSTO DI GAND
| GANSO, EMIL | American | 1895- | |
| 2549. Winter Morning | 14-1/2 x 22 | PENN | 1.00 |

GANZIANI
| 2550. Piper of Dreams | 11 x 16 | CAC | 3.00 |

GARNERAY, LEBRETON
2551. Baltimore, View of	10 x 15	CFA	12.00
2552. Boston, View of	10 x 15	CFA	12.00
2553. New Orleans, View of	10 x 15	CFA	12.00
2554. New York, View of	10 x 15	CFA	12.00
2555. Philadelphia, View of	10 x 15	CFA	12.00

| GARRIDO, LEANDRO ROMAN | French | 1868-1909 | |
| 2556. Minuet | 24 x 32 | CFA | 10.00 |

GASSER, HENRY M.		1909-	
2557. Gondola	16 x 22-1/2	PENN	1.00
2558. Home Port	20 x 24	PENN	1.00
			1.98 (Pr.)
2559. Inland Cove	19-1/2 x 24	PENN	1.00
			1.98 (Pr.)
2560. Lover's Tree	16 x 22-1/2	PENN	1.00
2561. Peaceful Harbor	20 x 24	PENN	1.00
			1.98 (Pr.)
2562. Solitude	19-1/2 x 24	PENN	1.00
2563. Summer Inlet	24 x 30	CAC	15.00
2564. Surf, Sand and Rocks	19-1/2 x 24	PENN	1.00
			1.98 (Pr.)
2565. Tranquility	19-1/2 x 24	PENN	1.00
2566. Winter Harbor	18-1/2 x 24	PENN	1.00
2567. Harbor Scenes (4)	10 x 13	PENN	1.00 set

        Inland Cove
        Peaceful Harbor
        Surf, Sand and Rocks
        Winter Harbor

GASTEIGER	German	1871-	
2568. Camellias in Bloom	30 x 24	CAC	7.50
2569. Poinsettias	20 x 18	CAC	7.50

GAUGUIN, PAUL	French	1848-1903	
2570. Les Alyscamps, Arles	10 x 8	ESH	1.00
2571. And the Gold of Their Bodies	8 x 10	ESH	1.00
2572. Arearea	27 x 33-1/2	NYGS	18.00
	17 x 22	PENN	1.00
2573. Aus Tahiti	31-1/2 x 25	NYGS	20.00
2574. The Bathers	23 x 29	CAC	18.00
2575. Beach at Tahiti	23 x 18	CFA	12.00
2576. The Big Tree	16 x 20	CFA	7.50
2577. Bonjeur, Monsieur Gauguin	20 x 24	DAC	6.00
2578. Breton Landscape	23 x 34	CFA	15.00

		18 x 24	DAC	6.00
2579.	Breton Village Under Snow	16 x 22	ESH	10.00
2580.	Bretonne	13 x 9	NYGS	5.00
2581.	The Call (The Appeal)	23 x 15-1/2	ESH	10.00
		10 x 8	ESH	1.00
2582.	Cavalier	14 x 9	NYGS	5.00
2583.	Contes Barbares (Barbaric Tales)	19 x 13	NYGS	10.00
2584.	Days of God	8 x 10	CAC	1.50
2585.	Entrance to a Village	19-1/2 x 23	PENN	1.00
2586.	Farm at Pouldu	8 x 10	ESH	1.00
2587.	Fatata Te Miti	22-1/2 x 30-1/2	NYGS	15.00
		18 x 24	PENN	1.00
		11 x 14	NYGS	3.00
2588.	Femmes Maoris	16-1/2 x 21	NYGS	16.00
2589.	Femmes de Tahiti	18 x 14	PENN	1.00
2590.	Flowers and Bowl of Fruit	16-1/2 x 24	PENN	1.00
2591.	Girl from Brittany in Prayer	25 x 18	NYGS	15.00
2592.	Haystacks	23-1/2 x 18	PENN	1.00
2593.	Ia Orana Maria (Hail Mary)	30 x 23	NYGS	15.00
2594.	I Raro Te Oviri	22-1/2 x 30-1/2	NYGS	15.00
		11 x 14	NYGS	3.00
2595.	Landscape at Arles	24 x 18	DAC	6.00
		10 x 8	ESH	1.00
2596.	Lane near Arles	8 x 10	ESH	1.00
2597.	Little Breton Girls by the Sea	24 x 18	PENN	1.00
2598.	Man with an Axe	10 x 8	ESH	1.00
2599.	Marie Henry	8 x 10	CAC	1.50
2600.	Maternity	22-1/2 x 14-1/2	ESH	10.00
		10 x 8	ESH	1.00
2601.	Mill in Britanny	18 x 22-1/2	ESH	10.00
		8 x 10	ESH	1.00
2602.	Nafea (When Do You Marry)	29 x 21	CFA	18.00
		23 x 18	HNA	5.95
		22-1/2 x 17	ESH	10.00
		10 x 8	ESH	1.00
2602.	Nature Morte	14 x 18	CAC	5.00
2603.	Nave Nave Mahana (Enchanting Sun)	22 x 30	ESH	15.00
		19 x 26	CFA	15.00
		8 x 10	ESH	1.00
2604.	Never More	12-1/2 x 24	PENN	1.00
2605.	The Offering	8 x 10	ESH	1.00
2606.	Out of Tahiti	31 x 25	CFA	18.00
2607.	Paysage de Bretagne	23 x 18	PENN	1.00
2608.	Poor Fisher	24 x 20	PENN	1.00

2609.	Red Dog	8 x 10	ESH	1.00
2610.	Reverie	9 x 7	CFA	1.00
2611.	Rider on the Coast	14 x 17	CAC	2.00
2612.	Riders on the Beach	25 x 29	NYGS	18.00
		15 x 18-1/2	PENN	1.00
2613.	Riders on the Coast	33 x 30	CAC	12.00
		29 x 23	CFA	12.00
2614.	Ta Matete (The Market)			
		26 x 33-1/2	NYGS	18.00
		24 x 30	ESH	15.00
		18 x 24	PENN	1.00
		18 x 23	HNA	5.95
		14 x 18	CAC	5.00
		8 x 10	ESH	1.00
2615.	Still Life and a Fan	10 x 12	IA	3.00
2616.	Still Life with Apples	25-1/2 x 29-1/2	NYGS	12.00
2617.	Tahitian Girl Crouching	8 x 7	CFA	1.00
2618.	Tahitian Landscape	26-1/2 x 21	NYGS	12.00
		23 x 17	CFA	10.00
2619.	Tahitian Mountains	26 x 36	NYGS	18.00
		22-1/2 x 31	NYGS	12.00
		14-1/2 x 20	NYGS	5.00
		6 x 7-1/2	NYGS	.50
2620.	Tahitian Village	33 x 26	CAC	10.00
2621.	Tahitian Women	14 x 18	CFA	4.00
		8 x 10	ESH	1.00
2622.	Te Raau Rahi	23-1/2 x 29-1/2	NYGS	15.00
2623.	Te Rerioa	18 x 24	PENN	1.00
				1.98 (Pr.)
2624.	Three Puppies	22 x 15	CAC	10.00
		10 x 8	MMA	.35
2625.	Two Tahitian Women	30 x 23	NYGS	15.00
		23 x 18	NYGS	12.00
2626.	Two Tahitian Women with Mangoes			
		30 x 23	CAC	15.00
		23 x 18	CAC	12.00
2627.	Vairumati	18 x 23	CAC	15.00
2628.	Vision After the Sermon	17 x 22	CAC	10.00
2629.	White Horse	30-1/2 x 20	ESH	15.00
		22 x 14	NYGS	7.50
		10 x 8	ESH	1.00
2630.	Why Are You Angry	17-1/2 x 24-1/2	AA	7.50
2631.	Woman on a White Horse	20 x 24	PENN	1.00
2632.	Woman with Flowers	28 x 18	CAC	7.50
2633.	Woman with Mango	20 x 12	PENN	1.00
2634.	Women Bathing	23 x 29-1/2	NYGS	18.00
2635.	Women of Tahiti	21-1/2 x 29	ESH	15.00
		11 x 14	IA	3.00
		8 x 10	ESH	1.00

2636. Women on the Beach   6 x 8   CFA   1.00
2637. Women with Mangoes   30 x 23   CAC   15.00
GAULLI, GIOVANNI BATTISTA (IL BACCICCIO)
                               Italian   1639-1709
2638. Tobias and the
      Archangel   5 x 15   IA   3.00
2639. Detail of No. 2638   11 x 15   IA   3.00
GEBERT, WALDEMAR   German   1877-
2640. Fishing Boats   19-1/2 x 27-1/2   ESH   8.00 (Pr.)
GEIGENBERGER, OTTO   German   1881-1946
2641. Environs of Rome   31 x 21-1/2   ESH   15.00
GELLÉE, CLAUDE   French   1600-1682
2642. Landscape   11 x 15   IA   3.00
2643. Landscape with Herd   12 x 7   CFA   4.00
2644. Landscape with
      Merchants   18 x 23   HNA   5.95
2645. Landscape with Trees   11 x 8   AR   3.50
2646. Seaport, Embarkation
      of St. Ursula   18 x 23   HNA   5.95
2647. Ship in Storm   12 x 9   CFA   4.00
GENOUD
2648. Lipari Island   12 x 16   CAC   10.00
GENT
2649. Magnolia   24 x 31   CAC   10.00
GENTH
2650. Spanish Dancers   20 x 30   CAC   10.00
GENTILE DA FABRIANO (GENTILE DI NICOLO DI GIOVANNI
      MASSI)   Italian   1360/70-1427/50
2651. Adoration of the Magi
      (Detail)   11 x 15   IA   3.00
2652. Coronation of the
      Virgin   32 x 23   IA   24.00
2653. Flight into Egypt   5 x 16   IA   3.00
2654. Madonna and Child   15 x 11   IA   3.00
GENTILESCHI, ORAZIO   Italian   1562-1647
2655. Annunciation   15 x 10   IA   3.00
GERARD, FRANCOIS   French   1770-1837
2656. Eros and Psyche   13 x 19   CFA   2.50
2657. Napoleon   12 x 9   IA   3.00
GERICAULT, JEAN-LOUIS THEODORE   French   1791-1824
2658. Horse Race   8 x 10   ESH   1.00
2659. Horses at Market   9 x 12   CFA   5.00
2660. Polish Trumpeter   15-1/2 x 12   NYGS   12.00
GEROME, LEON   French   1824-1904
2661. La Madeleine à Paris   20 x 24   CAC   15.00
2662. La Place de la
      Concorde à Paris   20 x 24   CAC   15.00
GERWIN, FRANZ
2663. Coke Furnace   27 x 36   CFA   15.00
2664. Pulse of Industry   26 x 36   NYGS   18.00
GESSNER, RICHARD
2665. Steel Works   21 x 41   ESH   15.00

GHERARDO DEL FORA	Italian	1444-1529	
2666. Choral Page	15 x 10	IA	3.00
2667. Missal Page with			
Annunciation	14 x 10	IA	3.00

GHIRLANDAIO, DOMENICO (BIGORDI, BENEDETTO DOMENICO)

	Italian	1449-1494	
2668. Adoration of the			
Shepherds	11 x 11	IA	3.00
2669. Angel Appearing to			
Zacharias	10 x 14-1/2	AR	4.00
2670. Annunciation	11 x 15	IA	3.00
2671. Birth of the Baptist	10 x 15	IA	3.00
2672. Birth of the Virgin	9 x 15	IA	3.00
2673. Five Women--Detail			
of No. 2672	11 x 15	IA	3.00
2674. Ludovica Tornabuoni--			
Detail of No. 2672	15 x 11	IA	3.00
2675. Last Supper	9 x 14	IA	3.00
2676. Old Man with a Child	15 x 11	IA	3.00
2677. Visitation	9 x 15	IA	3.00
2678. Giovanna Tornabuoni--			
Detail of No. 2677	15 x 11	IA	3.00
2679. Two Maids--Detail of			
No. 2677	15 x 11	IA	3.00
GHIRLANDAIO, RIDOLFO	Italian	1483-1561	
2680. Portrait of a Man			
(The Goldsmith)	15 x 11	IA	3.00
GIACOMETTI ALBERTO	Swiss	Contemporary	
2681. Head of the Artist's			
Mother	17 x 12	NYGS	18.00

GIAMBELLINO, IL   See BELLINI, GIOVANNI
GIANUZZI, GIULIO   See ROMANO, GIULIO

GIAQUINTO, CORRADO	Italian	1699-1755	
2682. Assumption of the			
Virgin	15 x 9	IA	3.00
GIBB, WILLIAM			
2683. Musical Instruments			
(12)	9 x 13	NYGS 20.00 set	
			or 2.00 ea.

       Bagpipes, Continental
       Bagpipes, Northumbrian and Lowlands
       Clavichord
       Drums of India
       Guitar
       Hellier Stradivarius
       Mandoline and Quinterna
       Organ, Champer
       Spinnet, Double
       Spinnet, Upright
       State Trumpet and Kettledrum
       Viola da Gamba

GILBERT, C. IVAR

2684. Landscapes--"Of Thee I Sing" (8)	9 x 12	DAC	1. 00 ea.
	6 x 8	DAC	. 60 ea.
GILBERT, JANE	American	Contemporary	
2685. Girl with Cat	14 x 10	CAC	6. 00
2686. Girl with Flowers	20 x 16	CAC	10. 00
GILLES, WERNER	German	1894-	
2687. Fishing	15 x 22	ESH	7. 50
GINELLI, L.			
2688. Peaceful Riviera	24 x 48	DAC	10. 00
GIORGIONE (BARBARELLI, GIORGIO) Italian		1478-1510	
2689. Adoration of the Shepherds	24 x 30	NYGS	16. 00
	19-1/2 x 24	PENN	1. 00
	6 x 7-1/2	NYGS	. 50
2690. The Bravo	13 x 11	IA	3. 00
2691. Boy with an Arrow	13 x 11	IA	3. 00
2692. Christ Supporting the Cross	16 x 8	IA	3. 00
2693. The Concert	11 x 14	IA	3. 00
2694. Head--Detail of No. 2693	15 x 11	IA	3. 00
2695. Concert Champetre (Pastoral Symphony)	11 x 13	IA	3. 00
2696. Double Portrait	13 x 11	IA	3. 00
2697. Evander and Aeneas	23 x 28	CAC	10. 00
2698. Landscape with Figures	10 x 14	IA	3. 00
2699. Laura	14 x 11	IA	3. 00
2700. The Mocked Christ	11 x 14	IA	3. 00
2701. Solomon's Judgment	14 x 11	IA	3. 00
2702. The Storm	17 x 15	IA	3. 00
2703. Three Philosophers	23 x 18	HNA	5. 95
	13 x 11	IA	3. 00
2704. Trial by Fire	14 x 11	IA	3. 00
GIOTTO DI BONDONE	Italian	1266-1336	
2705. Angel--Detail from "Madonna and Angels"	15 x 11	IA	3. 00
2706. Apparition Before the Chapter at Arles	8 x 8	IA	1. 50
2707. Ascension of Christ	11 x 12	IA	3. 00
2708. Ascension of St. John, the Evangelist	11 x 15	IA	3. 00
2709. Detail of No. 2708--St. John the Evangelist	15 x 11	IA	3. 00
2710. Detail of No. 2708	11 x 15	IA	3. 00
2711. Brother Leo Sees the Heavenly Throne	9 x 8	IA	1. 50
2712. Baptism of Christ	11 x 12	IA	3. 00
2713. Detail of No. 2712	14 x 11	IA	3. 00
2714. Canonisation of St. Francis	9 x 8	IA	1. 50

2715.	Christ on the Mount		
	of Olives	45 x 20	CAC	6.00
		30 x 16	CAC	1.50
2716.	The Clarisses		
	Mourning St. Francis	9 x 8	IA	1.50
2717.	Crucifixion	11 x 12	IA	3.00
2718.	Death of the Knight		
	of Celano	12 x 11	IA	3.00
		8 x 8	IA	1.50
2719.	Death and Obsequies		
	of St. Francis		
	(Assisi)	9 x 8	IA	1.50
2720.	Death of St. Francis		
	(S. Croce)	11 x 15	IA	3.00
2721.	Deposition	19 x 20	IA	7.50
		11 x 12	IA	3.00
2722.	Entry into Jerusalem	13 x 12	IA	3.00
2723.	Flight into Egypt	19 x 19	IA	7.50
		11 x 11	IA	3.00
2724.	Holy Family	30 x 16	CAC	1.50
2725.	Innocent III Approves		
	the Order	14 x 11	IA	3.00
2726.	Innocent III Dreams		
	of St. Francis	9 x 8	IA	1.50
2727.	Joachim and the		
	Shepherds	18 x 23	HNA	5.95
2728.	Judas Kiss	11 x 11	IA	3.00
2729.	Detail of No. 2728	15 x 11	IA	3.00
2730.	A Knight Verifies the		
	Stigmata	9 x 8	IA	1.50
2731.	Madonna and Child	15 x 11	IA	3.00
2732.	Marriage of the Virgin	11 x 12	IA	3.00
2733.	Meeting at the Golden		
	Gate	11 x 12	IA	3.00
2734.	Joachim and Anne--		
	Detail of No. 2733	15 x 11	IA	3.00
2735.	Miracle of the Source	15 x 11	IA	3.00
		10 x 8	IA	1.50
2736.	Nativity	11 x 14	IA	3.00
2737.	Noli Me Tangere	11 x 12	IA	3.00
2738.	Magdalen and Jesus--		
	Detail of No. 2737	15 x 11	IA	3.00
2739.	Presentation of the		
	Virgin	11 x 12	IA	3.00
2740.	Detail of No. 2739	13 x 11	IA	3.00
2741.	Resurrection of		
	Lazarus	11 x 12	IA	3.00
2742.	Detail of No. 2741	15 x 11	IA	3.00
2743.	St. Francis and the		
	Birds	21 x 18-1/2	ESH	10.00
2744.	St. Francis and the		
	Sultan	9 x 8	IA	1.50

2745. St. Francis Appearing			
to Gregory IX	9 x 8	IA	1.50
2746. St. Francis Being			
Honored by a Man	8 x 8	IA	1.50
2747. St. Francis Celebrates			
the Crib at Greccio	12 x 11	IA	3.00
	8 x 8	IA	1.50
2748. St. Francis Drives			
Out the Devils from			
Arezzo	9 x 8	IA	1.50
2749. St. Francis Dreaming			
a Palace	8 x 8	IA	1.50
2750. St. Francis Giving His			
Cloak	23-1/2 x 20-1/2	AA	12.00
	12 x 11	IA	3.00
	8 x 8	IA	1.50
2751. St. Francis Healing a			
Devotee	8 x 8	IA	1.50
2752. St. Francis Hearing the			
Voice of the			
Crucifix	9 x 8	IA	1.50
2753. St. Francis in the			
Chariot of Fire	14 x 11	IA	3.00
2754. St. Francis Liberates			
a Man from Prison	8 x 8	IA	1.50
2755. St. Francis Preaching			
Before Honorius III	14 x 11	IA	3.00
	8 x 8	IA	1.50
2756. St. Francis Receiving			
the Stigmata (Assisi)	8 x 8	IA	1.50
2757. St. Francis Receiving			
the Stigmata (S.			
Croce)	13 x 11	IA	3.00
2758. St. Francis Resuscitates			
a Woman	8 x 8	IA	3.00
2759. St. Francis Speaking			
to the Birds	20 x 18	CAC	10.00
	15 x 11	IA	3.00
	8 x 8	IA	1.50
2760. St. Francis Transported			
into Ecstasy	9 x 8	IA	1.50
2761. St. Francis Waives			
His Inheritance	13 x 11	IA	3.00
	9 x 8	IA	1.50
2762. Vision of a Brother			
and of the Bishop	9 x 8	IA	1.50

GIOTTO, SCHOOL OF

2763. Crucifixion and Saints	15 x 8	IA	3.00
2764. Dante, Portrait of	15 x 11	IA	3.00

GIOTTINO (MASO DI BANCO)   Italian   Ac. 1336-1350

2765. Deposition from the			
Cross	14 x 22	IA	3.00

GIOVANNI DA COMO   See GIOVANNI DA MILANO
GIOVANNI DA FIESOLE   See ANGELICO, FRA

GIOVANNI DA MILANO	Italian	Ac.	1349-1369
2766. Madonna and Child	15 x 9	IA	3.00
2767. Presentation in the Temple	15 x 10	IA	3.00
2768. Detail of No. 2767-- Two Heads	10 x 15	IA	3.00
GIOVANNI DEL BIONDO	Italian	Ac.	1377-1392
2769. Madonna and Saints	15 x 8	IA	3.00
GIOVANNI DI PAOLO	Italian	c.	1403-1482
2770. Flight into Egypt	18 x 23	HNA	5.95
2771. St. Jerome and the Lion	15 x 11	IA	3.00
2772. Virgin of Humility	15 x 11	IA	3.00
GIOVANNI PISANO See PISANO, GIOVANNI			
GIRALT LERIN			
2773. Danza Gitana, Granada	20 x 40	NYGS	15.00
GIRTIN			
2774. Rainbow over the Exe	11-1/2 x 19-1/2	NYGS	18.00
GISSING, ROLAND	Canadian		
2775. Bow River Valley (Banff, Alberta, Canada)	20 x 25	IA	7.50
2776. Foothills of the Rockies	20 x 25	IA	7.50
GIUSTO DI GAND	Flemish	c.	1440-1475
2777. Communion of the Apostles	11 x 12	IA	3.00
GLACKENS, WILLIAM J.	American		1870-1938
2778. Beach at Annisquam	16-1/2 x 20	NYGS	7.50
2779. Dream Ride	15 x 17	NYGS	5.00
2780. Hammerstein's Roof Garden	24 x 20	PENN	1.00
GLANNON, EDWARD JOHN	American		1911-
2781. Corner of the Pasture	12 x 18	CAC	3.00
GLICKLICH			
2782. Spring Song	17 x 13	CAC	3.50
	12 x 9	CAC	2.00
GLINTZ			
2783. Autumn Flowers	18 x 24	CAC	7.50
2784. Bell Flowers	21 x 28	CAC	9.00
2785. Sailing Harbour	21 x 28	CAC	9.00
GLITSCH			
2786. Camp Flowers	18 x 13	CAC	2.00
2787. Freisia	17 x 13	CFA	5.00
2788. Mimosa	17 x 13	CFA	5.00
GLORIA			
2789. Younger Than Spring- time (4)	12 x 9	DAC	.60 ea.
GLÜSING			
2790. On the High Seas	16 x 20	IA	6.00
GODRON, J. B.			

2791. Madonna	21 x 20	ESH	10.00
	13 x 12	ESH	5.00
GOES, HUGO VAN DER	Flemish	1440-1482	
2792. Adoration of the Magi	24-1/2 x 37	NYGS	18.00
	15 x 25	IA	7.50
2793. Holy Family	7 x 8	NYGS	.50
2794. Portinari Triptych	11 x 26	IA	10.00
2795. Floral Still Life--			
Detail of No. 2794	15 x 11	IA	3.00
2796. St. Victor and a			
Donor	19 x 16	IA	12.00
GOGH, VINCENT VAN See VAN GOGH, VINCENT			
GOLDING, CECIL	American	1908-	
2797. Adonis	39-1/2 x 12	NYGS	15.00
2798. American Robin	24-1/2 x 19-1/2	NYGS	10.00
	16 x 12	NYGS	5.00
2799. Detail of No. 2798	6 x 7-1/2	NYGS	1.00
2800. Autumn Leaves	30 x 25	NYGS	7.50
2801. Baltimore Oriole	24-1/2 x 19-1/2	NYGS	10.00
	16 x 12	NYGS	5.00
2802. Details of No. 2801 (2)	7-1/2 x 6	NYGS	1.00 ea.
2803. Blossom-Headed			
Parakeet	24-1/2 x 19-1/2	NYGS	10.00
	16 x 12	NYGS	5.00
2804. Detail of No. 2803	6 x 7-1/2	NYGS	1.00
2805. Blue and White	28 x 34	NYGS	10.00
2806. Blue Jay	24-1/2 x 19-1/2	NYGS	10.00
	16 x 12	NYGS	5.00
2807. Detail of No. 2806	6 x 7-1/2	NYGS	1.00
2808. Brown Thrasher	24-1/2 x 19-1/2	NYGS	10.00
	16 x 12	NYGS	5.00
2809. Details of No. 2808 (2)	7-1/2 x 6	NYGS	1.00 ea.
2810. Cardinal	30 x 24	CAC	10.00
	24-1/2 x 19-1/2	NYGS	10.00
	21 x 16	CAC	5.00
	16 x 12	NYGS	5.00
2811. Details of No. 2810 (2)	7-1/2 x 6	NYGS	1.00 ea.
2812. Caress	7-1/2 x 6	NYGS	1.00
2813. Christ Preaching on			
the Sea (After			
Hofmann)	22-1/2 x 36	IA	15.00
2814. Delight	16 x 12	NYGS	3.00
2815. Dixie Memories	28 x 34	NYGS	10.00
	20 x 24	NYGS	5.00
2816. Enchantment	7-1/2 x 6	NYGS	1.00
2817. Exaltation	16 x 12	NYGS	3.00
	7-1/2 x 6	NYGS	1.00
2818. Flowering Dogwood	25-1/2 x 31	NYGS	7.50
	17 x 21	NYGS	3.00
2819. Gaiety	7-1/2 x 6	NYGS	1.00
2820. Gladioli	7-1/2 x 6	NYGS	1.00
2821. Gleam o' Gold	28 x 34	NYGS	10.00

		20 x 24	NYGS	5.00
2822.	Gold and Silver	28 x 34	NYGS	10.00
2823.	Golden Harvest	23-1/2 x 35	NYGS	15.00
2824.	Grace	7-1/2 x 6	NYGS	1.00
2825.	Joy	7-1/2 x 6	NYGS	1.00
2826.	Keep 'Em Flying	20 x 16	CAC	2.50
		14 x 11	CAC	1.00
2827.	Queen of Flowers	28 x 34	CAC	10.00
		20 x 24	CAC	5.00
2828.	Rapture	7-1/2 x 6	NYGS	1.00
2829.	Red-Capped Fruit Dove	24-1/2 x 19-1/2	NYGS	10.00
		16 x 12	NYGS	5.00
2830.	Detail of No. 2829	7-1/2 x 6	NYGS	1.00
2831.	Red-Shafted Flicker	24-1/2 x 19-1/2	NYGS	10.00
		16 x 12	NYGS	5.00
2832.	Details of No. 2831 (2)	7-1/2 x 6	NYGS	1.00 ea.
2833.	Rose-Breasted Grosbeak	24-1/2 x 19-1/2	NYGS	10.00
		16 x 12	NYGS	5.00
2834.	Detail of No. 2833	6 x 7-1/2	NYGS	1.00
2835.	Temple Dancer	24 x 20	CAC	7.50
2836.	Tulips	17 x 21	CAC	3.00
2837.	Venus	39-1/2 x 12	NYGS	15.00
2838.	Yellow-Billed Cuckoo	24-1/2 x 19-1/2	NYGS	10.00
		16 x 12	NYGS	5.00
2839.	Detail of No. 2838	6 x 7-1/2	NYGS	1.00
GOLINKIN, JOSEPH WEBSTER		American	1896-	
2840.	Endeavor II and Ranger	23 x 17	CAC	15.00
2841.	Hambletonian	17 x 23	CAC	15.00
GONNER, P.		German		
2842.	Song Birds (6)	12 x 9	DAC	.24 ea.
		8 x 6	DAC	.16 ea.

       Bluebird
       Cardinal
       Goldfinch
       Goldfinch, Common
       Robin
       Rusty Blackbird

GOODMAN, ELSA				
2843.	Christ in Gethsemane (After Hofmann)	40 x 30	IA	12.00
GONZALES				
2844.	Personnage	15 x 11	NYGS	12.00
GORKY				
2845.	Agony	8 x 10	MMA	.35
GORTER, ARNOLD MARC		Dutch	1866-	
2846.	December	27 x 21	CAC	10.00
2847.	Spring	19 x 31	CAC	10.00
GOSSART, JAN See MABUSE				
GOULD, JOHN		English	1804-1881	

2848. Birds (16)	12 x 9	CAC	1.00 ea.
	8 x 6	CFA	1.00 ea.
2849. Birds (4)	16 x 12	NYGS	3.00 ea.
Brazilian Yellowtail			
Collared Inca			
Glittering Hummingbird			
Shining Sunbeam			

GOYA Y LUCIENTES, FRANCISCO DE   Spanish   1746-1828

2850. Be Careful with that Step	12 x 8	NYGS	2.00
2851. Blindman's Buff	18 x 23	HNA	5.95
	15 x 20	CAC	4.00
2852. Bullfight	18-1/2 x 24	NYGS	10.00
	16 x 24	PENN	1.00
2853. Don Manuel Osorio de Zuniga	30 x 23	NYGS	15.00
	19-1/2 x 15	NYGS	7.50
	13 x 10	NYGS	.50
	23 x 17-1/2	AP	5.00
	10 x 8	AP	.50
2854. Gossiping Women	16 x 40	NYGS	20.00
2855. Lady Reading a Letter	22-1/2 x 15-1/2	ESH	10.00
2856. Naked Maya	10 x 8	ESH	1.00
2857. Picnic	10 x 8	ESH	1.00
2858. Portrait of the Artist	17 x 13	CAC	7.50
2859. Portrait of Countess Casa-Flores	15 x 10	IA	3.00
2860. Portrait of Ferdinand VII	13 x 10	IA	3.00
2861. Senora Sabasa Garcia	24 x 18-1/2	PENN	1.00
	20 x 16	NYGS	7.50
2862. Spring	20 x 13	CFA	7.50
2863. Victor Guye	23 x 18	HNA	5.95
2864. Vintage	21 x 15	CAC	4.00
2865. Water Carrier	22 x 18	CAC	10.00

GOYEN, JAN VAN   Dutch   1596-1656

2866. Landscape, Dordrecht	9-1/2 x 16	AR	4.00

GOZZOLI, BENOZZO   Italian   1420-1497

2867. Angel (Head)	15 x 11	IA	3.00
2868. Angel Adoring (2)	15 x 11	IA	3.00 ea.
2869. Angels Adoring (2)	11 x 15	IA	3.00 ea.
2870. Angel Gardener	11 x 15	IA	3.00
2871. Angel Gardener (2)	15 x 11	IA	3.00 ea.
2872. Journey of the Magi: Emperor Paleologue	15 x 11	IA	3.00
2873. Emperor Paleologue-- Detail of No. 2872	11 x 15	IA	3.00
2874. Journey of the Magi: Lorenzo Il Magnifico	15 x 11	IA	3.00
2875. Lorenzo Il Magnifico-- Detail of No. 2874	11 x 15	IA	3.00
2876. Piero dei Medici--			

	Details of No. 2874 (2)	11 x 15	IA	3. 00 ea.
2877.	Journey of the Magi: Giuliano dei Medici	15 x 11	IA	3. 00
2878.	Giuliano dei Medici-- Detail of No. 2877	11 x 15	IA	3. 00
2879.	Marriage of St. Catherine	7 x 11	IA	3. 00
2880.	Miracle of St. Dominic	9 x 13	IA	3. 00
2881.	St. Augustine Brought to School	11 x 13	IA	3. 00
2882.	St. Augustine Leaving Rome for Milan	11 x 12	IA	3. 00
2883.	St. Augustine Teaching Philosophy	11 x 13	IA	3. 00
2884.	Tower of Babel, Details (2)	11 x 15	IA	3. 00 ea.
2885.	Tower of Babel, Details (2)	15 x 11	IA	3. 00 ea.

GRABWINKLER, P.

2886.	Fall of the Year	12 x 16	IA	2. 50

GRADL, HERMANN

2887.	River View	22-1/2 x 28	ESH	10. 00

GRAF, URS   Swiss   1485-1529

2888.	Place of Execution	9 x 9-1/2	AR	3. 00

GRANDMA MOSES   See MOSES
GRANT, GORDON   American   1875-

2889.	Harbor Traffic	17 x 21-1/2	NYGS	5. 00
2890.	In with the Tide	25 x 30	CAC	7. 50
2891.	Wind and Tide	16-1/2 x 21-1/2	NYGS	7. 50
2892.	Winter Landscape	20 x 25	CAC	7. 50

GRANT, (SIR) FRANCIS   Scotch   1803-1878

2893.	Breakfast Scene at Melton	20-1/2 x 28	NYGS	15. 00
2894.	Melton Breakfast	21 x 28	CAC	24. 00
2895.	Quorn Hounds	20 x 27	CAC	25. 00
2896.	Sir Richard Sutton	17 x 28	CAC	25. 00
2897.	Sir Richard Sutton and the Quorn Hounds	20 x 34	CAC	36. 00

GRAU-SALA, EMILIO   Spanish   1911-

2898.	Can-Can	26 x 17-1/2	NYGS	15. 00
2899.	Vaudeville Artist No. 1	18 x 15	CAC	10. 00

GRAULÉ

2900.	Blossom Valley	24 x 48	DAC	10. 00
		11 x 14	DAC	2. 80
2901.	Country Autumn	24 x 48	DAC	10. 00
		11 x 14	DAC	2. 80
2902.	Far from Town	24 x 48	DAC	10. 00
		11 x 14	DAC	2. 80
2903.	Passing Showers	24 x 48	DAC	10. 00
		11 x 14	DAC	2. 80

GRAVES, MORRIS	American	1910-	
2904. Bird Searching	30 x 15	NYGS	15.00
2905. Blind Bird	8 x 10	MMA	.35
2906. Duck Resting	19 x 30	CFA	7.50
2907. Duckling	13 x 17	CFA	5.00
2908. Maribou	17 x 25	CAC	5.00
2909. Woodpeckers	30-1/2 x 21	NYGS	12.00
GRAY, MARIE CHILTON	American	1888-	
2910. Delphinium and White			
Peonies	25 x 30	CAC	7.50
GRECO, EL (DOMENICO THEOTOCOPULI)			
	Spanish	1541-1614	
2911. Annunciation	25 x 17	NYGS	12.00
2912. Apostles Peter and			
Paul	26 x 22-1/2	NYGS	12.00
2913. Christ Blessing	23 x 18	HNA	5.95
2914. Christ Driving the			
Traders from the			
Temple	20 x 24	IA	12.00
2915. Christ Healing the			
Blind Man	28 x 35	IA	15.00
2916. Laocoon	23 x 18	HNA	5.95
2917. Mater Dolorosa	26 x 20	NYGS	18.00
	20-1/2 x 14-1/2	ESH	10.00
	10 x 8	ESH	1.00
2918. Mary Magdalen	21-1/2 x 16-1/2	NYGS	12.00
2919. St. Jerome	28-1/2 x 24-1/2	NYGS	15.00
2920. St. Martin and the			
Beggar	24 x 12-1/2	NYGS	12.00
	24 x 13	PENN	1.00
	10 x 5	NYGS	.50
2921. View of Toledo	28 x 25	NYGS	15.00
	24 x 21-1/2	NYGS	12.00
	14 x 12-1/2	NYGS	4.00
	8 x 7	NYGS	.50
2922. The Virgin with St.			
Ines and St. Thecla	24 x 12-1/2	NYGS	7.50
GREEK ART			
2923. Antiquities (3)	9 x 24 (1)	AR	
	8-1/2 x 12 (2)	AR	12.00
			set of 3
2924. Apollo's Oxen Stolen			
by Hermes (Detail			
of Vase)	10 x 13	ESH	8.00
2925. Chariot (Detail of			
Vase)	10 x 17	ESH	8.00
2926. Ganymede Pursued by			
Zeus (Detail of Vase)	15-1/2 x 12	ESH	8.00
2927. Stag (Detail of Vase)	10 x 17	ESH	8.00
2928. The Vix Vase:			
Quadriga	23 x 30	ESH	15.00
GREEN, M. GHIGLION	French	1913-	

2929. L'Eglise St. Pierre	20 x 25	RL	10.00
2930. Haymakers	19 x 24	RL	10.00
2931. Ile de la Cité	20 x 25-1/2	RL	12.50
2932. Modern French Bouquet	20 x 16	PENN	1.00

GREENE, ELMER

2933. Antique Plate	24 x 30	CAC	7.50
2934. Basket of Sunshine	24 x 36	CAC	10.00
2935. Blue Bowl	24 x 30	CAC	7.50
2936. Brass Vase	24 x 30	CAC	7.50
2937. Chinese Basket	22 x 33	CAC	7.50
2938. Gardenia	20 x 16	IA	3.50
2939. Garden's Gift	24 x 30	CAC	7.50
2940. Garnet Vase	24 x 30	CAC	7.50
2941. Harmony	24 x 30	CAC	7.50
2942. Magnolia	24 x 30	CAC	7.50
2943. Medley of Spring	24 x 36	CAC	10.00
2944. Orchid and White	22 x 33	CAC	7.50
2945. Satin Gown	22 x 26	CAC	7.50
2946. Symphony of Flowers	24 x 30	CAC	7.50

GREENWOOD, MARION   American   Contemporary

2947. Haitian Dancers	12 x 18	NYGS	10.00

GREER, A. D.

2948. Blue and White	25 x 30	CAC	7.50
2949. Bouquet of Asters	30 x 25	CAC	7.50
2950. Glade Water	25 x 30	CAC	7.50
2951. May Blossoms	25 x 30	IA	7.50
2952. Wild Irish Roses	28 x 34	CAC	10.00

GRELLETTE

2953. Sacred Heart of Jesus	20 x 16	CAC	6.00
	12 x 9	CAC	2.00
2954. Sacred Heart of Mary	20 x 16	CAC	6.00
	12 x 9	CAC	2.00

GREUZE, JEAN-BAPTISTE   French   1725-1805

2955. Broken Jug	13 x 11 oval	IA	3.00
2956. Broken Pitcher	18 x 14	CAC	7.50
2957. Dairymaid	13 x 11 oval	IA	3.00
2958. Dead Bird	14 x 11	IA	3.00
2959. L'Enfant à l'Ecuelle	14 x 8	NYGS	4.00
2960. Head of a Girl	16 x 14	CAC	5.00
	14 x 10	CAC	4.00
2961. Little Girl with a Dog	14 x 11	IA	3.00
2962. Milk Maid	18 x 14	CAC	7.50
	12 x 10	CAC	2.50
	11 x 9	CAC	5.00
2963. Study of a Woman	17 x 13	CAC	5.00
2964. Wool Winder	20 x 16-1/2	NYGS	10.00
2965. Young Girl with a Bird	16 x 13	CAC	5.00

GRIFFITH, E. N.

2966. Bachelor's Friends	24 x 31	CFA	15.00
	6 x 7	CFA	1.00

GRIMM, PAUL

2967.	Bouquet	19-1/2 x 27-1/2	ESH	8.00 (Pr.)
2968.	Desert Beauty	16 x 20	ESH	5.00 (Pr.)
2969.	Grandmother and Child	19-1/2 x 27-1/2	ESH	8.00 (Pr.)
2970.	Joshua	16 x 20	ESH	5.00 (Pr.)
2971.	Jucca, California	16 x 20	ESH	5.00 (Pr.)
2972.	Mexico	16 x 20	ESH	5.00 (Pr.)
2973.	Old Mission	12 x 16	ESH	3.00 (Pr.)
2974.	Old Weaver	16 x 20	ESH	5.00 (Pr.)
2975.	View into Mountains	19-1/2 x 23-1/2	ESH	8.00 (Pr.)
GRIMOU, ALEXIS		French	1678-1733	
2976.	Girl Pilgrim	14 x 10	IA	3.00
2977.	Youthful Pilgrim	14 x 10	IA	3.00
GRIS, JUAN		Spanish	1887-1927	
2978.	Black Palette	18 x 23	HNA	5.95
2979.	Breakfast	8 x 10	MMA	.35
2980.	Checkerboard	16 x 20	CFA	7.50
		11 x 14	AR	5.00
2981.	Le Compotier	24-1/2 x 20	NYGS	12.00
2982.	Guitar and Flowers	8 x 10	MMA	.35
2983.	Guitarist	23 x 15	AR	5.00
2984.	Harlequin	20 x 13	CFA	7.50
2985.	Maker of Preserves	24 x 20	CAC	12.00
2986.	Nature Morte	10 x 14	NYGS	12.00
2987.	Still Life	22 x 28	NYGS	18.00
2988.	Still Life with Open Book	16 x 20	NYGS	10.00
2989.	Violin and Glasses	19 x 24	CAC	15.00
GRISOT, P.		French	1911-	
2990.	After Rehearsal	24 x 19	RL	10.00
GRITCHENKO				
2991.	Coimbra	18-1/2 x 11	NYGS	12.00
GROFE, MARY				
2992.	Roses and Larkspur	14 x 15	CFA	1.50
2993.	Zinnias and Larkspur	14 x 15	CFA	1.50
GROMAIRE, MARCEL		French	1892-	
2994.	Brooklyn Bridge	18-1/2 x 22-1/2	ESH	10.00
GROPPER, WILLIAM		American	1897-	
2995.	America--Its Folklore (Map)	22 x 32-1/2	NYGS	5.00
2996.	Cossacks	14 x 18	CAC	10.00
2997.	Diogenes	18 x 12	CAC	10.00
2998.	Equestrienne	26 x 20	NYGS	15.00
2999.	On Stage	18 x 14	CAC	10.00
3000.	Races	18 x 14	CAC	10.00
3001.	Senate	14 x 18	NYGS	10.00
3002.	Senate	15 x 20	MMA	5.00
3003.	The West	16 x 20	CAC	10.00
3004.	Woodcutter	18 x 14	CAC	10.00
GROSE, DAVID				
3005.	Blackberry Patch	10 x 30	AA	12.00
3006.	Locust Trees	10 x 30	AA	12.00
GROSS				

3007.	Landscape	14 x 23	PENN	1.00

GROSZ, GEORGES   German (Res. U. S.) 1893-c. 1945

3008.	Central Park	17-1/2 x 13-1/2	NYGS	5.00
3009.	Manhattan	16 x 22	CAC	15.00
3010.	Manhattan Harbor	22 x 16-1/2	NYGS	10.00

GROTH

| 3011. | Bullfight | 16 x 22 | CAC | 24.00 |

GRUND

| 3012. | Walk in the Park | 24 x 18 | DAC | 6.00 |

GRUENEWALD (OR GRÜNEWALD), MATTHIAS
                              German   c. 1470-1531

3013.	Angel Concert with			
	Madonna and Child	20 x 22	CAC	12.00
3014.	Angel Musician	23 x 18	ESH	10.00
3015.	Ascension	30 x 19	CAC	18.00
3016.	Christ on the Cross	20 x 22	CAC	12.00
3017.	Concert of the Angels	13 x 21	CAC	5.00
3018.	Moonlight	23 x 29	CAC	10.00
3019.	Portrait of a Saint in			
	Prayer	14 x 11-1/2	AR	4.00
3020.	Stuppach Madonna	33-1/2 x 28	NYGS	10.00
3021.	Virgin and St. John	31 x 25	ESH	15.00

GUASTA, BENVENUTO DI GIOVANNI DEL
                              Italian   1436-1518

3022.	Angels (Detail from			
	the Virgin and			
	Saints)	15 x 11	IA	3.00

GUARDI, FRANCESCO DE'   Italian   1712-1793

3023.	Arco E. Marina	12 x 21	CFA	12.00
3024.	Brenta Canal	12 x 21	CFA	12.00
3025.	Bridge at Venice	12 x 20	DAC	4.00
3026.	Canale della Giudecca	17-1/2 x 26	RL	15.00
3027.	Colonnades	30 x 23	CFA	15.00
3028.	Departure of the			
	Bocentauro	20 x 30	ESH	15.00
3029.	Doge's Palace, Venice	18 x 23	HNA	5.95
		17 x 23	AR	15.00
3030.	Fantastic Landscape	15-1/2 x 40	NYGS	18.00
3031.	Grand Canal	22 x 40	CFA	25.00
3032.	Grand Canal Rialto			
	Bridge	12 x 18	CFA	7.50
3033.	Peristylium of a Villa	8 x 6	IA	3.00
3034.	La Place Saint-Marc	9-1/2 x 13-1/2	NYGS	4.00
3035.	Rio dei Mendicanti at			
	Venice	8 x 6	IA	3.00
3036.	Ruins on the Seashore	14 x 10	CFA	1.50
3037.	Seascape with Archway	9 x 15	IA	3.00
3038.	Scene in Venice	23 x 34	CFA	20.00
3039.	Venetian Scene	12 x 20	DAC	4.00
3040.	Venice	10 x 15	NYGS	4.00
3041.	View of the Canale di			
	Brenta	9 x 15	IA	3.00

3042.	View of the Laguna at			
	Venice	10 x 15	IA	3.00
3043.	View on the Canna-			
	reggio	16 x 25	NYGS	12.00
GUBA, R.				
3044.	Along the Coast	19 x 27	CFA	7.50
3045.	Idle Hours	24 x 28	CFA	10.00
3046.	Sailing Boats	23-1/2 x 31-1/2	ESH	10.00 (Pr.)
		16 x 20	ESH	5.00 (Pr.)
GUBLER, MAX				
3046.	Old Man and the Sea	39 x 27	CFA	30.00
GUDIOL				
3047.	Motherhood	26 x 19	NYGS	12.00
GUERCINO, IL (BARBIERI, GIOVANNI FRANCESCO)				
		Italian	1591-1666	
3048.	Ecce Homo	14 x 11	IA	3.00
GUERIN, FRANCOIS		French	1735-1791	
3049.	Lady Reading with			
	Child	10 x 12	CFA	4.00
3050.	Lady Writing with			
	Child	10 x 12	CFA	4.00
GUERMACHEFF, MICHEL				
3051.	Lengthening Shadows	19 x 22-1/2	CAC	5.00
3052.	Sunset Glory	19 x 22-1/2	CAC	5.00
GUILLAUMIN, ARMAND		French	1841-1927	
3053.	Pointe de la Baumette,			
	Agay	18 x 23	HNA	5.95
3054.	Sail Boats	21-1/2 x 27	NYGS	12.00
		8 x 10	ESH	1.00
GUERVAL				
3055.	Ballet (4)	11 x 14	DAC	1.20 ea.
		8 x 10	DAC	.80 ea.
GUIDI, TOMMASO See MASACCIO				
GUIDO DA SIENA		Italian	13th Century	
3056.	Madonna and Child	15 x 10	IA	3.00
GUIDONE				
3057.	Frate Guido di S.			
	Galgano	14 x 9	IA	3.00
GUION, MOLLY		American	1910-	
3058.	Easter Lilies	24 x 20	NYGS	10.00
3059.	Jade and China	24 x 20	NYGS	7.50
3060.	Rose Goddess	24 x 20	NYGS	7.50
3061.	Yellow Roses	24 x 20	NYGS	10.00
GUYS, CONSTANTIN		French	1805-1892	
3062.	La Caleche	7 x 10	NYGS	4.00
3063.	Dancer	12 x 9	AR	5.00
3064.	English Family Outing	10 x 8	ESH	1.00
3065.	Horse and Carriage	8 x 10	ESH	1.00
3066.	Hyde Park	8 x 10	ESH	1.00
3067.	Ladies at the Theatre	7 x 10	CFA	5.00
3068.	Lady in Blue and			
	Green	12 x 8-1/2	AR	5.00

3069. Two Ladies in a
      Theatre Box   7 x 10   AR   5.00

H

HAGEDORN, KARL	German (Res. England)	1889-	
3070. Rough Waters	17 x 24	CFA	6.00
HAKENBECK			
3071. Peter at the Zoo	20 x 14	AP	5.00
HALL, HAINES	American	Ac. 1959	
3072. Gardenias	17 x 18	IA	3.00
	9 x 10	IA	3.00
3073. Magnolia Blossoms	17 x 18	IA	3.00
	9 x 10	IA	1.00
HALLIDAY, EDWARD	English	1902-	
3074. Prince Philip, Duke			
of Edinburgh	20 x 15	CAC	7.50
HALS, FRANZ	Flemish	1580-1666	
2075. La Bohemienne	22-1/2 x 20	NYGS	20.00
3076. Bohemian Girl	24 x 20	PENN	1.00
3077. Family Group	14 x 25	CAC	10.00
3078. Gypsy	15 x 14	CFA	5.00
	12 x 11	IA	3.00
3079. Hille Bobbe	19 x 16	CAC	4.00
	7 x 6	NYGS	.50
3080. Jester	26 x 23	CFA	18.00
	26 x 22	CAC	35.00
	22 x 16	CAC	18.00
	10 x 8	AP	.50
3081. Laughing Cavalier	29 x 23	NYGS	48.00
	19 x 15	CAC	15.00
	16-1/2 x 13	NYGS	5.00
	12 x 9	CAC	2.00
	10 x 8	AP	.50
3082. Mulatto	14 x 12	AP	5.00
3083. Portrait of Jasper			
Schade von Westrum	24 x 18	DAC	6.00
3084. Portrait of an Officer	23 x 18	HNA	5.95
3085. Rommelpot Player	24 x 18	CFA	15.00
3086. Singing Boy	7 x 6	NYGS	.50
3087. Singing Boys	23 x 18	HNA	5.95
	10 x 8	AP	.75
HAMILTON, W.			
3088. Times of Day (4)	12 x 10	CFA	25.00 set
HAN JO-CHO			
3089. Sparrows in Rice			
Field	10" oval	NYGS	8.00
HANFT, W.			
3090. Beechen Alley	23-1/2 x 31-1/2	IA	10.00
3091. Birches	22-1/2 x 30	IA	10.00
3092. Spring	18 x 23-1/2	IA	6.00
3093. Sunny Way	24 x 32	CAC	10.00

3094. Sylvan Silence	24 x 32	CAC	10.00
HANKEY, WILLIAM LEE	English	1869-	
3095. Anchors Aweigh	20 x 24	CAC	6.00
3096. Arrival in Port	20 x 24	CAC	6.00
3097. Awaiting the Tide	26 x 31	CAC	10.00
3098. Breton Harbour	18 x 22	CAC	7.50
3099. Coombe Village, Oxford-shire	20 x 24	CAC	6.00
3100. Departing Fishermen	20 x 24	CAC	6.00
3101. Drifting	22 x 28	CAC	10.00
3102. Fish Quay, St. Ives	18 x 22	CAC	7.50
3103. Fisherman's Cove	25-1/2 x 31	NYGS	10.00
3104. Gay Normandy	20 x 24	CAC	6.00
3015. Mentone	18 x 22	CAC	5.00
3106. Mussel Boats, Honfleur	18 x 22	CAC	7.50
3107. Quaint Brittany	20 x 24	CAC	6.00
3108. St. Tropez Harbor	20 x 24	CAC	6.00
3109. Summer in Devonshire	25 x 31	NYGS	10.00
3110. Village Pond, Oxfordshire	20 x 24	CAC	6.00
HAPP, HANS	German	1889-	
3111. Candlelight	27 x 23	ESH	12.00
3112. Old Well	27-1/2 x 23	ESH	12.00
HARBART, GERTRUDE			
3113. Nickel Plate Road	17 x 40	NYGS	18.00
HARDER, ALEXANDER	German	1901-	
3114. Harbor	23-1/2 x 31-1/2	ESH	10.00 (Pr.)
3115. Hunt	23-1/2 x 31-1/2	ESH	10.00 (Pr.)
3116. Old Fisherman	19 x 15	CAC	3.50
HARDY, HEYWOOD			
3117. Breaking Cover	22 x 30	CAC	25.00
3118. Lost Scent	22 x 30	CAC	25.00
3119. Sporting Scene	20 x 26	CFA	5.00
	17 x 25	CAC	5.00
HARLOW, HARRY M.	American	1882-	
3120. Mrs. Waddell and Children	25 x 32	CAC	10.00
HARNETT, WILLIAM M.	American	1848-1892	
3121. Antique Violin	25 x 16	CAC	7.50
3122. Bard of Avon	24 x 18	AA	10.00
3123. Emblems of Peace	21 x 26	CFA	12.00
	6 x 7	CFA	1.00
3124. Evening's Comfort	9 x 12	CFA	3.00
3125. Faithful Colt	22 x 17	PENN	1.00
			1.98 (Pr.)
3126. Just Dessert	21 x 25	CFA	15.00
	6 x 7	CFA	1.00
3127. Literature	14 x 19	CFA	5.00
	6 x 7	CFA	1.00
3128. Music and Good Luck	32 x 35	CFA	15.00
3129. Music and Literature	23-1/2 x 31-1/2	NYGS	15.00
	11 x 14	NYGS	3.00
3130. My Gems	18 x 23	HNA	5.95

3131. Old Models	30 x 16	CFA	15.00
3132. Old Refrain	22-1/2 x 15-1/2	NYGS	7.50
3133. Smoking	14 x 19	CFA	5.00
	6 x 7	CFA	1.00
HARRIES, LESLIE	English		
3134. Mixed Summer Bowl	19 x 15	RL	3.50
HARRISON, BERNARD	English (Res. France)		
3135. Early Morning, Pont D'Avignon	18-1/2 x 22-1/2	RL	7.50
HARRISON, CLAUDE	English	1922-	
3136. Cowboys and Indians	18 x 24	RL	7.50
HARRISON, JOHN CYRIL	English	1898-	
3137. Alpine Stream	24 x 31	CAC	15.00
3138. Mallard Rising	13 x 19	CAC	5.00
3139. Passing Mallards	18 x 24	CFA	7.50
3140. Widgeon on Tideway	18 x 24	CFA	7.50
HART, B. LEN			
3141. Spring Landscape	19 x 27	RL	10.00
HART, ERNEST			
3142. Cocker Spaniels	16 x 22	NYGS	7.50
3143. English Setters	16 x 22	NYGS	7.50
3144. Irish Setters	16 x 22	NYGS	7.50
3145. Pointers	16 x 22	NYGS	7.50
HART, GEORGE OVERBURY "POP" American		1868-1933	
3146. Bahamas	12 x 19	NYGS	5.00
HART, JAMES M.	American	1828-1901	
3147. View on the Hudson	19 x 25-1/2	NYGS	10.00
HARTLEY, MARSDEN	American	1878-1943	
3148. Fish House, New England	15 x 20	NYGS	7.50
3149. Fox Island, Maine	20 x 25	PENN	1.00
3150. Wild Roses	22 x 28	NYGS	15.00
HARTUNG, HANS	German-French	1904-	
3151. Painting T 1962 L 7	8-1/2 x 37	ESH	13.00
HARVEY, HAROLD	English	1874-1942	
3152. Blue Door, Newlyn	22 x 18	CAC	5.00
3153. Cornish Homestead	17 x 21	RL	5.00
3154. Tea Time, Newlyn	22 x 18	RL	6.00
HASEGAWA			
3155. Ming Horse	30 x 40	CAC	45.00
HASSAM, CHILDE	American	1859-1935	
3156. Bailey's Beach	22 x 24	NYGS	10.00
3157. Church at Old Lyme	27 x 24	IA	12.00
	10 x 8	AP	.50
3158. Golden Afternoon, Oregon	29-1/2 x 39	NYGS	18.00
3159. Winter Nightfall in the City	14-1/2 x 19	NYGS	5.00
HASSELL, CLEMENTS	English		
3160. Blue Window in Cassis	24 x 20	CAC	10.00
HAVELL, ROBERT, JR.	American	1793-1878	
3161. The Blenheim Leaving			

	Star Hotel	10 x 16	CAC	12.00
3162.	Land of Promise	26 x 36	AA	15.00
3163.	Partridge Shooting	11 x 15	CAC	24.00
3164.	Pheasant Shooting	11 x 15	CAC	24.00
3165.	Shootings (4)	8 x 12	CAC	24.00 set
3166.	Snipe Shooting	11 x 15	CAC	24.00
3167.	Wild Duck Shooting	11 x 15	CAC	24.00
3168.	View of Ossining	30 x 40	CAC	18.00
		28 x 37-1/2	NYGS	18.00

HAWTHORNE, CHARLES WEBSTER   American   1872-1930

3169.	Trousseau	22 x 22	CAC	7.50

HAYMSON, JOHN   American   Contemporary

3170.	Arlington, Va. , Robert E. Lee Home	20 x 16	AA	7.50
3171.	Autos, Old	12 x 30	AA	10.00
3172.	Balloon No. 1	30 x 12	AA	10.00
3173.	Balloon No. 2	30 x 12	AA	10.00
3174.	Banjo	30 x 12	AA	10.00
3175.	Blast Furnace	30 x 12	AA	10.00
3176.	Blue Vase	30 x 12	AA	10.00
3177.	Boston, Mass. , Old North Church	20 x 16	AA	7.50
3178.	Boston, Mass. , Old South Meeting House	20 x 16	AA	7.50
3179.	Charleston, S. C. , Dock Street Theatre	16 x 12	AA	5.00
3180.	Charleston, S. C. , Garden Gate	16 x 12	AA	5.00
3181.	Charleston, S. C. , Meeting Street	16 x 12	AA	5.00
3182.	Charleston, S. C. , St. Philip's Church	16 x 12	AA	5.00
3183.	Charlottesville, Va.: Thomas Jefferson's Home, Monticello	18 x 24	AA	12.00
3184.	Chicago, Ill.: Aerial View	24 x 18	AA	10.00
3185.	Chicago, Ill., Boulevard Bridge	20 x 16	AA	7.50
		12 x 9	AA	2.00
3186.	Chicago, Ill., Michigan Boulevard	20 x 16	AA	7.50
		12 x 9	AA	2.00
3187.	Chicago, Ill., Water Tower	24 x 18	AA	10.00
3188.	Corn	12 x 30	AA	10.00
3189.	Driftwood	12 x 30	AA	10.00
3190.	Fire Engines, Old	12 x 30	AA	10.00
3191.	Florence, Italy: Piazza	12 x 16	AA	5.00
3192.	Grain Elevator	20 x 16	AA	7.50
3193.	Green Vase	30 x 12	AA	10.00

3194. Jamaica: Kingston	16 x 12	AA	5.00
3195. Jamaica: Street Scene	16 x 12	AA	5.00
3196. Locomotives, Old	12 x 30	AA	10.00
3197. London, England: Changing the Guard	16 x 12	AA	5.00
3198. London, England: Changing the Guard, Buckingham Palace	12 x 30	AA	10.00
3199. London, England: London Bridge	12 x 30	AA	10.00
3200. London, England: Mansion House	16 x 12	AA	5.00
3201. London England: Old Curiosity Shop	16 x 12	AA	5.00
3202. London, England: Tower Bridge	16 x 12	AA	5.00
3203. Los Angeles, Calif., Civic Center	16 x 20	AA	7.50
3204. Mexico: Fountain	12 x 16	AA	5.00
3205. Mexico: Market at Patzinaro	16 x 12	AA	5.00
3206. Mexico: Taxco	12 x 16	AA	5.00
3207. Mexico: Taxco Cathedral	16 x 12	AA 16 x 12	5.00
3208. Nassau: Gregory's Arch	16 x 12	AA	5.00
3209. Nassau: Waterfront	16 x 12	AA 12 x 16	5.00
3210. New England Harbors (6)	12 x 16	AA	5.00 ea.
Boothbay (2)			
Gloucester (2)			
Rockport (2)			
3211. New Orleans: Lace Balconies	20 x 16	AA	7.50
3212. New Orleans: Old Residence	20 x 16	AA	7.50
3213. New Orleans: Prete House	30 x 12	AA	10.00
3214. New Orleans: Vieux Carré	30 x 12	AA	10.00
3215. New York: Central Park	30 x 12	AA	10.00
3216. New York: Central Park Lake	16 x 20	AA	7.50
3217. New York: Central Park Skating	30 x 12	AA	10.00
3218. New York: Central Park, Winter Night	30 x 12	AA	10.00
3219. New York: Downtown Skyline	12 x 30	AA	10.00
3220. New York: Fifth Avenue	18-1/2 x 15	NYGS	6.00

3221. New York: Fulton Market	16 x 20	AA	7.50
3222. New York: George Washington Bridge	12 x 30	AA	10.00
3223. New York: Grand Central Terminal	18-1/2 x 15	NYGS	6.00
3224. New York: Lever House	20 x 16	AA	7.50
3225. New York: Lower Park Avenue	20 x 16	AA	7.50
3226. New York City No. 1 (8)	9 x 12	AA	10.00 sheet
3227. New York City No. 2 (7)	9 x 12	AA	9.00 sheet
3228. New York: The Plaza	16 x 20	AA	7.50
3229. New York: Public Library	15 x 18-1/2	NYGS	6.00
3230. New York: Rockefeller Center	20 x 16	AA	7.50
3231. New York: Rockefeller Plaza	15 x 18-1/2	NYGS	6.00
3232. New York: St. Patrick's Cathedral No. 1	20 x 16	AA	7.50
3233. New York: St. Patrick's Cathedral No. 2	20 x 16	AA	7.50
3234. New York: Statue of Liberty	30 x 12	AA	10.00
3235. New York: Skyline	20 x 16	AA	7.50
3236. New York: Skyline, Lower New York from Brooklyn	12 x 30	AA	10.00
3237. New York: Stock Exchange	20 x 16	AA	7.50
3238. New York: Stock Exchange	30 x 12	AA	10.00
3239. New York: United Nations Secretariat	30 x 12	AA	10.00
3240. New York: United Nations Skyline	12 x 30	AA	10.00
3241. New York: U.S. Treasury Building	20 x 16	AA	7.50
3242. New York: Vanderbilt Avenue	20 x 16	AA	7.50
3243. New York: Washington Square	20 x 16	AA	7.50
3244. Paris, France: Arc de Triomphe	24 x 10	AA	8.00
3245. Paris, France: Boulevard des Italiens	16 x 12	AA	5.00
3246. Paris, France: Les Bouquinistes	30 x 12	AA	10.00

3247. Paris, France: Kiosk and Café	16 x 12	AA	5.00
3248. Paris, France: Left Bank	30 x 12	AA	10.00
3249. Paris, France: Louvre	15 x 30	AA	15.00
3250. Paris, France: La Madeleine	30 x 12	AA	10.00
3251. Paris, France: Moulin Rouge	16 x 12	AA	5.00
3252. Paris, France: Notre Dame	12 x 27	AA	10.00
3253. Paris, France: Palais Justice	15 x 30	AA	15.00
3254. Paris (8)	12 x 9	AA	2.00 ea.

Book Stalls
Deux Lions
Flower Market
Montmartre
On the Seine
L'Opera
Sacre Coeur
Vieux Montmartre

3255. Paris, France: Petite Rue	24 x 10	AA	8.00
3256. Paris, France: Place du Tertre	18 x 24	AA	12.00
3257. Paris, France: Place Furstenberg	18 x 24	AA	12.00
3258. Paris, France: Rue de Rivoli	16 x 12	AA	5.00
3259. Paris, France: Sacre Coeur	12 x 27	AA	10.00
3260. Paris, France: Saint Germain	30 x 12	AA	10.00
3261. Philadelphia, Pa., Betsy Ross House	16 x 12	AA	5.00
3262. Philadelphia, Pa., Cradle of Liberty	20 x 16	AA	7.50
3263. Philadelphia, Pa., Elfreth's Alley	16 x 12	AA	5.00
3264. Philadelphia, Pa., Independence Hall	18 x 24	AA	12.00
3265. Philadelphia, Pa., Off Rittenhouse Square	20 x 16	AA	7.50
3266. Rome, Italy: Pantheon	12 x 16	AA	5.00
3267. Rome, Italy: St. Peter's	12 x 16	AA	5.00
3268. San Francisco, Calif., Cable Cars	20 x 16	AA	7.50
3269. San Francisco, Calif., Fishermen's Wharf	20 x 16	AA	7.50
3270. San Juan Capistrano			

Mission	16 x 20	AA	7.50
3271. Steamboats	12 x 30	AA	10.00
3272. Texas: Alamo	16 x 12	AA	5.00
3273. Texas: Cat Cracker	20 x 16	AA	7.50
3274. Texas: Oil Fields	20 x 16	AA	7.50
3275. Texas: Oil Refinery	30 x 12	AA	10.00
3276. Trotters	12 x 30	AA	10.00
3277. Universities: Cornell	16 x 12	AA	5.00
3278. Universities: Nassau Hall, Princeton	16 x 12	AA	5.00
3279. Universities: Yale	16 x 12	AA	5.00
3280. Universities: The Yard, Harvard	16 x 12	AA	5.00
3281. Valley Forge, Pa.	16 x 12	AA	5.00
3282. Venice, Italy: Canal	16 x 12	AA	5.00
3283. Venice, Italy: Gondolas	12 x 16	AA	5.00
3284. Venice, Italy: St. Marks	16 x 12	AA	5.00
3285. Washington, D.C.: Capitol	20 x 16	AA	7.50
3286. Washington, D.C.: Capitol at Night	20 x 16	AA	7.50
3287. Washington, D.C.: Jefferson Memorial	30 x 12	AA	10.00
3288. Washington, D.C.: Lincoln Memorial	12 x 30	AA	10.00
3289. Washington, D.C.: Mount Vernon, Va., Washington's Home	16 x 20	AA	7.50
3290. Washington, D.C.: National Gallery of Art	16 x 20	AA	7.50
3291. Washington, D.C.: Supreme Court Building	20 x 16	AA	7.50
3292. Washington, D.C.: Washington Monument	30 x 12	AA	10.00
3293. Washington, D.C.: White House	12 x 30	AA	10.00
3294. White Vase	30 x 12	AA	10.00
3295. Williamsburg, Va. (8)	12 x 9	AA	2.00 ea.

Bruton Church
The Capitol
Court House
Duke of Gloucester Street
Governor's Palace
Palace Gardens
Raleigh Tavern
Water's Coleman House

HAYS, WILLIAM JACOB	American	1872-1934	
3296. Westchester Hills	27 x 36	NYGS	15.00

HAYWARD, ARTHUR	English	1841-1917	
3297. Harbour, St. Ives	19 x 22-1/2	RL	6.00
HAYWARD, PETER			
3298. Aristocrats	25 x 30	CAC	7.50
3299. City Rain	24 x 40	DAC	8.00
3300. Off the Avenue	24 x 40	DAC	8.00
3301. Palm Cove	24 x 40	DAC	8.00
3302. Quiet City	24 x 40	DAC	8.00
3303. Windswept Palms	24 x 40	DAC	8.00
HEALY, GEORGE	American	1813-1894	
3304. Abraham Lincoln	27-1/2 x 20	NYGS	12.00
HEBLING, T.			
3305. Mozart	28 x 22	CFA	12.00
HECKEL, ERICH	German	1883-	
3306. White House in Dangast	18 x 23	HNA	5.95
HECHT, ZOLTAN	American	1890-	
3307. Skaters	16 x 20	CAC	10.00
HEEMSKERCK, EGBERT VAN	Dutch	1610-1680	
3308. Interior	14 x 11	IA	3.00
3309. Young Girl	21 x 16	NYGS	20.00
HEFFNER, J.			
3310. Black Forest Idyll	26 x 34	NYGS	12.00
3311. Spring Landscape	26 x 33	CFA	15.00
3312. Springtime	24 x 33	CFA	15.00
HEGETSCHWEILER, MAX	Swiss	1902-	
3313. Studio	12 x 14	CAC	10.00
HEGNER			
3314. Street at Nessebar	15 x 20	AP	5.00
HEIDINGSFELD, FRITZ	German	1907-	
3315. Coast of East Lake	21 x 27-1/2	ESH	8.00
3316. East Lake	21 x 28	ESH	8.00
3317. Ibiza	12 x 16	ESH	4.00
HEIMROD			
3318. General Store	9 x 12	DAC	1.20
	6 x 8	DAC	.60
3319. School Recess	9 x 12	DAC	1.20
	6 x 8	DAC	.60
3320. To the Fire	9 x 12	DAC	1.20
	6 x 8	DAC	.60
3321. Whistle Stop	9 x 12	DAC	1.20
	6 x 8	DAC	.60
HELCK, PETER	American	Contemporary	
3322. Cars, Famous Racing (4)	8 x 12	DAC	1.00 ea.
HELSTROM, BESSIE			
3323. White Hydrangeas	25 x 30	CFA	10.00
HEMPFING, WILHELM	German	1886-1951	
3324. Dreamer's Cove	22 x 30-1/2	IA	10.00
HENCKE, ALBERT			
3325. Dick Whittington	20 x 16	CFA	2.50
3326. Girl with Swing	16 x 20	CFA	2.50

3327. Goosey Goosey Gander	20 x 16	CFA	2.50
3328. Jack and the Beanstalk	20 x 16	CFA	2.50
3329. Little Red Riding Hood	20 x 16	CFA	2.50
3330. Mary and her Little Lamb	22 x 28	CFA	2.50
3331. Noah's Ark	28 x 40	CFA	15.00
3332. See Saw	16 x 20	CFA	2.50
HENDERSON, CHARLES COOPER English		1803-1877	
3333. Calais Express	15 x 25	AA	7.50
3334. Going Easy	13 x 24	CAC	10.00
3335. Got Hold	13 x 24	CAC	10.00
3336. Leeds to London	24 x 35	AA	15.00
3337. London Royal Mail	15 x 25	AA	7.50
HENNER, JEAN JACQUES	French	1829-1905	
3338. Fabiola	19 x 14-1/2	IA	7.50
	14 x 11	IA	3.00
	10 x 8	IA	1.50
3339. Reader	11 x 14	IA	3.00
HENNESSEY, PATRICK	Irish	1915-	
3340. Lake and Mountain	20-1/2 x 24-1/2	RL	10.00
3341. Last of Summer	20-1/2 x 24-1/2	RL	10.00
HENRI, ROBERT	American	1865-1929	
3342. Herself	20-1/2 x 17	NYGS	7.50
3343. Himself	20-1/2 x 17	NYGS	7.50
	8 x 6-1/2	NYGS	.50
HENRY, EDWARD LAMSON	American	1841-1919	
3344. Childhood of Rapid Transit	15 x 32-1/2	NYGS	36.00
		(H. C. Grav.)	
3345. Country Breakfast	18 x 26	DAC	6.00
3346. Days before Rapid Transit	13 x 34	NYGS	36.00
		(H. C. Grav.)	
3347. Home Again	24 x 40	CFA	12.00
3348. The 9:45 Accommodation, Stratford, Conn.	15 x 30	AA	12.00
3349. Off the Main Road	18 x 26	DAC	6.00
3350. Old Dutch Church	18 x 34	NYGS	36.00
		(H. C. Grav.)	
3351. Saint John's Church	21-1/2 x 17-1/2	NYGS	30.00
		(H. C. Grav.)	
3352. The Planet	15 x 32	NYGS	36.00
		(H. C. Grav.)	
HENRY, GEORGE	Scotch		
3353. Over the Downs	20 x 25	RL	7.50
HENRY, MICHEL	French	1928-	
3354. Bronze and Grey	30 x 15	RL	15.00
HENRY, PAUL	Irish	1880-1958	
3355. Connemara Cottages	16 x 20	RL	5.00
3356. Roadside Cottage, Lough Inagh	16 x 20	RL	5.00
HERMES			
3357. Donkey Ride	16 x 12	CFA	5.00

HERRING, JOHN FREDERICK	English	1795-1865	
3358. Breaking Cover	17-1/2 x 30-1/2	NYGS	10.00
	13 x 20-1/2	NYGS	5.00
	6-1/2 x 11	NYGS	1.00
3359. The Death	17-1/2 x 30-1/2	NYGS	10.00
	13 x 20-1/2	NYGS	5.00
	6-1/2 x 11	NYGS	1.00
3360. Fox Hunting Scenes (4)	9 x 16	IA	2.50 ea.
Breaking Cover			
The Death			
Full Cry			
The Meet			
3361. Full Cry	17-1/2 x 30-1/2	NYGS	10.00
	13 x 20-1/2	NYGS	5.00
	6-1/2 x 11	NYGS	1.00
3362. The Meet	17-1/2 x 30-1/2	NYGS	10.00
	13 x 20-1/2	NYGS	5.00
	6-1/2 x 11	NYGS	1.00
HERRING-HARRIS			
3363. Full Cry (4)	20 x 32	AA	24.00 ea.
HERVE, JULES	French	1887-	
3364. Bois de Boulogne	22-1/2 x 28	RL	12.50
3365. Les Jardins des			
Tuileries (4)	11 x 14	DAC	2.00 ea.
HESS, JULIUS			
3366. Landscape with Pines	30 x 23	ESH	10.00
HESSELIUS, JOHN	American	1728-1778	
3367. Charles Calvert	24 x 19	NYGS	12.00
HEUBERGER, F.			
3368. Silent Sentinels	25-1/2 x 29	RL	12.50
HEWES, MADELINE			
3369. The Blessing Strive	24 x 30	CFA	15.00
HIBBARD, ALDRO THOMPSON	American	1886-	
3370. Covered Bridge	24 x 32	IA	10.00
3371. Little Town of Weston	24 x 32	IA	10.00
HICKS, EDWARD	American	1780-1849	
3372. Peacable Kingdom	18 x 24	PENN	1.00
	17-1/2 x 23	NYGS	10.00
	5-1/2 x 7-1/2	NYGS	.50
3373. Residence of David			
Twining	16 x 19	IA	7.50
HIDALGO, ALEJANDRO RANGEL	Mexican	Contemporary	
3374. Consuelo	20 x 15	NYGS	7.50
3375. Going to Market	15-1/2 x 12	NYGS	5.00
	7-1/2 x 6	NYGS	1.50
3376. Indita	20 x 15	NYGS	7.50
	7-1/2 x 6	NYGS	1.50
3377. Indito	20 x 15	NYGS	7.50
	7-1/2 x 6	NYGS	1.50
3378. Jose	20 x 15	NYGS	7.50
	7-1/2 x 6	NYGS	1.50

3379. Little Bird Vendor	15-1/2 x 12	NYGS	5.00
	7-1/2 x 6	NYGS	1.50
3380. Little Caballero	20 x 15	NYGS	7.50
	7-1/2 x 6	NYGS	1.50
3381. Little Flower Vendor	15-1/2 x 12	NYGS	5.00
	7-1/2 x 6	NYGS	1.50
3382. Little Senorita	20 x 15	NYGS	7.50
	7-1/2 x 6	NYGS	1.50

HIGGINS, VICTOR

3383. Fiesta Day	30 x 32	IA	18.00

HILAIR, JEAN BAPTISTE   French   1753-1822

3384. Music Lesson	12 x 11 Oval	IA	3.00
3385. Reading	12 x 11 Oval	IA	3.00

HILL, J. S.

3386. Bevy of Quails	18-1/2 x 24	AA	15.00

HILLIER, TRISTRAM

3387. Country Lane	20 x 24	RL	10.00
3388. Flooded Meadow	18 x 24	RL	10.00

HINDU ART

3389. Arajah and his Favorite	10 x 8	ESH	1.00
3390. Four Birds	8 x 10	ESH	1.00
3391. High Lord and his Chosen One	8 x 10	ESH	1.00
3392. Horse and Groom (Kotah School)	8 x 10	ESH	1.00
3393. Kangra--Krishna and Radha	8 x 10	ESH	1.00
3394. Kotah--Groom Caparisoned Horse	8 x 10	ESH	1.00

HIROSHIGE

3395. Koyoenkyo Bridge	26 x 9	PENN	1.00
3396. Season's First Snow	19 x 38-1/2	PENN	1.00
3397. Snow Landscape	26 x 8-1/2	PENN	1.00

HIRSCH, JOSEPH   American   1910-

3398. Philosopher	24-1/2 x 18-1/2	NYGS	15.00

HITCHCOCK, GEORGE   American   1850-1913

3399. Flight into Egypt	24 x 36	NYGS	15.00

HOBBEMA, MEINDERT   Dutch   1638-1709

3400. Avenue, Middleharnis, Holland	26 x 35	NYGS	18.00
	13-1/2 x 18-1/2	NYGS	5.00
3401. Avenue of Trees	8 x 10	AP	.50
3402. Landscape with Falconer	28 x 37-1/2	NYGS	24.00
3403. Landscape, Wooded Road	29 x 35-1/2	NYGS	15.00
3404. View on a High Road	26 x 35-1/2	NYGS	20.00
3405. Village Avenue	18 x 26	DAC	6.00
3406. Village near a Pool	18 x 23	HNA	5.95
3407. Watermill with Great Red Roofs	24 x 36	CFA	18.00

3408. Watermill with the			
Red Roof	18 x 24	DAC	6.00
	12 x 16	DAC	2.00

HOBBIE, LUCILLE

3409. Antique Shops (4)	11 x 14	DAC	2.00 ea.
	6 x 8	DAC	.60 ea.
3410. Blue Door	11 x 14	DAC	2.00
	6 x 8	DAC	.60
3411. Roadside Chat	11 x 14	DAC	2.00
	6 x 8	DAC	.60
3412. Spinning Wheel	11 x 14	DAC	2.00
	6 x 8	DAC	.60
3413. Turn of the Road	11 x 14	DAC	2.00
	6 x 8	DAC	.60

HODLER, FERDINAND   Swiss   1853-1918

3414. Breithorn	18 x 23	HNA	5.95
3415. Meditation	22-1/2 x 16	NYGS	10.00
3416. Woodland	19 x 26	NYGS	12.00

HOFER, KARL   German   1878-1955

3417. Girls Throwing			
Flowers	28 x 22	CAC	12.00
3418. Italian Landscape	24 x 29	NYGS	18.00
3419. Italian Landscape,			
Agnuzzo	25 x 36	NYGS	15.00
3420. Landscape at Muzzano	15-1/2 x 20-1/2	AP	5.00
	8 x 10	AP	.60
3421. Musicians	30 x 25	NYGS	24.00
3422. Still Life with Grape-			
fruit	18 x 23	NYGS	12.00
3423. Still Life with Lemons	18-1/2 x 22	NYGS	20.00
3424. Three Masks	19-1/2 x 16	IA	6.00
	10 x 8	AP	.75

HOFMANN, HEINRICH   German   1824-1911

3424a Christ and the Rich			
Young Ruler	27 x 36	IA	15.00
	19 x 24	IA	5.00
	8 x 9-1/2	IA	10.00
			(Grav.)
	7-1/2 x 9	IA	.50
3425. Christ at Thirty-			
three	20 x 16	IA	4.00
	12 x 9	IA	1.00
	9-1/2 x 7-1/2	NYGS	.50
3426. Christ at Twelve	20 x 16	IA	4.00
	9-1/2 x 7-1/2	NYGS	.50
3427. Christ in the Garden			
of Gethsemane	39-1/2 x 28	IA	24.00
	30 x 22	IA	10.00
	24 x 17-1/2	IA	5.00
	20 x 16	IA	6.00
	20 x 14-1/2	IA	4.00
	12 x 9	IA	3.50
	10 x 7	NYGS	.50

3428.	Christ in the Temple	27 x 36	IA	15.00
3429.	Christ Preaching on the Sea	6-1/2 x 10	IA	10.00 (Grav.)
3430.	Christ with Mary and Martha	8 x 10	IA	10.00 (Grav.)
3431.	Christus	10 x 8	IA	10.00 (Grav.)
3432.	Good Shepherd	21 x 28	IA	5.00
3433.	In the Forest	23-1/2 x 31-1/2	ESH	10.00 (Pr.)
3434.	The Lord's Image (I am the Truth)	30 x 22	NYGS	10.00
		10 x 7-1/2	NYGS	.50
3435.	The Saviour	20 x 16	IA	4.00
		10 x 8	IA	.50

HOGARTH, WILLIAM   English   1697-1764

3436.	Graham Children	22-1/2 x 25	AP	12.00
		8 x 10	AP	.50
3437.	Shrimp Girl	10 x 8	AP	.50

HOITSU, SAKAI   Japanese   1761-1828

3438.	Chrysanthemums	29-1/2 x 10	NYGS	18.00
3439.	Peonies and Chrysanthemums	29-1/2 x 10	NYGS	18.00

HOKUSAI

3440.	Iran Courtesan	26 x 11	PENN	1.00

HOLBEIN, HANS, THE YOUNGER   German   1497-1543

3441.	Anne of Cleves, Queen of England	14 x 10	IA	3.00
3442.	B. von Hartenstein	10 x 8	AP	.25
3443.	Edward VI as a Child	22 x 17	NYGS	7.50
		8 x 6	NYGS	.50
3444.	Lady Lee	10 x 8	AP	.25
3445.	Merchant George Gisze	34-1/2 x 30-1/2	NYGS	20.00
		25 x 22	CFA	15.00
		26 x 23	NYGS	22.00
		25-1/2 x 22-1/2	IA	15.00
		7 x 6	NYGS	.50
		10 x 8	AP	.60
3446.	Portrait of an Elderly Man	7 x 5	NYGS	.50
3447.	Portrait of Erasmus	14 x 11	IA	3.00
3448.	Portrait of Henry VIII	13 x 11	IA	3.00
3449.	Portrait of a Lady	20 x 15	CFA	7.50
3450.	Portrait of a Man	18 x 13-1/2	AJ	7.50
3451.	Portrait of Richard Southwell	14 x 11	IA	3.00
3452.	Self-Portrait	9 x 7	IA	3.00
3453.	Sir Thomas More	28-1/2 x 23	NYGS	15.00
		8 x 6	NYGS	.50

HOLE, WILLIAM

3453.	Christ Weeping over Jerusalem	10 x 15	IA	10.00

	7 x 10	IA	10.00
			(Grav.)
HOLESCH, DE			
3454. Chargers	20 x 26	PENN	1.00
3455. Courtship	24 x 20	PENN	1.00
3456. Quartet	26 x 19	PENN	1.00
3457. Rehearsal	26 x 19	PENN	1.00
HOLLAND			
3458. Federal Hall	17-1/2 x 22	PENN	1.00
HOLST, JOHANNES			
3459. Schooner	22 x 31	IA	15.00
HOLY, A			
3460. Boats in Harbour	18 x 23	CFA	10.00
3461. Street near Harbor	18 x 23	CFA	10.00
HOMER, WINSLOW	American	1836-1910	
3462. Boys in a Pasture	15 x 22	PENN	1.00
3463. Breezing Up	19-1/2 x 31	NYGS	15.00
	16 x 25	PENN	1.00
			1.98 (Pr.)
	15 x 24	NYGS	10.00
3464. Bridle Path, White Mountains	18 x 23	HNA	5.95
3465. Coming Storm	13 x 19-1/2	NYGS	5.00
3466. Country School	22 x 40	CFA	12.00
3467. Croquet Scene	18 x 24	DAC	6.00
	15 x 25	NYGS	12.00
	12 x 16	DAC	2.00
3468. Eight Bells	18 x 21	PENN	1.00
3469. Flower Garden and Bungalow, Bermuda	12 x 18	AJ	6.00
3470. Fog Warning	16-1/2 x 26	PENN	1.00
	8 x 10	AP	.50
	13 x 21	AP	3.00
3471. Gulf Stream	18-1/2 x 30	AA	10.00
	11 x 20	NYGS	7.50
3472. Herring Net	18-1/2 x 30	NYGS	12.00
	18 x 26	DAC	6.00
3473. Hudson River Logging	13 x 19	NYGS	7.50
3474. Moonlight at Woods Island Light	8 x 10	AP	.50
3475. Negro Cabins and Palms	8 x 10	AP	.50
3476. Northeaster	25-1/2 x 37-1/2	NYGS	15.00
	8 x 10	AP	.50
	7 x 11	NYGS	.50
3477. North Woods Club, Adirondacks	12-1/2 x 18	AJ	6.00
3478. Palm Tree, Nassau	19-1/2 x 13-1/2	NYGS	10.00
	18 x 12	AJ	6.00
	9 x 6	NYGS	.50
3479. Portage	14 x 21	NYGS	5.00
3480. Rapids, Hudson River	15 x 21-1/2	NYGS	7.50

3481. Shell Heap	18 x 12-1/2	NYGS	7.50
3482. Skating at the Central Park	12-1/2 x 19	NYGS	5.00
3483. Sloop, Bermuda	13-1/2 x 19-1/2	NYGS	10.00
	12-1/2 x 18	AJ	6.00
3484. Snap the Whip	24 x 38	AA	15.00
3485. Sponge Fishing, Bahamas	14 x 18-1/2	NYGS	7.50
3486. Stowing the Sail, Bahamas	14 x 22	AP	7.50
	13-1/2 x 21-1/2	NYGS	7.50
3487. Turkey Buzzard	12 x 8	AJ	6.00
3488. Weaning the Calf	19 x 30	NYGS	12.00
3489. Weather Beaten	16 x 27-1/2	PENN	1.00
3490. Watercolors (Portfolio) (6)	9-1/2 x 14	PENN	1.98 set

        Bermuda
        Boatman
        Breezing Up
        Diamond Shoal
        Lost on the Grand
          Banks
        Rum Cay

HOOCH, PIETER DE	Dutch	1629-1683	
3491. Card Players	29 x 25	CFA	18.00
3492. Courtyard of Dutch House	8 x 10	AP	.50
3493. Dutch Courtyard	19-1/2 x 16-1/2	NYGS	10.00
	7-1/2 x 6-1/2	NYGS	.50
3494. Dutch Courtyard with Pump	8 x 10	AP	.50
3495. Interior of a Dutch House	18-1/2 x 16	NYGS	5.00
3496. The Mother	27 x 29-1/2	NYGS	24.00
3497. Pantry	20 x 19	AP	5.00
3498. Storage Room	8 x 10	AP	.50
3499. Woman Peeling Apples	22 x 17-1/2	IA	15.00
HONTHORST, GERARD (GHERARDO DELLE NOTTI)			
	Dutch	1590-1656	
3500. Adoration of the Infant Jesus	11 x 15	IA	3.00
3501. Almond Blossoms	23-1/2 x 31-1/2	ESH	10.00 (Pr.)
3502. Bavarian Lake	12 x 16	ESH	3.00 (Pr.)
3503. Forest View	19-1/2 x 27-1/2	ESH	8.00 (Pr.)
3504. Lake of Garda	19-1/2 x 27-1/2	ESH	8.00 (Pr.)
3505. Landscape	19-1/2 x 27-1/2	ESH	8.00 (Pr.)
	12 x 16	ESH	3.00 (Pr.)
3506. Moorland	12 x 16	ESH	3.00 (Pr.)
3507. Sunflowers	23-1/2 x 31-1/2	ESH	10.00 (Pr.)
HOPPER, EDWARD	American	1882-	
3508. Captain Strout's House	13 x 19	CFA	5.00

3509. Circus Wagon	13 x 19	CFA	5.00
3510. Ground Swell	15 x 21	NYGS	5.00
3511. House on Pamet River	15 x 19	NYGS	5.00
3512. Lighthouse, Two			
Lights	8 x 10	AP	.50
3513. Marshall's House	13 x 19	CFA	5.00
3514. Rockland Harbor,			
Maine	13 x 19	CFA	5.00
3515. Seven A.M.	18 x 24	PENN	1.00

HOPPMAN, HEIN

3516. Fishing Boats on			
Shore	18 x 24	ESH	10.00

HOPPNER, JOHN   English   1758-1810

3517. Little Bo Peep			
(Miss Harriet Ann			
Seale)	31 x 25	NYGS	12.00
	24 x 19-1/2	NYGS	10.00
	18 x 14	CFA	5.00

HORTER, EARL

3518. Gloucester Docks	14 x 19	NYGS	5.00

HOSCH

3519. Bavarian Lake	23-1/2 x 31-1/2	ESH	10.00 (Pr.)

HOUSTON, ROBERT   Scotch   1891-

3520. Autumn Birches,			
Loch Lomond	17-1/2 x 22-1/2	RL	5.00
3521. Firth of Clyde	18 x 24	CFA	5.00
3522. Homewards	19 x 22-1/2	RL	5.00
3533. Isle of Arran	18 x 24	CFA	5.00

HOUTMAN, M.

3534. Basket of Fruit	13 x 15	CFA	7.50
3535. Bowl of Fruit	13 x 15	CFA	7.50

HOWARD

3536. Seascape	19 x 32-1/2	PENN	1.00

HOWLAND, ALFRED C.

3537. Buffalo Hunt	17-1/2 x 23-1/2	PENN	1.00
3538. Fourth of July			
Parade	24 x 39-1/2	NYGS	15.00

HUBER, WOLF   German   1480-1549

3539. Adoration of the			
Kings	28 x 18	NYGS	20.00
3540. Annunciation to			
Joachim	28 x 18	NYGS	20.00
3541. Flight into Egypt	22 x 22	NYGS	20.00
3542. Joachim and Anna	28 x 18	NYGS	20.00
3543. Landscape	13 x 18	AR	7.50

HUET, J. B.

3544. L'Apres Midi	9 x 11	CFA	6.00
3545. Le Matin	9 x 11	CFA	6.00
3546. Le Midi	9 x 11	CFA	6.00
3547. Summer	9 x 11	CFA	6.00

HUGO, JEAN   French   1894-

3548. Autumn Honeymoon	9 x 12	NYGS	2.00
	6 x 7-1/2	NYGS	1.00

3549. Harbor	18 x 24	NYGS	15.00
3550. Honeymoon by the Bay	15 x 18	NYGS	10.00
	6 x 7-1/2	NYGS	1.00
3551. Honeymoon by the River	15 x 18	NYGS	10.00
	9 x 12	NYGS	2.00
	6 x 7-1/2	NYGS	1.00
3552. Honeymoon in the Country	15 x 18	NYGS	10.00
	6 x 7-1/2	NYGS	1.00
3553. Honeymoon in the Hills	6 x 7-1/2	NYGS	1.00
3554. Honeymoon in Paris	15 x 18	NYGS	10.00
	9 x 12	NYGS	2.00
	6 x 7	NYGS	1.00
3555. Honeymoon in the Snow	9 x 12	NYGS	2.00
	6 x 7-1/2	NYGS	1.00
3556. Honeymoon in the Spring	6 x 7	NYGS	1.00
3557. Pastoral Honeymoon	9 x 12	NYGS	2.00
	6 x 7-1/2	NYGS	1.00
3558. Seacoast Honeymoon	6 x 7-1/2	NYGS	1.00
3559. Seaside Honeymoon	15 x 18	NYGS	10.00
	9 x 12	NYGS	2.00
	6 x 7-1/2	NYGS	1.00
3560. Sylvan Honeymoon	15 x 18	NYGS	10.00
	6 x 7-1/2	NYGS	1.00

HULDAH (HULDAH CHERRY JEFFE)

	American	Contemporary	
3561. After the Race	20 x 16	NYGS	7.50
	14 x 11	NYGS	3.00
	7-1/2 x 6	NYGS	1.00
3562. Annette	7-1/2 x 6	NYGS	1.00
3563. Au Café	20 x 16	NYGS	7.50
	14 x 11	NYGS	3.00
	7-1/2 x 6	NYGS	1.00
3564. Au Jardin	25 x 20	NYGS	12.00
	20 x 16	NYGS	7.50
	14 x 11	NYGS	3.00
	7-1/2 x 6	NYGS	1.00
3565. Detail of No. 3564	14 x 11	NYGS	3.00
3566. Avant le Rideau	25 x 20	NYGS	12.00
	14 x 11	NYGS	3.00
	7-1/2 x 6	NYGS	1.00
3567. Before the Race	20 x 16	NYGS	7.50
	14 x 11	NYGS	3.00
	7-1/2 x 6	NYGS	1.00
3568. Big Brother	20 x 16	NYGS	7.50
	14 x 11	NYGS	3.00
	7-1/2 x 6	NYGS	1.00
3569. By the Seashore	24 x 36	NYGS	15.00
3570. Cafe - Promenade	24 x 36	NYGS	15.00
	11 x 14	NYGS	3.00

3571. Detail of No. 3570	25 x 20	NYGS	12.00
	14 x 11	NYGS	3.00
	7-1/2 x 6	NYGS	1.00
3572. Curtain Time	15 x 39-1/2	NYGS	12.00
	7 x 14	NYGS	3.00
3573. Elise	7-1/2 x 6	NYGS	1.00
3574. Flower Market	20 x 25	NYGS	12.00
	11 x 14	NYGS	3.00
3575. Detail of No. 3574	25 x 20	NYGS	12.00
	14 x 11	NYGS	3.00
	7-1/2 x 6	NYGS	1.00
3576. His Rose	20 x 16	NYGS	7.50
	14 x 11	NYGS	3.00
	7-1/2 x 6	NYGS	1.00
3577. Ice Cream Vendor	25 x 20	NYGS	12.00
	20 x 16	NYGS	7.50
	14 x 11	NYGS	3.00
	7-1/2 x 6	NYGS	1.00
3578. In Central Park	25 x 20	NYGS	12.00
	20 x 16	NYGS	7.50
	14 x 11	NYGS	3.00
	7-1/2 x 6	NYGS	1.00
3579. La Jeune Ballerina	25 x 20	NYGS	12.00
	14 x 11	NYGS	3.00
	7-1/2 x 6	NYGS	1.00
3580. La Sylphide	24 x 30	NYGS	12.00
3581. Les Deux Camarades	25 x 20	NYGS	12.00
	20 x 16	NYGS	7.50
	14 x 11	NYGS	3.00
	7-1/2 x 6	NYGS	1.00
3582. Detail of No. 3581	14 x 11	NYGS	3.00
3583. Little Sister	20 x 16	NYGS	7.50
	14 x 11	NYGS	3.00
	7-1/2 x 6	NYGS	1.00
3584. Louise	7-1/2 x 6	NYGS	1.00
3585. Marianne	7-1/2 x 6	NYGS	1.00
3586. May Bud	20 x 16	NYGS	7.50
	14 x 11	NYGS	3.00
	7-1/2 x 6	NYGS	1.00
3587. Maytime	15 x 29-1/2	NYGS	12.00
	7 x 14	NYGS	3.00
3588. Mignon	7-1/2 x 6	NYGS	1.00
3589. Mimi	7-1/2 x 6	NYGS	1.00
3590. Mois de Mai	31-1/2 x 10	NYGS	12.00
	20 x 6	NYGS	4.00
3591. Premiere au Rendezvous	25 x 20	NYGS	12.00
	20 x 16	NYGS	7.50
	14 x 11	NYGS	3.00
	7-1/2 x 6	NYGS	1.00
3592. Printemps	31-1/2 x 10	NYGS	12.00
	20 x 6	NYGS	4.00

3593. Suzanne	7-1/2 x 6	NYGS	1.00
3594. Sailboat Pond	25 x 20	NYGS	12.00
	20 x 16	NYGS	7.50
	14 x 11	NYGS	3.00
	7-1/2 x 6	NYGS	1.00
3595. Tavern on the Green	25 x 20	NYGS	12.00
	20 x 16	NYGS	7.50
	14 x 11	NYGS	3.00
	7-1/2 x 6	NYGS	1.00
3596. Yvonne	7-1/2 x 6	NYGS	1.00
HUMMEL			
3597. Madonna and Child	17-1/2 x 22	IA	10.00
	11 x 14	IA	3.00
	7 x 9-1/2	IA	1.20
HUNT, V.			
3598. Harvest Time	24 x 40	DAC	8.00
3599. Little Gardeners	24 x 40	DAC	8.00
HUNT, W. HOLMAN	English	1827-1910	
3600. Light of the World	28 x 14	IA	6.00
	24 x 12	IA	4.50
	19 x 10	IA	2.50
	12 x 6	IA	.60
HUNT, WILLIAM			
3601. Hurdy-Gurdy Boy	26 x 20	CFA	7.50
HUNTINGTON			
3602. Abraham Lincoln	24 x 18	DAC	6.00
HURD, PETER	American	1904-	
3603. Rancheria	12-1/2 x 22	PENN	1.00
	12 x 22	NYGS	5.00
3604. Rio Hondo	22 x 29	NYGS	12.00
HUTTER, WOLFGANG	Austrian	Contemporary	
3605. Lovers	18-1/2 x 26	NYGS	12.00
HUYGENS			
3606. Profusion of Beauty	20 x 16	PENN	1.00
HUYSUM, JAN VAN	Dutch	1682-1749	
3607. Vase of Flowers	14 x 11	IA	3.00
HYAMS, MARTHA			
3608. Bird Lovers	12 x 21	NYGS	7.50
3609. Story Teller	12 x 21	NYGS	7.50
HYAMS, WILLIAM	English	1878-	
3610. Boston Stump, Lincolnshire	16 x 12	RL	1.50
3611. Bramber, Sussex	16-1/2 x 20	RL	3.50
3612. Castle Coombe	12 x 16	RL	1.50
3613. Chichester	12 x 16	RL	1.50
3614. Church on the Hill, Near Lewes	12 x 16	RL	1.50
3615. Clifton Suspension	12 x 16	RL	1.50
3616. Devon Cottage	16-1/2 x 20	RL	3.50
3617. Devonshire Village in the Teign Valley	16 x 12	RL	1.50
3618. East Gate and Tower, Wells	16 x 12	RL	1.50

3619.	Edinburgh Castle	12 x 16	RL	1.50
3620.	Great Clock, Rouen	16 x 12	RL	1.50
3621.	Greenwich	12 x 16	RL	1.50
3622.	Lincoln	16 x 12	RL	1.50
3623.	Llandoger Tavern, Bristol	12 x 16	RL	1.50
3624.	Meaux sur Marne	12 x 16	RL	1.50
3625.	Norfolk Village	12 x 16	RL	1.50
3626.	Notre-Dame	12 x 16	RL	1.50
3627.	Old Dieppe	16 x 12	RL	1.50
3628.	Romney, Kent	12 x 16	RL	1.50
3629.	St. Mary Redcliffe from the River	16 x 12	RL	1.50
3630.	Salisbury Cathedral	16 x 12	RL	1.50
3631.	Stirling Castle	12 x 16	RL	1.50
3632.	Tenterden, Kent	12 x 16	RL	1.50
3633.	Tower of London	12 x 16	RL	1.50
3634.	Wells from the Bishop's Garden	12 x 16	RL	1.50
3635.	Welsh Valley	12 x 16	RL	1.50
3636.	West Front, Wells Cathedral	12 x 16	RL	1.50
3637.	Ypres Gate, Rye	12 x 16	RL	1.50

I

IBARRARAN, JOSÉ
3638. Sacred Heart of
       Jesus   22-1/2 x 16   IA   3.00
                            12-1/2 x 9   IA   .60
IBARZ ROCA, MIGUEL   Spanish   1920-
3639. Costa Catalina, St.
       Pol   17 x 39   NYGS   18.00

3640. Little Harbor (Ibiza) 21 x 39   NYGS   18.00
IKONS, RUSSIAN
3641. Ikons (12)   8 x 10   AJ   15.00 set
                                                  or 1.50 ea.

Crucifixion (15th Century)
Descent into Hell (Northern School, 15th to 16th
    Centuries)
Last Judgement (16th to 17th Centuries)
Nativity (Moscow School, 15th Century)
Old Testament Trinity (15th Century)
Presentation of a Miracle
Raising of Lazarus (15th Century)
Raising of Lazarus (Novgorod School, 15th
    Century)
St. Leontius of Rostow (16th Century)
St. Nicholas, Bishop of Myra (Novgorod School,
    12th Century)
Scenes from Life of St. George (Novgorod School,
    16th Century)

Transfiguration of Christ

3642.	Nativity	28 x 21	NYGS	20.00

IMMEL, PAUL J.

3643.	Anemonies	16 x 16	AA	2.50
3644.	Cosmos	16 x 16	AA	2.50
3645.	Dahlias	16 x 16	AA	2.50
3646.	Dainty Bess Rose	16 x 16	AA	2.50
3647.	Daisies	16 x 16	AA	2.50
3648.	Gettysburg Address	20 x 16	AA	5.00
3649.	Moss Rose	16 x 16	AA	2.50
3650.	Phlox	16 x 16	AA	2.50
3651.	Wall Flowers	16 x 16	AA	2.50

INDIA, FRANCESCO See TORBIDO, IL

INDUNO, GEROLAMO   Italian   1827-1890

3652.	Antiquary	15 x 11	IA	3.00

INGRES, JEAN AUGUSTE DOMINIQUE

French   1780-1890

3653.	Comtesse D'Hausson-ville	30 x 21-1/2	NYGS	15.00
3654.	Gounod, Charles	12 x 9	NYGS	3.00
3655.	Gounod, Madame Charles	12 x 9	NYGS	3.00
3656.	Mlle. Riviere	23 x 18	HNA	5.95
3657.	Mme. Riviere	10 x 8	NYGS	.50
3658.	Petite Baigneuse	10 x 8	ESH	1.00
3659.	Raoul Rochette	12 x 9	AR	3.00
3660.	Reclining Odalisque	16 x 30	ESH	15.00
		8 x 10	ESH	1.00
3661.	The Source	15 x 7	IA	3.00
		10 x 8	AP	.60
3662.	The Spring	15 x 7	CFA	2.50
3663.	Turkish Women	9" circle	NYGS	.50

INNESS, GEORGE   American   1825-1894

3664.	After a Summer Shower	8 x 10	AP	.50
3665.	Autumn Oaks	20 x 30	NYGS	12.00
		6 x 9-1/2	NYGS	.50
3666.	June	18 x 28	PENN	1.00
				1.98 (Pr.)
3667.	Lackawanna Valley	18 x 23	HNA	5.95
3668.	Passing Shower	12 x 19	NYGS	5.00
3669.	Peace and Plenty	31 x 45	AJ	20.00
		20-1/2 x 30	IA	12.00
		16-1/2 x 24	PENN	1.00
		7 x 10-1/2	NYGS	.50

IRANIAN ART--Fifth Century B.C.

3670.	Archer of the Royal Guard, Facing Right	30 x 11	ESH	15.00
3671.	Archer of the Royal Guard, Facing Left	30 x 11	ESH	15.00
3672.	Lion	20 x 36-1/2	ESH	13.00

ITAYA, FOUSSA			
3673. Intruder	18 x 23	RL	7.50
IVERD, EUGENE			
3674. Admiration	21 x 14	CFA	7.50
3675. Happy Days	22 x 28	CFA	7.50
3676. Looking Forward	22 x 28	CFA	7.50
3677. Old and New	22 x 28	CFA	7.50

J

JACOB, ALEXANDRE	French	1876-	
3678. Ferry	18 x 13	RL	5.00
3679. L'Hiver	14 x 17-1/2	RL	5.00
3680. Le Printemps	14 x 17-1/2	RL	5.00
3681. Spring in Normandy	18 x 13	RL	5.00
3682. Winter in the Marshes	22 x 18	RL	7.50
3683. Winter's Peace	24 x 19-1/2	RL	7.50
3684. Winter Sun	23-1/2 x 30	RL	10.00
JACOBSEN, AUGUST	Norwegian	1868-	
3685. Shady Nook	22 x 30-1/2	IA	10.00
	17 x 23-1/2	IA	6.00
	12 x 16	IA	2.50
JACOPO DEL SELLAIO	Italian	1442-1493	
3686. Banquet of the Queen Vasti	11 x 15	IA	3.00
JACQUE			
3687. Sheepfold	8 x 10	AP	.60
JACUS, JEAN	French	1926-	
3688. Age of Light	18 x 24	RL	7.50
3689. Ships of Thought	20 x 24	RL	7.50
3690. Timeless City	19 x 25	RL	7.50
JAFFE, ARTHUR	American	Contemporary	
3691. Autumn's Paint Box	10-1/2 x 15	AJ	3.00
3692. Cosmos	12 x 8-1/2	AJ	1.50
3693. Garden Wall with Grinnel Glacier	8-1/2 x 12	AJ	1.50
3694. Greeting the Sunrise	28 x 22	AJ	10.00
3695. Montana Mountains	12 x 8-1/2	AJ	1.50
3696. St. John's Garden	12 x 8-1/2	AJ	1.50
3697. Spring	19-1/2 x 39	IA	5.00
3698. Spring in the Air	10-1/2 x 15	AJ	3.00
3699. Spring in the Hills	10-1/2 x 15	AJ	3.00
3700. Sugar Maples	10-1/2 x 15	IA	3.00
3701. Sunny Autumn	19-1/2 x 39	IA	5.00
JAMBOR, LOUIS	Hungarian	1884-	
3702. Enchanted Hour	24 x 30	NYGS	7.50
	8 x 10	NYGS	1.00
3703. Jesus of Nazareth	21 x 16	IA	1.50
	12 x 9	IA	.75
3704. The Lord's Supper	24-1/2 x 18	IA	5.00
	17 x 12-1/2	IA	2.00

3705. Twinkle Toes	24 x 30	NYGS	7.50
	8 x 10	NYGS	1.00
3706. Winter Sunset	24 x 30	NYGS	7.50
	8 x 10	NYGS	1.00
JAMIESON, MITCHELL	American	1915-	
3707. Convoy Entering			
Mers-El-Kebir	12 x 18	NYGS	3.00
3708. Gray Morning	12 x 18	NYGS	3.00
JANCH, MICHAEL			
3709. Garden Flowers	20 x 15-1/2	NYGS	7.50
	14 x 11	NYGS	4.00
JANK, ANGELO	German	1868-1935	
3710. Full Cry	24 x 33	NYGS	15.00
JANSEM, JEAN			
3711. Still Life	24 x 31	IA	18.00
JANSSENS, ABRAHAM	Flemish	1575-1632	
3712. Dutch Interior	16-1/2 x 20	AP	5.00
3713. The Peace	15 x 11	IA	3.00
JAPAN (Various Artists)			
3714. Dancer	10 x 8	ESH	1.00
3715. Beauty Adjusting			
Combs	39-1/2 x 17	PENN	1.00
3716. Beauty with Attendant	39-1/2 x 17	PENN	1.00
3717. Conquering Eagle	20 x 28	PENN	1.00
3718. Four Horses	17 x 35	PENN	1.00
3719. Horses Gamboling (2)	40 x 12-1/2	PENN	1.00 ea.
3720. Moon Guitar	30 x 10	PENN	1.00
			1.98 (Pr.)
3721. Peacock in Paradise	20 x 28	PENN	1.00
3722. Portfolio (8)	14 x 9	PENN	2.98 set

Hiroshige - View of Fuji with Cherry Blossoms
          View of Sumida
          View 42 of Tokaido
          View 13 of Tokaido
Hokusai - Fuji in Clear Weather
Utamaro - Courtesan (2)
Yeisan - Gaido

3723. Seasons (4)	8 x 10	DAC	1.60 ea.
	6 x 8	DAC	.60 ea.
3724. Zither	30 x 10	PENN	1.00
			1.98 (Pr.)
JACQUES, PIERRE	Swiss	1913-	
3725. Blooming Orchard	21 x 30	NYGS	12.00
3726. Enchanted Road	21 x 26	NYGS	10.00
3727. Rolling Wheatfields	16 x 39-1/2	NYGS	15.00
3728. Yacht Basin, Geneva	21 x 30	NYGS	12.00
JAWLENSKY, ANDREJ ALEXEJEWITSCH			
	Russian	1902-	
3729. Mediterranean at			
Marseilles	17 x 26	NYGS	22.00
3730. Stream in Murnau	19-1/2 x 21	NYGS	12.00
3731. Variation	20-1/2 x 15	NYGS	20.00

JOHN, C. R. D'OYLY	English	1906	
3732. Café Bar	17 x 21-1/2	RL	6.00
3733. Down to the Beach, Capferrat	17 x 21-1/2	RL	6.00
3734. Old Archway	17 x 25	RL	7.50
3735. Old Bridge, Venice	17 x 24-1/2	RL	7.50
3736. Ponte Vecchio, Florence	17 x 24-1/2	RL	7.50
3737. Santa Margarita	17 x 25	RL	7.50
3738. Valbonne	17 x 21-1/2	RL	6.00
JOHNSON, AVERY			
3739. Bahama Chores	16 x 22	CFA	10.00
3740. Bahama Morning	16 x 22	CFA	10.00
JOHNSON, CECILE			
3741. Harbor Towns (4)	12 x 30	DAC	4.00 ea.
	16 x 15	DAC	1.20 ea.
JOHNSON, EASTMAN	American	1824-1906	
3742. The Boy Lincoln	8 x 10	AP	.50
3743. Old Stage Coach	22 x 40	CFA	12.00
3744. Scissors Grinder	26 x 20	CFA	7.50
JONES, JOE	American	1909-	
3745. Chapel in the Park	24 x 20	NYGS	20.00
3746. Quiet Cove	11-1/2 x 18	NYGS	7.50
3747. Rockport	24 x 36	NYGS	15.00
3748. Setting Sail	18 x 36	NYGS	15.00
	11-1/2 x 18	NYGS	7.50
JONGKIND, J. B.	Dutch	1819-1891	
3749. Harbor at Honfleur	7 x 9	NYGS	.50
3750. Marine	8 x 10	ESH	1.00
3751. River Meuse	14 x 20	NYGS	7.50
3752. View of Grenoble	9 x 14-1/2	AP	2.00
JORDAENS, JACOB	Flemish	1593-1678	
3753. Pan and Syrinx	14 x 11	IA	3.00
3754. Satyr and the Peasant	13 x 11	IA	3.00
JOSY			
3755. Eiger Monch und Jungfrau	14 x 17-1/2	IA	3.00
3756. Grindelwald mit Wetterhorn	14 x 17-1/2	IA	3.00
3757. Jungfrau (von Wengen aus)	14 x 17-1/2	IA	3.00
3758. Jungfrau mit Lutschine	14 x 17-1/2	IA	3.00
3759. Kochelsee	14 x 17-1/2	IA	3.00
3760. Lake Como	14 x 18	IA	3.00
3761. Ostersee	14 x 17-1/2	IA	3.00
3762. Portofino	14 x 17-1/2	IA	3.00
3763. Wetterstein mit Garmisch Partenkirchen	14 x 17-1/2	IA	3.00
3764. Zugspitze mit Eibsee	14 x 17-1/2	IA	3.00
JOUAULT, A.			

3765. Flower Market,			
Madagascar	22 x 28-1/2	RL	12.50
JULES, MERVYN	American	1912-	
3766. Circus	8 x 10	AP	.50
3767. Cobblers	14-1/2 x 18-1/2	NYGS	5.00
3768. Hot Jazz	14 x 17	AR	10.00
3769. Little Hippo	8 x 10	AP	.25
JULIO, A.			
3770. Bella Vista	24 x 36	DAC	6.00
JUNGHANNS, JULIUS PAUL	Austrian	c. 1876-1958	
3771. Coming Home	19 x 32-1/2	ESH	15.00
3772. The Hunt	20 x 27	ESH	8.00

K

KAGIE, JAN			
3773. Pines on the Dunes	19-1/2 x 30	RL	7.50
KAHILL, JOSEPH B.	American	1882-	
3774. Collector	20 x 24	NYGS	7.50
	11 x 14	NYGS	3.00
KAISER			
3775. Summer Vista	23 x 31	CFA	15.00
KALCKREUTH, P.			
3776. Fishing Boats	18 x 25	CFA	7.50
3777. High Sea	26 x 39	IA	15.00
	13 x 19	IA	5.00
3778. High Sea No. 2	13 x 19	CFA	5.00
3779. Sailing Home	23 x 17	CFA	7.50
3780. Waves	18 x 23	CFA	7.50
KANDINSKY, WASSILY	Russian	1866-1944	
3781. Arrow Composition	16 x 22-1/2	ESH	10.00
3782. Capricious Line	27 x 14	AA	15.00
3783. Composition #711	16-1/2 x 23	AP	10.00
3784. Composition, 1934	17-1/2 x 23	NYGS	10.00
3785. Dream Improvisation	27-1/2 x 27-1/2	NYGS	18.00
3786. Heavenly Bodies	21-1/2 x 16	PENN	1.00
3787. Improvisation #10	8 x 10	ESH	1.00
3788. Improvisation #30	28 x 28	CFA	15.00
3789. Improvisation XIX	27 x 31-1/2	IA	18.00
3790. Intersecting Lines	24 x 35	CFA	18.00
3791. Lyrisches	17 x 23-1/2	PENN	1.00
3792. Points in a Bow	23 x 18	HNA	5.95
3793. Poster	26 x 21	PENN	1.00
3794. Poster	28 x 20	PENN	1.00
3795. Symmetrical Accord	24-1/2 x 31-1/2	NYGS	18.00
3796. Traversing Line	24-1/2 x 35-1/2	NYGS	18.00
3797. Yellow Triangle	18 x 25	IA	7.50
KANELBA, RAYMOND	Polish (Res. France) 1897-		
3798. Little Musician	14 x 11-1/2	NYGS	10.00
KARFOIL, BERNARD	American	1886-1952	
3799. Laurent Pony Cart	16 x 20	NYGS	5.00
	8 x 10	AP	.50
KARGER, JOSEF	Austrian	1901-	

3800. First Thaw	24 x 48	DAC	10.00
	9 x 17-1/2	DAC	2.00
3801. Romantic Rome	24 x 48	DAC	10.00
3802. Summer in			
Amsterdam	24 x 48	DAC	10.00
KASSEL, F.			
3803. A Boy and his Dog	24 x 20	DAC	6.00
	12 x 10	DAC	1.20
3804. Daily Task	24 x 20	DAC	6.00
	12 x 10	DAC	1.20
3805. Girl with Basket	24 x 20	DAC	6.00
	12 x 10	DAC	1.20
3806. Grandmother's Pride	24 x 20	DAC	6.00
	12 x 10	DAC	1.20
3807. Little Helper	24 x 20	DAC	6.00
	12 x 10	DAC	1.20
3808. Spinning Wheel	24 x 20	DAC	6.00
	12 x 10	DAC	1.20
3809. Three Generations	24 x 20	DAC	6.00
	12 x 10	DAC	1.20
KATZ, MANÉ	Russian (Res. France) 1894-		
3810. Torah	25-1/2 x 20	AA	15.00
KAULBACH, GEORG	German	1866-1945	
3811. Artist's Daughter	21 x 14	CAC	5.00
	7 x 6	CAC	1.00
3812. Gretel	12 x 9	NYGS	1.50
	7-1/2 x 6	NYGS	1.00
3813. Hansel	12 x 9	NYGS	1.50
	7-1/2 x 6	NYGS	1.00
KAUTZKY, TED	American	1896-1953	
3814. Cape Ann Harbor	13 x 18	PENN	1.00
3815. Church Street	25 x 30	CFA	10.00
3816. Connecticut Hills	20 x 24	CAC	6.00
3817. Country Holiday	20 x 24	CAC	6.00
3818. Fisherman's Harbor	20 x 24	CAC	6.00
3819. Hilltop Haven	22 x 28	CFA	7.50
3820. Looking Eastward	13 x 18	PENN	1.00
3821. Normandy Road	22 x 28	CFA	7.50
3822. October Sunshine	20 x 24	CAC	6.00
3823. Peaceful Cove	22 x 28	CFA	7.50
3824. Quiet Inlet	13 x 18	PENN	1.00
3825. Schooner in Harbor	20 x 24	CAC	6.00
3826. Sunny Brittany	22 x 28	CFA	7.50
3827. Village Street	25 x 30	CFA	10.00
3828. Winter in New England	20 x 24	CAC	6.00
KAYMAR			
3829. Nature Studies (6)	28 x 13-1/2	AA	7.50 ea.
Fall (2)			
Grape Leaves			
Queen Anne's Lace			
Summer (2)			
KEANE, MARGARET	American	Contemporary	

3830. Awakening	12 x 9	WK	3.00
3831. Black Dress	20 x 10	WK	10.00
3832. Bull Fight Day	12 x 9	WK	2.00
3833. Circa (jg)	23 x 35	WK	15.00
3834. Coffee Break	24 x 27	WK	15.00
3835. Destiny	12 x 9	WK	2.00
3836. Edge of Summer	12 x 9	WK	2.00
3837. Emerging	12 x 9	WK	3.00
3838. Escape	35 x 20	WK	20.00
3839. Farmer's Daughter	12 x 9	WK	2.00
3840. Freshmen	12 x 9	WK	3.00
3841. In Between	28 x 19	WK	15.00
3842. Many Views	9 x 12	WK	3.00
3843. Mother and Child	30 x 18	WK	15.00
3844. On the Beach	34 x 22	WK	15.00
3845. On the Threshold	34 x 21	WK	15.00
3846. Reflection	12 x 9	WK	3.00
3847. Reply	12 x 9	WK	3.00
3848. Secret	30 x 14	WK	10.00
3849. Storm	12 x 9	WK	3.00
3850. Three Harlequins	29 x 23	WK	15.00
3851. Transition	12 x 9	WK	3.00
3852. Youth	24 x 12	WK	10.00
KEANE, WALTER	American	Contemporary	
3853. Alone	29 x 37	WK	25.00
3854. At the Fair	12 x 9	WK	3.00
3855. Backstage	31 x 19	WK	15.00
3856. Beachhead	12 x 24	WK	15.00
3857. Ballerina	12 x 9	WK	2.00
3858. Blond Boy	12 x 9	WK	2.00
3859. Boy and his Dog	12 x 9	WK	3.00
3860. Dragon on Parade	9 x 12	WK	2.00
3861. First Grail	12 x 9	WK	3.00
3862. Girl and her Cat	12 x 9	WK	3.00
3863. Girl of China	29 x 14	WK	20.00
3864. Grant Avenue, San Francisco	28 x 18	WK	15.00
3865. Gypsies	12 x 9	WK	2.00
3866. Little Ones	12 x 9	WK	3.00
3867. Lookout	40 x 18	WK	15.00
3868. Lost	12 x 9	WK	2.00
3869. No Dogs Allowed	24 x 12	WK	15.00
3870. Peace on Earth	28 x 33	WK	25.00
3871. Rejected	12 x 9	WK	3.00
3872. Runaway	40 x 14	WK	25.00
3873. Stray	24 x 12	WK	15.00
3874. Steep Climb	40 x 20	WK	20.00
3875. Waif	30 x 14	WK	20.00
3876. Waiting for Grand-mother	12 x 9	WK	3.00
3877. Watching	12 x 9	WK	3.00
KEANE, WILLIAM			
3878. Old Banjo	25 x 16	CFA	7.50

KEARFOTT, ROBERT RYLAND	American	1890-	
3879. Dress Rehearsal	24 x 40	DAC	8.00
	12 x 20	DAC	2.00
	8 x 12	DAC	1.00
KEEN, LILA MOORE			
3880. Camelias (6)	20 x 16	AA	3.50 ea
	16 x 12	AA	2.50 ea
Alba Fimbriata (White)	16 x 12		
Chandieri Elegans	20 x 16		
Dr. W. G. Lee	20 x 16		
Japonica Triphosa (White)	16 x 12		
Latifolia	20 x 16		
Rev. John Bennett	20 x 16		
KEISEKI			
3881. Summer	24 x 10	CAC	12.00
KEITH, WILLIAM	American	1839-1911	
3882. Cypress Point	17 x 40	NYGS	15.00
	11 x 26	NYGS	7.50
KELLY, (SIR) GERALD	English	1879-	
3883. Abraham Lincoln	18 x 15	NYGS	5.00
	9 x 7-1/2	NYGS	1.50
	9 x 7	CAC	1.00
3884. Basketmakers in Seville	19-1/2 x 25	RL	12.50
3885. Burmese Dancer in Pink	16 x 11-1/2	RL	7.50
3886. Burmese Dancer in Yellow	16 x 11-1/2	RL	7.50
3887. Saw Ohn Nyun	24 x 19	RL	15.00
KEMP-WELCH, LUCY	English	1868-	
3888. Behind the Plow	16 x 20	CAC	5.00
	8 x 10	AP	.50
KENNEDY, CECIL	English	1905-	
3889. Daffodils and Narcissi	17 x 14	RL	2.50
3890. Delphiniums and Lillies	10 x 8	CFA	1.00
3891. Nasturtiums	14 x 17	RL	2.50
KENT, ROCKWELL	American	1882-	
3892. Mount Equinox, Winter	20-1/2 x 26	NYGS	10.00
3893. Winter, a View of Monhegan, Maine	28 x 35-1/2	NYGS	18.00
	16-1/2 x 22	NYGS	7.50
	8 x 10	AP	.50
	6 x 7-1/2	NYGS	.50
	5 x 7	NYGS	.50
KERR, VERNON			
3894. Glowing Surf	24 x 48	IA	15.00
3895. Incoming Tide	20 x 40	IA	12.00

3896. Laguna Surf	24 x 48	IA	15.00
KESSEL, VAN			
3897. Gold Goblet and			
Flowers	16 x 22	ESH	10.00
KEYSER, THOMAS DE	Dutch	1596-1667	
3898. Portrait of an Old			
Woman	15 x 11	IA	3.00
KING, PAUL	American	1867-1947	
3899. Dream	24 x 20	AA	7.50
3900. Magnolias	28 x 31	CAC	10.00
3901. Mystery of the East	24 x 20	NYGS	7.50
3902. Peace	24 x 20	AA	7.50
KING, HENRIETTA	American		
3903. Ten P. M.	18 x 22	CAC	5.00
KIRCHBACH, GOTTFRIED	German	1888-1942	
3904. Christ and the			
Children	15 x 21	CAC	3.00
KIRCHNER, ERNST LUDWIG	German	1880-1938	
3905. Davos in the Snow	18 x 23	HNA	5.95
3906. Klostersu Mountain	26 x 25	CFA	18.00
3907. Self-Portrait with			
Model	8 x 10	AP	1.00
3908. Two Ladies in the			
Street	8 x 10	MMA	.35
KISLING, MOISE (OR MAURICE)	Polish	1891-	
3909. Woman with a Shawl	24 x 17	PENN	1.00
KISSELOWA, JELENA A.	Russian	1878-	
3910. Russian Peasant			
Woman	8 x 10	AP	.50
KLEE, PAUL	Swiss	1879-1940	
3911. Actor's Mask	16 x 14-1/2	AR	12.00
3912. Arab Song	26 x 18	NYGS	12.00
3913. Around the Fish	18 x 25	MMA	7.50
3914. Banner at the			
Pavilion	16 x 24	CFA	10.00
3915. Bird Garden	18 x 26-1/2	AA	15.00
3916. Blossoms in the			
Twilight	13 x 31	CFA	12.00
3917. Blue Head	19-1/2 x 13	AR	10.00
	10 x 7	AR	2.00
3918. Blue Night	19 x 29-1/2	ESH	15.00
3919. Boats and Cliffs	13 x 20	CAC	5.00
3920. By the Troutstream	12 x 9	NYGS	10.00
3921. Caprice in February	20 x 15	CFA	7.50
3922. Castle and Sun	23 x 18	HNA	5.95
3923. Chapel, 1917	12-1/2 x 7	NYGS	10.00
3924. Columns and Crosses	16-1/2 x 22	NYGS	12.00
3925. Composition, 1914	8 x 10	AP	.50
3926. Dancer	21 x 21	NYGS	15.00
3927. Drummer	8 x 10	AP	.75
3928. Ecstasy	8 x 10	AP	.75
3929. Equals Infinity	8 x 10	MMA	.35
3930. Fish Magic	23-1/2 x 30	NYGS	18.00

		8 x 10	AP	.75
3931.	Flower Girl	16 x 19	AR	10.00
3932.	Fruit D'Azur	8 x 10	AP	.75
3933.	Gold Fish	19 x 27-1/2	NYGS	15.00
3934.	Indian Story	16 x 20	PENN	1.00
				1.98 (Pr.)
3935.	Landscape of the Past	9 x 10	NYGS	10.00
3936.	Landscape, Yellow			
	Birds	19 x 24	CFA	12.00
		8 x 10	AP	.50
3937.	Legend of the Nile	27 x 24	NYGS	18.00
3938.	Lying Down	16-1/2 x 27	NYGS	15.00
3939.	Main and Side Roads	8 x 10	AP	.25
3940.	Man on a Tight Rope	12 x 7-1/2	NYGS	3.00
3941.	Mask, 1939	16 x 17	AR	7.50
		21 x 22	AR	10.00
3942.	Nestling Birds	17 x 23	AR	12.00
3943.	Once from the Gray			
	of Night Emerged	8 x 10	AP	.75
3944.	Oriental Castle	10 x 12	NYGS	10.00
3945.	Picture Album	24 x 22-1/2	NYGS	15.00
3946.	Picture Sheet	8 x 10	AP	.50
3947.	Pink-Yellow, Windows			
	and Roofs	12 x 9-1/2	NYGS	10.00
3948.	Portrait of Moe	18 x 24	PENN	1.00
3949.	Red Waistcoat	22-1/2 x 15	ESH	10.00
		10 x 8	AP	.75
3950.	Revolution of the			
	Viaduct	24 x 19-1/2	NYGS	15.00
3951.	Rich Harbour	13-1/2 x 29-1/2	NYGS	12.00
3952.	River Regulizing			
	Territory	14 x 21	IA	12.00
3953.	Senecio, 1922	16 x 14-1/2	AR	12.00
3954.	Sinbad the Sailor	16 x 23	PENN	1.00
				1.98 (Pr.)
3955.	Small Rhythmic			
	Landscape	11 x 9	NYGS	10.00
3956.	They're Biting	12 x 9	AR	3.00
3957.	Tomcat, 1930	10 x 13	NYGS	10.00
3958.	Traveling Circus	25 x 19-1/2	NYGS	15.00
3959.	Twittering Machine	8 x 10	MMA	.35
3960.	Understanding One	21 x 15	AR	12.00
		10 x 7	AR	2.00
3961.	Underwater Garden	23 x 18	HNA	5.95
3962.	Warning of the			
	Ships	8 x 10	AP	.75

KLEPICH, FRED

3963.	Sunday Walk	16 x 20	IA	5.00

KLIN, LEO

3964.	The Deer	23-1/2 x 18	NYGS	7.50

KLITGAARD, GEORGINA   Danish-American   1893-

3965.	Daisies	19 x 13	NYGS	5.00

KLUGE, CURT	German	1886-1940		
3966. Elysée Club	22 x 22	RL	15.00
3967. Fleurs	21-1/2 x 18	RL	7.50
3968. Lady of the Sampans	25 x 20	RL	12.50
3969. La Madeleine	20 x 24	CAC	10.00
3970. Notre Dame de Paris	20 x 24	RL	10.00
3971. Paris in Autumn	22 x 22	RL	15.00
KNATHS, KARL	American	1891-	
3972. Cin-Zin	20 x 24	NYGS	12.00
KNELL, KARL	Swiss	1880-1954	
3973. Man of War Cutter	6 x 10	CFA	5.00
3974. 92 Gun Battleship	6 x 10	CFA	5.00
3975. 36 Gun Frigate	6 x 10	CFA	5.00
3976. Sloop of War	6 x 10	CFA	5.00
KNIGHT, (DAME) LAURA	English	1877-	
3977. Beach	8 x 10	AP	.50
3978. Carnival	20 x 26	CFA	12.00
3979. Lamorna Cove	16-1/2 x 25	RL	7.50
3980. Month of May	20 x 16	CAC	6.00
3981. Normandy	22 x 28	CAC	10.00
KOBELL			
3982. Deer Hunter	15 x 12	NYGS	12.00
3983. Landscape near Munich	16 x 21	NYGS	12.00
3984. View on the Lake	15 x 13	NYGS	12.00
KOHLER, FRITZ	German	1887-	
3985. River Landscape	23 x 29	ESH	12.00
KOKOSCHKA, OSKAR	Austrian	1886-	
3986. Amsterdam	23-1/2 x 33	NYGS	18.00
3987. Augustus Bridge, Dresden	21 x 31	AR	15.00
3988. Boat in Dogana, Venice	25 x 31-1/2	NYGS	18.00
3989. Castles in Amsterdam	24 x 33	CAC	15.00
3990. Charles Bridge, Prague	24 x 30	DAC	8.00
3991. Clown with Dog	22-1/2 x 15-1/2	NYGS	10.00
3992. Coliseum, Rome	24-1/2 x 33-1/2	NYGS	18.00
3993. Courmayeur	24-1/2 x 35-1/2	NYGS	20.00
3994. Delphi	25 x 35	CFA	18.00
3995. Karlsbruck	18 x 28	CFA	12.00
3996. Karlsbrucke in Prague	19-1/2 x 27-1/2	NYGS	12.00
3997. London, Tower Bridge	23-1/2 x 29	NYGS	18.00
3998. Lyon	26-1/2 x 35-1/2	NYGS	20.00
3999. Mandril	23-1/2 x 19	PENN	1.00
4000. Matterhorn	27 x 35-1/2	NYGS	20.00
4001. Polperro, Cornwall	16 x 23	AP	7.50
4002. Portrait of Dr. Tietse and Wife	8 x 10	MMA	.35
4003. Roses at Villaneuve	18 x 23	NYGS	12.00
4004. Salzburg	25 x 35-1/2	NYGS	15.00
4005. Self-Portrait, 1913	23 x 14	NYGS	10.00

4006. Tempest	8 x 10	AP	7.50
4007. Terrace Gardens at Richmond	25 x 36	NYGS	18.00
4008. Venice, St. Maria della Salute	25-1/2 x 35	NYGS	18.00
4009. View of Dresden	16 x 23	NYGS	10.00
4010. View of the Rhone Valley	18 x 23	HNA	5.95
KOLBE, GEORGE	German	1877-1947	
4011. Hands	9 x 11	CFA	3.50
KOMAROMI-KACZ, ENDRÉ	Hungarian	1880-1950	
4012. Christ and the Little Children	28 x 39	IA	15.00
	17 x 24	IA	7.50
	10 x 14	IA	3.00
4013. Madame Butterfly	18 x 30	CFA	10.00
4014. Suffer the Little Children	28 x 40	NYGS	15.00
	17 x 24	NYGS	7.50
	10 x 14	NYGS	3.00
KONDIG			
4015. Geranium and Begonia	19 x 15	CAC	5.00
KONRAD, IGNACE			
4016. Breaking Cover	9 x 16	CAC	2.50
4017. Concours Hippique	21 x 29	CAC	9.00
4018. The Death	9 x 16	CAC	2.50
4019. Full Cry	9 x 16	CAC	2.50
4020. Joy of the Gallop	13-1/2 x 19	IA	5.00
4021. Mare and Foal in the Paddock	13 x 19	CAC	5.00
4022. The Meet	9 x 16	CAC	2.50
4023. The Meeting	21 x 29	IA	10.00
4024. Out to Grass	13 x 19	CAC	5.00
4025. Steeplechase	21 x 29	IA	10.00
4026. Thoroughbreds at Large	13-1/2 x 19	IA	5.00
KOONING, WILLIAM DE	Dutch (Res. U. S.)	1904-	
4027. Woman I	8 x 10	MMA	.35
KORTHALS, JAN (OR JOHANNES)	Dutch	1916-	
4028. Ceylon	14 x 18	DAC	2.00
4029. Paris Street Scenes (6)	11-1/2 x 7-1/2	DAC	1.00 ea.

           Boulevard St. Denis
           Montmartre, Rue du Chevalier de la Barre
           Place du Petit Pont
           Rue de Clignancourt
           Rue Geoffroy Liangevin
           Rue St. Denis

KOSA, EMIL JEAN	French (Res. U. S.)	1903-	
4030. Junction at Acton	14 x 19	CFA	5.00
4031. Meeting Place	24 x 36	CFA	15.00
4032. Meeting Place	16 x 24	CFA	6.00

4033. Pirates Cove	14 x 19	CFA	5.00
KOZLOW, RICHARD	American		
4034. Mirador	20 x 24	IA	12.00
KRAUS, AUGUST	German	1868-1934	
4035. Summer day	22 x 31	CFA	12.00
KREIBACH			
4036. Albert Schweitzer	8 x 10	AP	1.00
KRIESCH, LAURA	Hungarian	1879-	
4037. Confectioner in Cairo	11 x 15	CFA	7.50
4038. Fruit Market	11 x 15	CFA	7.50
4039. In the Hammam	11 x 15	CFA	7.50
4040. Return from the Oasis	11 x 15	CFA	7.50
KRINGS, H.			
4041. Smoker	19 x 16	CFA	10.00
4042. Young Mother	19 x 16	CFA	10.00
KROGER, FLORENCE	American		
4043. Arabesque	24 x 36	DAC	8.00
4044. Babies (2)	12 x 16	DAC	1.20 ea.
	9 x 12	DAC	.80 ea
	6 x 8	DAC	.40 ea.
Sweet Dreamer			
Wake-Up Time			
4045. The Boy Jesus	24 x 20	IA	5.00
	20 x 16	PENN	1.00
			1.98 (Pr.)
	18 x 15	IA	3.00
	10 x 8	IA	.50
4046. Days of Chivalry (4)	11 x 14	DAC	2.00 ea.
Day Dreamer			
Lovers' Lane			
Promenade			
Sunday Strollers			
4047. Golden Years (4)	16 x 7	DAC	1.20 ea.
Bibliophile			
Horticulturist			
Ornithologist			
Scholar			
4048. The Good Shepherd	10 x 8	DAC	.48
4049. Happy Family (4)	12 x 9	DAC	.60 ea.
Mom			
Pop			
Oswald			
Penelope			
4050. Jack	10 x 8	CAC	1.50
4051. Jill	10 x 8	CAC	1.50
4052. Kitten Portraits (4)	14 x 11	DAC	1.20 ea.
	10 x 8	DAC	.80 ea.
4053. Madonna and Child	20 x 16	PENN	1.00
			1.98 (Pr.)
4054. Religious Art (4)	16 x 20	DAC	3.00 ea.
	8 x 10	DAC	.50 ea.
Christ at Twelve			

The Lord's Image
Madonna and Child
Mary

KROLL, LEON	American	1884-	
4055. Nina	15 x 19	CAC	10.00
4056. Willows	14 x 20	NYGS	7.50
KRONBERG, LOUIS			
4057. Dancer in Pink	24 x 18	CFA	7.50
	19 x 14	CFA	3.00
4058. Dancer in White	24 x 18	CFA	7.50
	19 x 14	CFA	3.00
KRUGER, ERNA	German	1883-	
4059. Spring Sunshine	24 x 32	IA	10.00
4060. Summer Landscape	24 x 32	IA	7.50
	17-1/2 x 23-1/2	IA	5.00
4061 Summer's Glory	24 x 32	IA	10.00
4062. When the Leaves			
Begin to Fall	24 x 32	IA	7.50
	17-1/2 x 23-1/2	IA	5.00
KRUMMACHER, KARL	German	1867-1955	
4063. Cornfield	18 x 27	CFA	7.50
4064. Spring Blossoms	19 x 27	CFA	7.50
KUHN, WALT	American	1880-1949	
4065. Blue Clown	24 x 20	NYGS	12.00
4066. Dressing Room	24 x 18	PENN	1.00
KUJAL			
4067. Spring Blossoms	24 x 48	DAC	10.00
KUNDIG, R.			
4068. Landscape with Lake	24 x 29	CFA	12.00
KUNIYOSHI, YASUO	American	1893-1953	
4069. I'm Tired	19 x 14-1/2	NYGS	5.00
4070. Japanese Toy Tiger			
and Odd Objects	13-1/2 x 19-1/2	NYGS	5.00
4071. Objects on a Sofa	8 x 10	AP	.25
KUNTZ, ROGER	American	1926-	
4072. Apartment Houses	16 x 12	CAC	12.00
4073. Arcade	12 x 16	CAC	12.00
4074. Backstage	16 x 12	CAC	12.00
4075. Bar Lesperance	16 x 12	CAC	12.00
4076. Intermission	16 x 12	CAC	12.00
4077. Latin Quarter Hotel	16 x 12	CAC	12.00
4078. New Orleans Square	12 x 16	CAC	12.00
4079. Old New Orleans	12 x 16	CAC	12.00
4080. Sidewalk Cafe	12 x 16	CAC	12.00
KUPETSKY			
4081. Flute Player	20 x 16	CAC	10.00
KURZ, LOUIS (OR EMIL)	Austrian (Res. U. S.) 1833-1921		
and			
ALLISON, ALEXANDER			
4082. Assault of Fort			
Sanders	15 x 21	CAC	2.00
4083. Battle of Antietam	15 x 21	CAC	2.00

4084.	Battle of Atlanta	15 x 21	CAC	2.00
4085.	Battle of Bull Run	15 x 21	CAC	2.00
4086.	Battle of Cedar Creek	15 x 21	CAC	2.00
4087.	Battle of Champion Hill	15 x 21	CAC	2.00
4088.	Battle of Chancellorsville	15 x 21	CAC	2.00
4089.	Battle of Chattanooga	15 x 21	CAC	2.00
4090.	Battle of Chickamauga	15 x 21	CAC	2.00
4091.	Battle of Cold Harbor	15 x 21	CAC	2.00
4092.	Battle of Corinth	15 x 21	CAC	2.00
4093.	Battle of Five Forks	15 x 21	CAC	2.00
4094.	Battle of Fort Donelson	15 x 21	CAC	2.00
4095.	Battle of Franklin	15 x 21	CAC	2.00
4096.	Battle of Fredericksburg	15 x 21	CAC	2.00
4097.	Battle of Gettysburg	15 x 21	CAC	2.00
4098.	Battle of Kennesaw Mountain	15 x 21	CAC	2.00
4099.	Battle of Lookout Mountain	15 x 21	CAC	2.00
4100.	Battle of Missionary Ridge	15 x 21	CAC	2.00
4101.	Battle of the Monitor and the Merrimack	15 x 21	CAC	2.00
4102.	Battle of Nashville	15 x 21	CAC	2.00
4103.	Battle of Olustee	15 x 21	CAC	2.00
4104.	Battle of Opequon	15 x 21	CAC	2.00
4105.	Battle of Pea Ridge	15 x 21	CAC	2.00
4106.	Battle of Resaca	15 x 21	CAC	2.00
4107.	Battle of Shiloh	15 x 21	CAC	2.00
4108.	Battle of Spotsylvania	15 x 21	CAC	2.00
4109.	Battle of Stone River	15 x 21	CAC	2.00
4110.	Battle of the Wilderness	15 x 21	CAC	2.00
4111.	Battle of Williamsburg	15 x 21	CAC	2.00
4112.	Battle of Wilson's Creek	15 x 21	CAC	2.00
4113.	Capture of Fort Fisher	15 x 21	CAC	2.00
4114.	Fall of Petersburg	15 x 21	CAC	2.00
4115.	Fort Pillow Massacre	15 x 21	CAC	2.00
4116.	Siege of Vicksburg	15 x 21	CAC	2.00
4117.	Storming of Fort Wagner	15 x 21	CAC	2.00
KUTTER, JOSEPH		Luxemburgian	1894-1941	
4118.	Calvi on Corsica	25-1/2 x 31-1/2	NYGS	15.00
4119.	Clown	23-1/2 x 19-1/2	IA	15.00

L

LADUREAU, PIERRE	French	1881-	
4120. River Marne	23 x 29	CFA	20.00
LA FRESNAYE, ROGER DE	French	1885-1925	
4121. Conquest of the Air	8 x 10	MMA	.35
LA GONG			
4122. Balinese Dancer #1	26 x 13	CFA	20.00
4123. Balinese Dancer #2	26 x 13	CFA	20.00
LAKEN			
4124. Hunting Recollec-tions (6)	10 x 13	CAC	30.00 ea.
LAM			
4125. Jungle	8 x 10	MMA	.35
LAMPI, JOHANN BAPTIST	Austrian	1751-1830	
4126. Elisabeth, Princess of Wurttenberg	15 x 11	IA	3.00
LA MANOLA			
4127. Adeline Plunkett	14 x 10	CAC	2.50
LAMPRECHT, ANTON	German	1901-	
4128. Gay Flowers	26 x 20	ESH	10.00
LAMSWEERDE, FRANS VAN			
4129. Early Culture (6)			
Egyptian (2)	24 x 12	DAC	4.00 ea.
Incan (2)	12 x 24	DAC	4.00 ea.
Grecian (2)	24 x 12	DAC	4.00 ea.
4130. Heirlooms (4)	7 x 16	DAC	2.00 ea.
Engine Pumper			
Iron Kettle			
Spinning Wheel			
Steam Train			
4131. Shangri-La Landscapes (4)	12 x 30	DAC	6.00 ea.
	6 x 15	DAC	1.40 ea.
LANCRET, NICOLAS	French	1690-1743	
4132. L'Automne	9 x 12	IA	10.00 (Grav.)
4133. Autumn	12 x 14	CFA	15.00
	11 x 14	CFA	10.00
	10 x 14	IA	3.00
4134. Cage	14 x 10	IA	3.00
4135. La Camargo Dansant	18-1/2 x 26	NYGS	10.00
	9 x 12	IA	10.00
4136. Dancing	16-1/2 x 22	IA	10.00
4137. Golden Days	17 x 22	CFA	10.00
4138. In the Golden Days of Old	16-1/2 x 22	IA	10.00
4139. Innocence	22 x 22 Lozenge	CAC	7.50
	16 x 16 Lozenge	CAC	5.00
	11 x 11 Lozenge	CFA	2.50

		10-1/2 x 10-1/2 Lozenge	IA	3.00
		8 x 8-1/2 Lozenge	IA	1.75
4140.	Menuett	9 x 12	IA	10.00
4141.	Music Lesson	22 x 22 Lozenge	CAC	7.50
		16 x 16 Lozenge	CAC	5.00
		1J x 11 Lozenge	CFA	2.50
		10-1/2 x 10-1/2 Lozenge	IA	3.00
		8 x 8-1/2	IA	1.75
4142.	Pastorale--Dancing	17 x 22	CFA	10.00
4143.	Picnic After the Hunt	23-1/2 x 29	NYGS	12.00
4144.	La Princesse de Cleves	16 x 19-1/2	NYGS	7.50
4145.	Le Printemps	9 x 12	IA	10.00 (Grav.)
4146.	Spring	12 x 14	CFA	15.00
		11 x 14	CFA	10.00
		10 x 14	IA	3.00
4147.	Summer	17 x 22-1/2	ESH	10.00
		12 x 14	CFA	15.00
		10 x 14	IA	3.00
4148.	Winter	12 x 14	CFA	15.00
		10 x 14	IA	3.00
4149.	Winter, the Skaters	8 x 10	ESH	1.00

LANDORI

4150.	Interlude	31 x 21	CFA	16.00
4151.	Modern Ballet	14 x 34	CFA	15.00
4152.	Riders on the Beach	13 x 34	CFA	15.00

LANDSEER, (SIR) EDWIN HENRY English   1802-1873

4153.	Dignity and Impudence	8 x 10	AP	.50
4154.	Distinguished Member of the Humane Society	16 x 20	CAC	5.00
		9 x 12	CAC	2.00
4155.	Monarch of the Glen	26 x 20	CAC	7.50
		12 x 9	CAC	2.00
4156.	Shoeing the Mare	8 x 10	AP	.50

LANE, HARRY   American   1891-

4157.	Anemones	16 x 20	CFA	2.50
		13 x 16	CFA	1.50
4158.	Cyclamen	20 x 16	CFA	2.50
		16 x 13	CFA	1.50
4159.	Magnolias	20 x 16	CFA	2.50
		16 x 13	CFA	1.50
4160.	Pansies	16 x 20	CFA	2.50
		13 x 16	CFA	1.50
4161.	Primroses	20 x 16	CFA	2.50
		16 x 13	CFA	1.50

4162. Roses	20 x 16	CFA	2.50
	16 x 13	CFA	1.50
LANE, ROBERT BRYAN			
4163. Optimist	21 x 16	CFA	5.00
LA PAGLIA, ANTHONY	American		
4164. Song Birds (8)	22-1/2 x 18-1/2	NYGS	7.50 ea.
	16 x 12	NYGS	3.00 ea.

       Blue Grosbeak
       Blue Jay
       Cardinal
       Chickadees and Peonies
       Painted Bunting
       Redstart and Hydrangeas
       Summer Tanager
       Yellow Palm Warbler

LAPICQUE, CHARLES	French	1898-	
4165. Before the Start	16 x 26	PENN	1.00
LAREUSE, JEAN	French	1923-	
4166. Femmes D'Elegance (4)	12 x 10	DAC	1.00 ea.
LARGILLIERE, NICOLAS DE	French	1656-1746	
4167. Mlle. Dubois	28 x 22	IA	10.00
4168. Self-Portrait with			
Wife and Daughter	11 x 15	IA	3.00
LARSEN, OLE	Swedish	1907-	
4169. Teamwork	25 x 30	IA	7.50
LASINIO			
4170. Planets (6)	13 x 16	CFA	10.00 ea.
LASZLO, ALEXIUS DE	Hungarian-English	1869-1937	
4171. Roosevelt, Theodore	23-1/2 x 18	NYGS	12.00
LATOUR, MAURICE QUENTIN DE	French	1704-1788	
4172. Nativity (Rennes)	8 x 10	ESH	1.00
4173. Nativity (Louvre)	8 x 10	ESH	1.00
4174. Fortune Teller	16 x 19-1/2	AP	7.50
4175. Prisoner	19 x 12-1/2	ESH	10.00
LAUFMAN, SIDNEY	American	1891-	
4176. Summer Landscape	13 x 17	CAC	10.00
LAURENCIN, MARIE	French	1885-1956	
4177. Arabesque	21 x 18	CAC	15.00
4178. Dancers	18 x 22-1/2	ESH	10.00
4179. Les Deux Amies	22 x 18-1/2	NYGS	10.00
	14 x 11-1/2	NYGS	3.00
4180. Four Girls	14 x 20	CAC	15.00
4181. Girl in Red	23 x 18	HNA	5.95
	17 x 14	CFA	5.00
4182. Girl with Flowers	14 x 11	DAC	2.80
4183. Girl with Lillies	12 x 18	CAC	15.00
4184. Girl with Rose	17 x 21	CAC	15.00
4185. Helene	21 x 18	CAC	15.00
4186. In the Park	26-1/2 x 19	NYGS	12.00
	20 x 14	NYGS	7.50
	10 x 8	AP	.25
	8-1/2 x 6	NYGS	.50

4187. Jeanette	16 x 13	CAC	6.00
4188. La Princesse de Cleves	16 x 19	CAC	7.50
4189. Rosette Girl with			
Fan	19 x 14	CAC	12.00
4190. Self-Portrait	16 x 13	CAC	6.00
4191. La Jeune Mere	22 x 18-1/2	NYGS	10.00
	14 x 11-1/2	NYGS	3.00
4192. Sisters	26 x 32	PENN	1.00
	24 x 30	DAC	8.00
	11 x 14	DAC	2.80
4193. Yvette, Girl with			
Mandolin	19 x 14	CAC	12.00
	16 x 13	CAC	6.00
LAURENS, PAUL ALBERT	French	1870-	
4194. Head	11-1/2 x 9	NYGS	15.00
LAURJAN			
4195. Red Sideboard	17 x 22	CAC	10.00
LAURRAIN, CLAUDE See GELLEE, CLAUDE			
LAUTERBURG			
4196. Geraniums	30 x 25	CAC	15.00
LAUTH, ROBERT	German	1896-	
4197. Paris	20 x 23-1/2	IA	8.00
LAUTREC See TOULOUSE-LAUTREC, HENRI DE			
LAVAUX, GREGOIRE	French		
4198. Autumn Afternoon	14-1/2 x 17-1/2	RL	5.00
4199. Autumn Morning	24 x 30	CAC	10.00
4200. Chanson D'Automne	21 x 17-1/2	RL	5.00
4201. Coming Spring	14 x 17-1/2	RL	5.00
4202. Le Vieux Moulin	21 x 17-1/2	RL	5.00
LAVREINCE, N.	French-Swedish	1737-1807	
4203. Le Concert Agreeable	11 x 14	CFA	12.00
4204. La Partie de Musique	11 x 14	CFA	12.00
LAVRILLIER, G.	French	Contemporary	
4205. Red and White Roses	22-1/2 x 18	RL	6.00
LAWRENCE, (SIR) THOMAS	English	1769-1830	
4206. Calmady Children	28" circle	NYGS	10.00
	20" circle	NYGS	7.50
	9" circle	NYGS	1.50
4207. Countess Grosvenor	11 x 9	CFA	6.00
4208. Fluyder Children	28 x 17	NYGS	12.00
4209. Hon. Mrs. Ashley	10 x 8	CFA	6.00
4210. Lady Templeton and			
her Son	31 x 21-1/2	NYGS	12.00
4211. Master Lambton	28 x 21-1/2	IA	12.00
	14 x 11	IA	3.00
	10 x 8	AP	.50
4212. Detail of No. 4211.	14 x 11	IA	3.00
4213. Miss Croker	20 x 16	AA	5.00
	18 x 14	CFA	5.00
4214. Miss Murray	28 x 21-1/2	IA	12.00
	14 x 11	IA	3.00
	10 x 8	CFA	6.00

4215. Detail of No. 4214.	14 x 11	IA	3.00
4216. Miss West	27 x 22	NYGS	10.00
	7-1/2 x 6	NYGS	.50
4217. Pinkie	30-1/2 x 22	NYGS	12.00
	26 x 20	PENN	1.00
			1.98 (Pr.)
	24 x 16-1/2	NYGS	10.00
	24 x 16	CFA	10.00
	20 x 16	AA	5.00
	18 x 14	CFA	5.00
	18 x 13	NYGS	5.00
	14 x 10	NYGS	3.00
	12 x 9	NYGS	1.50
	10 x 8	AP	.50
4218. Portrait of Lord Seaham as a Boy	20 x 16	IA	6.00
	14 x 11	IA	2.50
LAWRENCE			
4219. Roses (4)	12 x 9	CFA	3.00 ea.
4220. Roses--Black Background (8)	12 x 9	CFA	5.00 ea.
LAYTON			
4221. Antique Shop	10 x 30	CAC	10.00
4222. Maison Dubois	23 x 10	CAC	7.50
4223. Mal's Restaurant	25 x 12	CAC	10.00
4224. March Gallery	30 x 10	CAC	10.00
4225. Perfume Shop	10 x 30	CAC	10.00
4226. Twelfth Step Cafe	30 x 10	CAC	10.00
4227. Village Cafe	23 x 10	CAC	7.50
4228. Wade Gallery	25 x 12	CAC	10.00
LEADER, B. W.			
4229. By Mead and Stream	16-1/2 x 28-1/2	NYGS	15.00
4230. Gleam before the Storm	18 x 27-1/2	NYGS	15.00
4231. Way to the Village Church	17-1/2 x 27	NYGS	15.00
LE BAS, EDWARD	English	1904-	
4232. Port near the Spanish Border	15 x 30	RL	10.00
LEBOURG			
4233. Paris, Le Pont Neuf	13 x 22-1/2	ESH	10.00
LE BRETON, CONSTANT	French	1895-	
4234. Ducal Palace	20 x 24	CAC	10.00
4235. Grand Canal	20 x 24	CAC	12.00
4236. Landscape with Boats	19 x 23	CFA	10.00
4237. Quiet Estuary	19 x 24	RL	10.00
4238. View of Baltimore	10 x 14	CFA	12.00
4239. Boston, View of	10 x 14	CFA	12.00
4240. Boston, View of, II	10 x 14	CFA	12.00
4241. Los Angeles, View of	9 x 13	CFA	12.00
4242. New York-Brooklyn, View of	10 x 14	CFA	12.00

4243. New York--Trans- Atlantic, View of	10 x 14	CFA	12.00
4244. Philadelphia, View of	10 x 14	CFA	12.00
4245. Sacramento, View of	10 x 14	CFA	12.00
LE BRUN, ELISABETH VIGÉE	French	1755-1842	
4246. Anna	20 x 10	NYGS	7.50
4247. Madame Elizabeth Le Brun	11 x 9	CFA	6.00
4248. Madame Le Brun and her Daughter	17 x 13	NYGS	5.00
4249. Marie Antoinette and her Children	10 x 8	ESH	1.00
4250. Mrs. Molé-Raymond	14 x 10	IA	3.00
4251. Self-Portrait	13 x 11	IA	3.00
4252. Detail of No. 4251-- Head	15 x 11	IA	3.00
4253. Self-Portrait with Daughter	14 x 11	IA	3.00
LE CERVIN			
4254. Matterhorn	27 x 35	CAC	12.50
LECLAIR, CHARLES		1914-	
4255. Bouquets (6)	12 x 9	DAC	.40 ea.
LECOMTE, PAUL EMILE	French	1877-1950	
4256. Mevagissey Harbour	17 x 21	RL	5.00
4257. Mouth of the Rance at Dinard	19-1/2 x 30	RL	10.00
4258. Old House	18 x 23	PENN	1.00
LEDER, A.			
4259. Fruits and Flowers	20 x 40	DAC	8.00
	9 x 17-1/2	DAC	2.00
LEE, DORIS E.	American	Contemporary	
4260. Apple Pickers	10 x 16	NYGS	5.00
4261. Corn Pickers	10 x 16	NYGS	5.00
4262. Thanksgiving	9 x 13	NYGS	3.00
	8 x 11	NYGS	1.50
4263. Tropical Bird	12 x 18	NYGS	10.00
4264. Winter in the Cat- skills	14 x 20	NYGS	5.00
LEE-HANKEY See HANKEY, WILLIAM LEE			
LEGARES, JOSE OLIVET			
4265. In the Foothills	25 x 35	NYGS	15.00
LEGER, FERNAND	French	1881-	
4266. Abstraction	25 x 20	CAC	15.00
4267. Big Julie	8 x 10	MMA	.35
4268. Blue Basket	24-1/2 x 19	NYGS	12.00
4269. Composition	11 x 8	AP	2.00
4270. Guitare	13 x 9	NYGS	12.00
4271. Mother and Child	16 x 22-1/2	ESH	10.00
4272. Nature Morte	10 x 7	NYGS	12.00
4273. Sitting Woman	10 x 8	AP	.75
4274. Three Women	8 x 10	MMA	.35
4275. Yellow Flowers in a Blue Vase	26 x 20	AP	12.00

LEEMPUTTER
    4276. Homeward Bound   20 x 26   CAC   7.50
LEHUCHER
    4277. Anemones   21 x 27   CAC   7.50
    4278. Spring Flowers   21 x 27   CAC   7.50
LEIBL, WILHELM   German   1844-1900
    4279. Three Women in
          Church   21 x 13   NYGS   5.00
    4280. Old Woman in Church   21 x 13   CAC   5.00
LEIGH, WILLIAM R.   American   1866-1955
    4281. Bull Diving   22 x 18   CFA   7.50
    4282. Bull Dogging   22 x 18   CFA   7.50
    4283. Double Crosser   22 x 18   CFA   7.50
    4284. Greased Lightning   22 x 18   CFA   7.50
LEIPOLD, KARL   German   1864-1943
    4285. Dutch Sailboats   21 x 29   CAC   12.00
    4286. Old Dutch Mill   29 x 25   CAC   10.00
    4287. Rialto Bridge   22 x 26   CAC   10.00
LEITH-ROSS, HARRY   American   1886-
    4288. Northern Lake   19 x 27   IA   10.00
    4289. Old Mill   19 x 27   IA   10.00
LELONG, PIERRE EMILE   American   1908-
    4290. Paris Street Scenes
          (20)   9-1/2 x 12 (12)   IA   3.50 ea.
                        12 x 9-1/2 (8)   IA   3.50 ea.
                    L'Arc de Triomphe
                    Les Bouquinistes
                    Les Champs-Elysees
                    La Conciergerie
                    Les Invalides
                    La Madeleine
                    Moulin Rouge
                    Notre Dame
                    Notre Dame (L'Abside)
                    Notre Dame et la Seine
                    L'Opera
                    Le Pantheon
                    Place de la Concorde
                    Place du Tertre
                    Place Vendome
                    Pont Alexandre III
                    Pont Neuf
                    Rue Norvins
                    La Tour Eiffel
LAMASSON, PAUL
    4291. Bicycle   10 x 8   CFA   1.50
    4292. Carnival   8 x 10   CFA   1.50
    4293. Carousel   10 x 8   CFA   1.50
    4294. French Provincial
          Subjects (4)   11 x 14   DAC   2.00 ea.
               Circus on Wheels
               Passers-By

		Side Show		
		Snow Flurry		
4295.	Holiday Inn	8 x 10	CFA	1.50
4296.	Village Square	8 x 10	CFA	1.50
LENBACH, FRANZ VON		German	1836-1904	
4297.	Shepherd Boy	16 x 22	IA	7.50
LEONARDO DA VINCI		Italian	1452-1519	
4298.	Annunciation	6 x 14	IA	3.00
4299.	Angel -- Detail of			
	No. 4298	15 x 11	IA	3.00
4300.	Beatrice D'Este	8 x 10	AP	.60
4301.	Head of the Saviour	14 x 11	IA	3.00
		10 x 8	ESH	1.00
		10 x 7-1/2	IA	1.75
4302.	Last Supper			
	(Unrestored)	16 x 32	IA	15.00
		13 x 23	IA	7.50
		11-1/2 x 22	NYGS	4.00
		8 x 10	AP	.50
		7 x 11	IA	1.75
	(Restored)	20 x 40	NYGS	10.00
		15 x 30	NYGS	5.00
		14 x 25	PENN	1.00
		10 x 20	NYGS	2.50
		9 x 15	IA	3.00
		5-1/2 x 12	NYGS	.50
4303.	Leda and the Swan	14 x 11	IA	3.00
4304.	Mona Lisa (La Gioconda)	21 x 14-1/2	AP	5.00
		19 x 13	CFA	7.50
		18-1/2 x 12-1/2	NYGS	5.00
		15 x 11	IA	3.00
		10 x 8	ESH	1.00
4305.	Portrait of Unknown			
	Woman	14 x 10	IA	3.00
4306.	St. John the Baptist	19 x 15	IA	7.50
		13 x 10	IA	3.00
		12 x 9	CFA	2.50
4307.	Self-Portrait			
	(Presumed)	14 x 11	IA	3.00
4308.	Virgin of the Rocks			
	(Detail)	22-1/2 x 19	ESH	10.00
		10 x 8	ESH	1.00
4309.	Virgin, Child and			
	St. Anne	21-1/2 x 15-1/2	IA	10.00
		14 x 11	IA	3.00
4310.	Head of St. Anne--			
	Detail of No. 4309	15 x 11	IA	3.00
LE PRINCE, JEAN BAPTISTE		French	1733-1781	
4311.	Russian Interior	7 x 6	AR	3.50
LEROLLE, HENRI		French	1848-1929	
4312.	Arrival of the			
	Shepherds	15-1/2 x 20	NYGS	4.00
		8-1/2 x 10-1/2	NYGS	.50

LEUTZE, EMANUEL G.	American	1816-1868
4313. Washington Crossing		
the Delaware	18 x 30	NYGS 12.00
	16 x 28	CAC 10.00
LEVI, JULIAN EDWIN	American	1900-
4314. New England Dock	13 x 10	CAC 10.00
LEVINE, JACK	American	1915-
4315. Old Testament		
Portraits (6)	10 x 8	NYGS 15.00 set
		or 3.00 ea.
Hillel		
King Asa		
King David		
King Saul		
Maimonides		
Yehudah		
LEVY, RUDOLF	German	1875-1943
4316. Still Life with		
Yellow Vase	24 x 30	CFA 15.00
LEWIS, EDMUND DARCH	American	1835-1910
4317. Landscape	22-1/2 x 36	NYGS 18.00
LEWSEY		
4318. Shoal Water	17 x 24	CAC 10.00
L'HERMITTE, LEON AUGUSTIN	French	1844-1925
4319. Haymaking	18-1/2 x 24-1/2	NYGS 7.50
4320. Supper at Emmaus	23 x 34	IA 18.00
LHOTE, ANDRE	French	1885-
4321. The Model	19 x 13	CFA 5.00
LIER, A.		
4322. Harvest	23 x 35	CFA 15.00
LIGNON		
4323. Clown	26-1/2 x 13	NYGS 16.00
LIMBOURG, POL DE	French	Ac. 1402-1416
4324. Book of Hours of the		
Duc de Berry (2)	10 x 8	ESH 1.00 ea.
LINARD		
4325. Bouquet of Flowers	17 x 22	CAC 10.00
LINDERUM		
4326. Ave Maria	20 x 14	NYGS 9.00
LIOTARD, JEAN ETIENNE	French	1702-1789
4327. Painter's Niece,		
Mlle. L	20 x 16	NYGS 16.00
4328. Portrait of a Lady	10 x 8-1/2	AR 4.00
4329. Young Girl Singing		
into a Mirror	24 x 20	CFA 10.00
LIPPI, FILIPPINO	Italian	1457-1504
4330. Angel Announcing	11" circle	IA 3.00
4331. Apparition of the		
Virgin to St.		
Bernard	12 x 11	IA 3.00
4332. Esther and Ahasverus	5 x 15	IA 3.00
4333. Madonna Adoring the		
Child	15 x 11	IA 3.00

4334. Madonna and Child	30 x 21-1/2	NYGS	12.00
4335. Portrait of an Old Man	13 x 10	IA	3.00
4336. Self-Portrait	15 x 11	IA	3.00
4337. Virgin Annunciate	11" circle	IA	3.00
LIPPI, (FRA) FILIPPO	Italian	1406-1469	
4338. Adoration of the Child	15 x 9	IA	3.00
4339. Angel Announcing	14 x 5	IA	3.00
4340. Madonna and Child and Stories from her Life	11" circle	IA	3.00
4341. The Virgin--Detail of No. 4340	15 x 11	IA	3.00
4342. Virgin with the Child and Two Angels	15 x 10	IA	3.00
4343. Virgin Adoring	24 x 18	IA	10.00
	24 x 18	IA	7.50
	15 x 11	IA	3.00
	11 x 8	IA	1.75
LIPCHITZ, JACQUES	French	1891-	
4344. Sauvetage	12-1/2 x 10	NYGS	12.00
LIPPINCOTT, EDWARD	American		
4345. Solid Comfort	24 x 30	DAC	8.00
LISMER			
4346. Rain in the North Country	22 x 28	NYGS	7.50
LISS, GIOVANNI See LYS, JAN VAN			
LITTLEJOHN, JOHN	English	1874-	
4347. Between Showers	18 x 22	CFA	10.00
LIVINGSTON, ALINE			
4348. Raggedy Romeo	16 x 21	AA	4.00
LLOVERAS, FEDERICO	Spanish	Contemporary	
4349. Bay of Naples	25-1/2 x 34	NYGS	18.00
4350. Bay of Palma de Mallorca	25-1/2 x 34	NYGS	18.00
	12 x 14	NYGS	4.00
4351. Castel S. Angelo	25-1/2 x 34	NYGS	18.00
	12 x 14	NYGS	4.00
4352. Columbus Monument, Barcelona	31-1/2 x 12	NYGS	12.00
4353. Giralda, Sevilla	31-1/2 x 12	NYGS	12.00
4354. Loire; Chateau d'Amboise	13-1/2 x 39	NYGS	18.00
4355. London, Houses of Parliament	17 x 39	NYGS	18.00
4356. Madrid, Puente di Segovia	17 x 39	NYGS	18.00
4357. Mallorca Harbor	13-1/2 x 39	NYGS	18.00
4358. Palma de Mallorca	13-1/2 x 39	NYGS	18.00
4359. Paris, Ile de la Cité	17 x 39	NYGS	18.00
4360. Paris, Le Pont Neuf	17 x 39	NYGS	18.00
4361. Parthenon, Athens	25-1/2 x 34	NYGS	18.00
	12 x 14	NYGS	4.00

4362. Piazza S. Pietro	25-1/2 x 34	NYGS	18.00
	12 x 14	NYGS	4.00
4363. San Marco, Venezia	31-1/2 x 12	NYGS	12.00
4364. Sorrento	17 x 39-1/2	NYGS	18.00
4365. Street in Chelsea	13-1/2 x 39-1/2	NYGS	18.00
4366. Venice	13-1/2 x 39	NYGS	18.00
4367. Windsor Castle	17 x 39	NYGS	18.00
LOCHNER, STEFAN	German	1400-1451	
4368. Adoration	22 x 24	CFA	15.00
	20 x 21	CFA	6.00
4369. Annunciation	30-1/2 x 33-1/2	NYGS	18.00
4370. Madonna in a Mystic Garden	12 x 10-1/2	NYGS	10.00
4371. Madonna in the Rose Garden	18-1/2 x 14-1/2	NYGS	12.00
4372. Madonna of the Rose Arbor	23 x 18	HNA	5.95
	18-1/2 x 14-1/2	IA	15.00
LOCKE, JUSTIN			
4373. Tata Domingo	24-1/2 x 10	IA	10.00
LOCKWOOD			
4374. Horses in Winter	8 x 10	AP	.50
LOCKWOOD, WARD	American	1894-	
4375. Fragments of Elegance	22-1/2 x 30	IA	15.00
4376. Young Sculptress	26 x 19	IA	10.00
LOEDERER			
4377. Brahms at Home	16 x 24	CAC	4.00
LOESCH, ERNST	German	1860-1946	
4378. Lilacs	26 x 22	IA	6.00
LOEWENGRUND			
4379. Rooftops	17 x 21	CAC	7.50
LOGAN, MAURICE			
4380. Old Dock	14 x 12	IA	7.50
LONG, STANLEY M.			
4381. Horse Wrangler	13-1/2 x 19-1/2	IA	6.00
4382. Meeting Place	13-1/2 x 19-1/2	IA	6.00
4383. Ranch Horses (4)	11 x 14	DAC	2.80 ea.
Breaking a Rough One			
Good Samaritan			
Reflections			
Wild Horses			
4384. Rest at Noon	13-1/2 x 19-1/2	IA	6.00
4385. Shady Pool	20 x 26	IA	7.50
4386. Trail Riders	13-1/2 x 19-1/2	IA	6.00
4387. Two Foals	20 x 26	IA	7.50
LONGHI, PIETRO	Italian	1702-1785	
4388. Dancing Master	14 x 11	IA	3.00
4389. Dentist	15 x 11	IA	3.00
4390. Familiar Concert	11 x 14	IA	3.00
4391. Kiss of the Hand	24 x 19	CFA	12.00
4392. Marriage	14 x 11	IA	3.00
4393. Tailor	24 x 19	CFA	12.00
	14 x 11	IA	3.00

LONGPRE, PAUL DE
   4394. Florals (8)   14 x 11   NYGS 2.50 ea.
         Delight (Rose)
         Enchanting
         Fairy Lustre
         Fleurs of Louis
         Gentle Waking
         Red Velvet
         White Prince
         Winsome

LORENZ, JOHANNES   German   1903-
    4395. Jugoslavia   6-1/2 x 15-1/2 ESH   4.00 (Pr.)
    4396. Matterhorn   6-1/2 x 15-1/2 ESH   4.00 (Pr.)
    4397. Pine Trees   6-1/2 x 15-1/2 ESH   4.00 (Pr.)
    4398. Riviera   6-1/2 x 15-1/2 ESH   4.00 (Pr.)

LORENZETTI, AMBROGIO Italian   c. 1348
    4399. Good Government 15 x 9   IA   3.00
    4400. Peace--Detail of No.
         4399   16 x 12   IA   3.00
    4401. Madonna and Child 15 x 9   IA   3.00
    4402. Madonna and Child
         and Two Saints   14 x 7   IA   3.00
    4403. Madonna and Saints 15 x 10   IA   3.00
    4404. St. Dorothea   15 x 10   IA   3.00

LORENZETTI, PIETRO   Italian   c. 1350
    4405. Birth of the Virgin 16 x 10   IA   3.00
    4406. Descent from the
         Cross   11 x 15   IA   3.00
    4407. Madonna and Saints
         John and Francis 11 x 15   IA   3.00

LORENZO DA SAN SEVERINO Italian   1445-1503
    4408. Virgin and St. Anne 15 x 7   IA   3.00

LORENZO DI CREDI (SCIARPELLONI, LORENZO)
                      Italian   1459-1537
    4409. Annunciation   13 x 11   IA   3.00
    4410. Virgin--Detail of
         No. 4409   10 x 8   IA   1.50
    4411. Holy Family   11" circle IA   3.00
    4412. Madonna and Child 15 x 11   IA   3.00
    4413. Madonna and Child
         with St. John   11" circle IA   3.00
    4414. Portrait of a Youth
         in a Black Cap   12 x 11   IA   3.00
    4415. Portrait of a Youth
         in a Red Cap   14 x 10   IA   3.00
    4416. Portrait of Verrocchio 15 x 10   IA   3.00

LORENZO DI PIETRO See VECCHIETTA, IL

LORENZO MONACO   Italian   1370-1425
    4417. Adoration of the Magi 10 x 15   IA   3.00
    4418. Crucifixion   9 x 15   IA   3.00

LORJOU, BERNARD   French   1908
    4419. Flowers and Pineapple 22 x 27-1/2 NYGS 15.00

4420. Green Dish	22-1/2 x 23	NYGS	18.00
4421. Red Sideboard	17-1/2 x 22-1/2	ESH	10.00
LORRAIN, CLAUDE See GELLEE, CLAUDE			
LOTIRON, ROBERT	French	1886-	
4422. Fishmongers	8 x 10	ESH	1.00
LOTTO, LORENZO	Italian	1480-1556	
4423. Gentleman with			
Gloves	14 x 11	IA	3.00
4424. Nativity	16 x 20	IA	6.00
4425. Portrait of Bernardo			
dé Rossi	14 x 11	IA	3.00
4426. Portrait of a Youth	11 x 12	IA	3.00
4427. St. Catherine of			
Alexandria	14 x 11	IA	3.00
4428. Three Ages of Man	11 x 14	IA	3.00
	8 x 10	AP	.60
4429. Virgin, Child and			
Two Saints	11 x 14	IA	3.00
LOUIS, NORBERT	German	1926-	
4430. Cities (4)	12 x 16	DAC	4.00 ea.
Amsterdam			
London			
New York			
Paris			
LOWRIE, AGNES POTTER	English-American	1892-	
4431. At the Seaside	20 x 24	NYGS	15.00
4432. Blue Compote	18 x 22	CFA	5.00
	6 x 8	CFA	1.00
4433. Children's Playground	18 x 24	NYGS	15.00
4434. Lancashire Village	14 x 20	NYGS	12.00
4435. Lobster	18 x 30	CFA	10.00
4436. Old Church and Steps	24 x 20	NYGS	15.00
4437. On the Sands, Berwick			
on Tweed	20 x 23-1/2	NYGS	15.00
4438. Red Compote	18 x 22	CFA	5.00
	6 x 8	CFA	1.00
4439. Watermelon	19 x 28	CFA	10.00
LOWRY, T. S.			
4440. Canals and Factories	24 x 29-1/2	NYGS	12.00
4441. Outside the Mill	11-1/2 x 20	NYGS	7.50
LUCAS			
4442. Aveyron	23 x 28	CAC	10.00
LUCE, MAXIMILIEN	French	1858-1941	
4443. Pastoral	25-1/2 x 36	NYGS	15.00
LUCIANI, SEBASTIANO See PIOMBO, SEBASTIANO DEL			
LUCIONI, LUIGI	American	1900-	
4444. Autumn Landscape	16 x 24	PENN	1.00
4445. Peace in the Valley	20 x 24	NYGS	10.00
4446. Route Seven	16 x 21	NYGS	7.50
4447. Sunlit Patterns	14 x 20	NYGS	7.50
4448. Vermont Pastoral	19-1/2 x 33	NYGS	10.00
LUDLUM			
4449. Ballerina	22 x 18	CAC	6.00

4450. Scheherazade	22 x 18	CAC	6.00

LUKA, M.
| 4451. Petite Fille | 18 x 14-1/2 | NYGS | 15.00 |
| 4452. Petit Saltimbanque | 18-1/2 x 13-1/2 | NYGS | 15.00 |

LUINI, BERNARDINO   Italian   1475-1532
4453. Head of the Virgin	10 x 8	AP	.50
4454. Little St. John with the Lamb	10 x 9	IA	1.50
4455. Madonna of the Carnation	17 x 16	AA	7.50
4456. Madonna of the Rose Bower	12 x 11	IA	3.00
4457. Portrait of a Lady	16 x 11	AR	5.00
4458. Silence	9 x 7	CFA	2.50

LUKS, GEORGE B.   American   1867-1933
| 4459. Guitar | 14-1/2 x 15 | NYGS | 5.00 |

LUNDBERG
| 4460. Portrait of Boucher | 12 x 9 | CFA | 2.50 |

LUPAS
4461. Johnson, Lyndon B.	13 x 17	NYGS	4.00
4462. Kennedy, John F.	28 x 20	NYGS	12.00
	16 x 13	NYGS	4.00
	13-1/2 x 10	NYGS	3.00
4463. Musicians (8)	14 x 11	CAC	3.00 ea.
	10 x 8	CAC	1.00 ea.

        Beethoven
        Brahms
        Dvorak
        Grieg
        Puccini
        Rachmaninoff
        Rossini
        Sibelius

LURCAT, JEAN   French   1892-
4464. Big Clowd	16 x 24	NYGS	12.00
4465. Brazil (Detail from KLM Tapestry)	8 x 10	ESH	1.00
4466. Colibri	22 x 16	NYGS	16.00
4467. Coq Blanc	23 x 15	NYGS	16.00
4468. Fleurs	22-1/2 x 17	NYGS	15.00
4469. Guerrier	23 x 14	NYGS	16.00
4470. Orion	42-1/2 x 30	ESH	15.00
4471. Papillon	16 x 22-1/2	NYGS	18.00
4472. Papillon Bleu	28 x 21-1/2	NYGS	16.00
4473. Poissons	16-1/2 x 27-1/2	NYGS	16.00

LUSCHNER
4474. Blossoms	15 x 11-1/2	ESH	8.00 (Pr.)
4475. Lago Maggiore	18 x 23-1/2	ESH	8.00 (Pr.)
4476. Venice	13-1/2 x 27-1/2	ESH	8.00 (Pr.)

LUTI, BENEDETTO   Italian   1666-1724
| 4477. Head of Cherub | 12 x 10 | IA | 3.00 |

LYNE, MICHAEL   English   1912-

4478. Beaufort at Worcester Lodge	15 x 21	RL	7.50
4479. Cotswold at Shipton Oliffe	15 x 21	RL	7.50
4480. Duke of Beaufort's Hunt	13 x 20	CFA	7.50
4481. Heythrop at Upper Slaughter	15 x 21	RL	7.50
4482. Royal Agricultural Beagles at Jarvis Quarry	15 x 21	RL	7.50
4483. Whadden Chase at Waterloo	15 x 21	RL	7.50
LYS, JAN VAN	German	c. 1629	
4484. Venus at the Mirror	14 x 11	IA	3.00

M

MABUSE (GOSSART, JAN)	Flemish	1470-1541	
4485. Adam and Eve	10 x 8	AR	3.00
4486. Adoration of the Kings	20 x 22	CAC	10.00
4487. Triptych Malvagna	11 x 15	IA	3.00
MAC DONALD, RICHARD	English	1919-	
4488. The Kite	20 x 32-1/2	RL	12.50
4489. Still Life with Thunder	28 x 17	RL	12.50
MAC GREGOR, R.			
4490. American Clipper "Lightning"	22 x 32	AA	10.00
4491. The "Ariel"	22 x 32	AA	10.00
4492. Before the Wind	24 x 32	AA	10.00
4493. Blue Waters	16 x 24	IA	5.00
4494. Cutty Sark	24 x 20	AA	7.50
4495. Outward Bound	16 x 24	IA	5.00
4496. Red Jacket	24 x 20	AA	7.50
4497. The Torrens	20 x 30	AA	8.00
MACKE, AUGUST	German	1887-1914	
4498. African Landscape	18 x 22	ESH	10.00
4499. Blue Girl Reading Book	23 x 17	PENN	1.00
4500. Children on the Water	16 x 22	ESH	10.00
4501. Girl with Blue Birds	22 x 30-1/2	NYGS	22.00
4502. Girls under the Trees	15 x 20	CAC	10.00
4503. Gladiolas	30 x 24	CAC	15.00
4504. Kandern	9-1/2 x 12-1/2	NYGS	12.00
4505. Landscape with Cow and Camel	18 x 21	CFA	15.00
4506. Millinery Shop at Promenade	20 x 29	CFA	15.00
4507. People on a Blue Lake	23-1/2 x 19	IA	15.00
4508. Port of Duisburg	17 x 15	CAC	5.00
4509. Yellow Coat	11-1/2 x 17-1/2	NYGS	16.00

4510. Zoological Gardens	19 x 31	NYGS	15.00
MACLET, ELISEE	French	1881-	
4511. Red Mill	20 x 28	NYGS	10.00
MAES, NICOLAES	Dutch	1632-1693	
4512. Asking a Blessing	20 x 24	DAC	6.00
4513. Duchess of Mazarin	20 x 15	CAC	10.00
4514. Old Woman Dozing over a Book	18 x 23	HNA	5.95
MAESTRO DEI CASSONI JARVES	Italian	15th Century	
4515. Griselda Legend	6 x 15	IA	3.00
MAESTRO DEL CASSONE ADIMARE			
4516. Marriage of Lisa Ricasoli and Boccaccio Adimari	9 x 15	IA	3.00
MAESTRO DI SAN FRANCESCO			
4517. St. Anthony	15 x 7	IA	3.00
MAGNASCO, ALESSANDRO	Italian	1667-1749	
4518. Baptism of Christ	24 x 30	NYGS	18.00
4519. Consignment of the Keys	7 x 9	NYGS	.50
4520. Count Gerolamo Colloredo	9 x 7	NYGS	.50
4521. Entertainment in a Garden	7 x 9	NYGS	.50
4522. Detail of No. 4521.	9 x 7	NYGS	.50
4523. Young Woman and Musician	10 x 7	NYGS	.50
MAGNUS, JOSEF	Austrian	1908-	
4524. Jenny Lind	28 x 22	IA	6.00
	20 x 16	IA	3.50
	12 x 9	IA	1.00
MAGRITTE, RENÉ	Belgian	1898-	
4525. Empire of Light	19-1/2 x 24-1/2	MMA	6.50
MAILLOL, ARISTIDE	French	1861-1944	
4526. Head of a Young Girl	20 x 24	NYGS	10.00
4527. Nude	8 x 10	NYGS	12.00
MAINARDI, SEBASTIANO	Italian	1460-1513	
4528. Madonna, Child and Angels	11" circle	IA	3.00
4529. Portrait of a Girl	10 x 6	CFA	1.00
4530. Portrait of a Man	17 x 13	NYGS	12.00
MAINO See MAYNO			
MAI-THU			
4531. The Class	10-1/2 x 30	ESH	15.00
4532. Game of Chess	8 x 34-1/2	ESH	18.00
4533. Recreation	10-1/2 x 30	ESH	15.00
MAJOR, HENRY	American	1889-	
4534. American Frolic	20-1/2 x 17	NYGS	6.00
	14 x 11	NYGS	2.00
	7-1/2 x 6	NYGS	1.00
4535. End of a Perfect Day	20-1/2 x 17	NYGS	6.00
	14 x 11	NYGS	2.00
	7-1/2 x 6	NYGS	1.00

4536. Gay Philosopher	20 x 16	NYGS	6.00
	14 x 11	NYGS	2.00
	7-1/2 x 6	NYGS	1.00
4537. In Love	20 x 16	NYGS	6.00
	14 x 11	NYGS	2.00
4538. On Top of the World	19 x 24	NYGS	6.00
	10-1/2 x 13	NYGS	2.00
4539. Philosopher's Heir	20 x 16	NYGS	6.00
	14 x 11	NYGS	2.00
	7-1/2 x 6	NYGS	1.00
4540. Philosopher's Offspring	20 x 16	NYGS	6.00
	14 x 11	NYGS	2.00
	7-1/2 x 6	NYGS	1.00
4541. Philosopher's Quartet	16 x 20	NYGS	6.00
	11 x 14	NYGS	2.00
4542. Philosopher's Wife	20 x 16	NYGS	6.00
	14 x 11	NYGS	2.00
	7-1/2 x 6	NYGS	1.00
MAKIELSKI, BRONISLAU	American	1901-	
4543. Blue Ridge Mountains of Virginia	25 x 30	IA	7.50
MALER, HANS	German	1488-1529	
4544. Maria of Burgundy	20 x 12	AJ	7.50
MALTHAUSER			
4545. Behold the Man	21 x 37	CAC	15.00
4546. Christ before Pilate	21-1/2 x 38	IA	12.00
4547. Golgatha	21 x 38	IA	12.00
MANCINI, DOMENICO	Italian	16th Century	
4548. Musician	13 x 11	IA	3.00
MANDON, EDOUARD	French	Contemporary	
4549. Song of the Surf	17-1/2 x 31	RL	7.50
4550. Tumbling Waves	16 x 32	RL	7.50
MANESSIER, ALFRED	French	1911-	
4551. Alleluia of the Fields	18-1/2 x 18-1/2	ESH	10.00
4552. Grown of Thorns	23 x 19	CFA	12.00
4553. Night	18 x 23	HNA	5.95
	15-1/2 x 21	IA	6.00
MANET, EDOUARD	French	1832-1883	
4554. Amazon	11 x 15	IA	3.00
4555. Balcony	9 x 6	NYGS	.50
4556. Ballet Espagnol	25 x 37	NYGS	18.00
4557. Bar at the Folies Bergere	21-1/2 x 28-1/2	NYGS	12.00
4558. Bar Maid at the Folies Bergere	24 x 18-1/2	PENN	1.00
	20-1/2 x 12-1/2	ESH	10.00
	10 x 8	NYGS	.50
	8 x 6	CFA	1.00
4559. Boy with a Sword	10 x 8	NYGS	.50
4560. Boy with Cherries	28 x 18	CAC	7.50
	22-1/2 x 18-1/2	ESH	10.00
	10 x 8	ESH	1.00

4561. Breakfast at the Studio	26 x 35	CFA	18.00
4562. Bunch of Flowers	14 x 10	AR	5.00
4563. Eel and Red-Mullet	10 x 12	IA	3.00
4564. Fifer	31-1/2 x 19	NYGS	15.00
	24 x 16	PENN	1.00
	23-1/2 x 14	NYGS	10.00
4565. Figure of a Boy	12 x 6	NYGS	3.00
4566. Flute Player	18 x 11	CFA	4.00
4567. Gare Saint-Lazare	18 x 23	HNA	5.95
4568. Girl at Folies Bergere	9 x 6	NYGS	.50
4569. Guitar and Sombrero	17-1/2 x 28	NYGS	15.00
4570. In a Boat	22 x 29-1/2	NYGS	16.00
	5-1/2 x 7-1/2	NYGS	.50
4571. Lola de Valence	15 x 11	IA	3.00
4572. Lunch in the Studio	27 x 35-1/2	NYGS	18.00
4573. Mlle. Marguerite	22 x 18	CFA	15.00
4574. Oellets and Clematites	8 x 10	ESH	1.00
4575. Olympia	8 x 12	CFA	2.50
4576. On the Balcony	10 x 8	ESH	1.00
4577. Les Paveurs, Rue de Berne	21 x 26	CAC	15.00
4578. Peonies	23 x 18	HNA	5.95
4579. Picnic	8 x 10	NYGS	.50
4580. Picnic on the Grass	9 x 12	CFA	2.50
4581. Pink Rose and Yellow Rose	12-1/2 x 9-1/2	NYGS	7.50
4582. Piper	10 x 8	ESH	1.00
4583. Plum	14 x 9	IA	3.00
4584. Port of Bordeaux	8 x 10	ESH	1.00
4585. Portrait of Mme. Blumer	24 x 19	PENN	1.00
	10 x 8	CFA	3.00
4586. Portrait of Irma Brunner	26 x 21	HNA	5.95
4587. Reading	7 x 9	NYGS	.50
4588. Roadmenders of Rue de Berne	21-1/2 x 26-1/2	NYGS	15.00
4589. Roses and Tulips in a Vase	18 x 11	CFA	5.00
4590. Self-Portrait	10 x 8	NYGS	.50
4591. Servant de Bocks	24 x 19	NYGS	12.00
4592. Serveuse de Bocks	9 x 7	NYGS	.50
4593. Study of a Woman	20 x 16	PENN	1.00
4594. Vase of Peonies	20 x 15-1/2	PENN	1.00
	10 x 8	ESH	1.00
	8 x 6	CFA	1.00
4595. Villa Bellevue	35 x 27	CAC	18.00
	25 x 20	CFA	12.00
	25 x 19	CAC	12.00
4596. Waitress Serving Beer	20 x 16-1/2	PENN	1.00
4597. Woman Bathing	15 x 11	IA	3.00

4598. Woman's Portrait	21 x 17	PENN	1.00
MANGUIN, HENRI CHARLES	French	1874-1943	
4599. Port of St. Tropez	22-1/2 x 18-1/2	ESH	10.00
MANTEGNA, ANDREA	Italian	1431-1506	
4600. Circumcision	15 x 7	IA	3.00
4601. Madonna and Child	20 x 16	CAC	10.00
	14 x 11	IA	3.00
4602. Madonna with			
Sleeping Child	17-1/2 x 13	NYGS	15.00
4603. Portrait of			
Elisabetta Gonzaga	14 x 10	IA	3.00
4604. St. George	15 x 7	IA	3.00
	10 x 5	NYGS	.50
4605. Virgin Enthroned			
with Saints	15 x 25	IA	10.00
MARATTA, CARLO	Italian	1625-1713	
4606. Holy Family	15 x 11	IA	3.00
4607. Holy Night	31 x 24	IA	12.00
	28 x 21	IA	10.00
	23-1/2 x 18	IA	7.50
	21 x 16-1/2	NYGS	9.00
	21 x 16	IA	4.00
	15 x 11	IA	3.00
4608. Detail of No. 4607			
(Horizontal)	15 x 20	IA	10.00
	11 x 15	IA	3.00
4609. Portrait of a Gentle-			
man	13 x 11	IA	3.00
4610. Portrait of a Man	13 x 11	IA	3.00
MARC, FRANZ	German	1880-1916	
4610a.Abstract Form	18 x 22	CFA	15.00
4611. Animals at Bay	18 x 23	HNA	5.95
4612. Blue Fox	12 x 16	ESH	4.00
4613. Blue Horses	17-1/2 x 30	NYGS	20.00
4614. Deer in Flower			
Garden	21-1/2 x 30	NYGS	18.00
4615. Deer in the Forest	21 x 32	CFA	18.00
	27 x 29-1/2	NYGS	24.00
	16 x 22	NYGS	15.00
4616. Gazelle	15 x 18	NYGS	15.00
	15 x 17-1/2	NYGS	5.00
	8 x 10	ESH	1.00
4617. Horse and Eagle	26 x 36	CAC	18.00
	26 x 35-1/2	IA	20.00
4618. Landscape with			
Horse	22 x 29	NYGS	22.00
	16 x 22	NYGS	15.00
4619. Little Blue Horse	22 x 28	NYGS	18.00
4620. Red and Blue Horses	10 x 13	CFA	7.50
4621. Red Deer	22 x 31-1/2	IA	18.00
	15 x 21	IA	10.00
4622. Red Horses	22 x 31-1/2	IA	18.00
	20-1/2 x 31	NYGS	18.00

	14 x 21	IA	5.00
	13 x 20	IA	10.00
4623. Sheep	21 x 28	NYGS	18.00
	16 x 23-1/2	PENN	1.00
4624. Stag in the Woods	21 x 31-1/2	IA	18.00
	14 x 21	IA	10.00
4625. Three Deer	23-1/2 x 31-1/2	NYGS	18.00
4626. Three Horses	18 x 23	HNA	5.95
	10-1/2 x 16	IA	5.00
4627. Tiger	30 x 27	NYGS	18.00
4628. Tower of Blue Horses	29 x 19	NYGS	18.00
	21 x 14	CFA	6.00
4629. Two Deer	22 x 31	CFA	18.00
4630. Two Sheep	19 x 29	NYGS	18.00
4631. Yellow Horses	20 x 31-1/2	NYGS	20.00
MARC, MARIA	German	1877-1955	
4632. Albi	8 x 12	CAC	1.50
4633. Angler's Paradise	25 x 12	CAC	2.50
4634. Avignon	16 x 20	CAC	4.00
4635. Bad Kreuznach	12 x 16	CAC	2.00
	8 x 12	CAC	1.50
4636. Baie de Menton	12 x 16	CAC	2.00
4637. Barche Isola dei Pescatori	8 x 12	CAC	1.50
4638. Basel	8 x 12	CAC	1.50
4639. Beilstein	12 x 16	CAC	2.00
4640. Bern	12 x 8	CAC	1.50
4641. Bernkastel	8 x 12	CAC	1.50
4642. Brook	25 x 12	CAC	2.50
4643. Bruges	12 x 8	CAC	1.50
4644. Chillon	8 x 12	CAC	1.50
4645. Clavadeleralp	8 x 12	CAC	1.50
4646. Coast of Italy	25 x 12	CAC	2.50
4647. Cochem	8 x 12	CAC	1.50
4648. Cordoba	12 x 8	CAC	1.50
4649. Cote D'Azur	8 x 12	CAC	1.50
4650. Cottage in Brittany	25 x 12	CAC	2.50
4651. Country Fair	12 x 25	CAC	2.50
4652. Dents du Midi	8 x 12	CAC	1.50
4653. Dinkelsbuhl	8 x 12	CAC	1.50
4654. Dreamy Corner	25 x 12	CAC	2.50
4655. Eiger Monch Jungfrau von Schynige Platte	16 x 20	CAC	5.00
4656. Erlach	12 x 16	CAC	2.00
4657. Evolene	8 x 12	CAC	1.50
4658. Fair Grounds	12 x 25	CAC	2.50
4659. Farm by the River	16 x 20	CAC	5.00
4660. Firenze	8 x 12	CAC	1.50
4661. Firenze, Palazzo Vecchio	8 x 12	CAC	1.50
4662. Firenze, Ponte Vecchio	8 x 12	CAC	1.50

4663.	Firenze, Panorama	12 x 16	CAC	2.00
4664.	Fluelen	8 x 12	CAC	1.50
4665.	Fribourg	12 x 16	CAC	2.00
4666.	Furstenau	12 x 16	CAC	2.00
4667.	Gandria	12 x 16	CAC	2.00
4668.	Geneve	8 x 12	CAC	1.50
4669.	Granada	12 x 8	CAC	1.50
4670.	Green Valley	14 x 25	CAC	3.00
4671.	Gribourg	12 x 16	CAC	2.00
4672.	Grindelwald	8 x 12	CAC	1.50
4673.	Harbor at Rockport, Mass.	16 x 20	CAC	4.00
4674.	Harbor in Brittany	25 x 12	CAC	2.50
4675.	Heidelberg	8 x 12	CAC	1.50
4676.	Innsbruck	8 x 12	CAC	1.50
4677.	Iserables	8 x 12	CAC	1.50
4678.	Isola Bella Sbocco Sul Lago	8 x 12	CAC	1.50
4679.	Isola Dei Pescatori Barche Alla Rivoca	8 x 12	CAC	1.50
4680.	Isola Dei Pescatori	8 x 12	CAC	1.50
4681.	Jungfrau	8 x 12	CAC	1.50
4682.	Kirmes	12 x 25	CAC	2.50
4683.	Lac Leman	12 x 16	CAC	2.00
4684.	Lago di Como Varenna	8 x 12	CAC	1.50
4685.	Lago di Como Nesso	8 x 12	CAC	1.50
4686.	Ligerz Cieresse	8 x 12	CAC	1.50
4687.	Little Flemish Town	25 x 12	CAC	2.50
4688.	The Lock	16 x 20	CAC	5.00
4689.	Luzern	8 x 12	CAC	1.50
4690.	Mallorca	8 x 12	CAC	1.50
4691.	Maloja	8 x 12	CAC	1.50
4692.	Martiques	16 x 20	CAC	5.00
4693.	Matterhorn	8 x 12	CAC	1.50
4694.	Menton	8 x 12	CAC	1.50
4695.	Michelstadt	8 x 12	CAC	1.50
4696.	Miltenberg	12 x 16	CAC	2.00
4697.	Montreux	8 x 12	CAC	1.50
4698.	Morcote	12 x 8	CAC	1.50
4699.	Morges	8 x 12	CAC	1.50
4700.	Mourillon	8 x 12	CAC	1.50
4701.	Murten	8 x 12	CAC	1.50
4702.	Mythen	8 x 12	CAC	1.50
4703.	Nordlingen	8 x 12	CAC	1.50
4704.	Oberengadin	12 x 16	CAC	2.00
4705.	Old Canal Bridge	25 x 12	CAC	2.50
4706.	Old Manor	14 x 25	CAC	3.00
4707.	Palma de Mallorca	12 x 16	CAC	1.50
4708.	Paris, la Madeleine	8 x 12	CAC	1.50
4709.	Paris, les Bouquinistes	8 x 12	CAC	1.50
4710.	Paris, Montmartre	16 x 20	CAC	5.00

		8 x 12	CAC	1.50
4711.	Paris, Notre Dame	18 x 24	CAC	10.00
		16 x 20	CAC	5.00
		8 x 12	CAC	1.50
4712.	Paris, Place de la Concorde	8 x 12	CAC	1.50
4713.	Paris, Place du Tertre	8 x 12	CAC	1.50
4714.	Pine Trees	25 x 12	CAC	2.50
4715.	Piz Bernina	12 x 16	CAC	2.00
4716.	Piz Roseg	12 x 8	CAC	1.50
4717.	Port Mejean	8 x 12	CAC	1.50
4718.	Quiet Stream	14 x 25	CAC	3.00
4719.	Rivaplana	8 x 12	CAC	1.50
4720.	Riverside Village	14 x 25	CAC	3.00
4721.	Riviera	25 x 12	CAC	2.50
4722.	Roma, Arco di Constantino	8 x 12	CAC	1.50
4723.	Rome, Piazza San Pietro	8 x 12	CAC	1.50
4724.	Rome, Tempie e Chiesa	12 x 16	CAC	2.00
4725.	Rosegtal Piz Roseg und Sellagruppe	16 x 20	CAC	5.00
4726.	Rothenburg	12 x 16	CAC	2.00
		8 x 12	CAC	1.50
4727.	Roundabouts	12 x 25	CAC	2.50
4728.	San Salvatore	8 x 12	CAC	1.50
4729.	Sarlat	12 x 16	CAC	2.00
4730.	Schaffhausen	16 x 12	CAC	2.00
		12 x 8	CAC	1.50
4731.	Sevilla	12 x 8	CAC	1.50
4732.	Small Canal	25 x 12	CAC	2.50
4733.	Solothurn	8 x 12	CAC	1.50
4734.	Southern Coast	14 x 25	CAC	3.00
4735.	Sunny Bay	14 x 25	CAC	3.00
4736.	St. Gallen	8 x 12	CAC	1.50
4737.	St. Luc	12 x 8	CAC	1.50
4738.	St. Moritz Bad	8 x 12	CAC	1.50
4739.	St. Moritz	12 x 8	CAC	1.50
4740.	St. Sophorin	8 x 12	CAC	1.50
4741.	St. Ursanne	12 x 8	CAC	1.50
4742.	Stein Am Rhein	12 x 16	CAC	2.00
4743.	Terrace by the Sea	25 x 12	CAC	2.50
4744.	Thunersee	8 x 12	CAC	1.50
4745.	Toledo	8 x 12	CAC	1.50
4746.	Treib	8 x 12	CAC	1.50
4747.	Urnersee	8 x 12	CAC	1.50
4748.	Vaumarcus	12 x 16	CAC	2.00
4749.	Venezia, Bacinio de San Marco	12 x 14	CAC	4.00
4750.	Venezia, Canale della Giudecca	12 x 14	CAC	4.00

4751. Werdenberg	20 x 30	CAC	18.00
4752. Zermatt	8 x 12	CAC	1.50
4753. Zuoz	12 x 8	CAC	1.50
4754. Zurich	8 x 12	CAC	1.50
MARCHAND, ANDRÉ	French	1877-1951	
4755. Basket of Tomatoes	20 x 25	CAC	15.00
4756. Quinces	18 x 22-1/2	ESH	10.00
MARCOUSSIS, LOUIS C.	Polish	1884-	
4757. Goldfish Bowl	10-1/2 x 30	ESH	15.00
MAREES, HORST DE	German	1896-	
4758. Rowers	27 x 33	NYGS	22.00
4759. St. Martin and the Beggar	37 x 24	NYGS	24.00
MARESCHI, MICHELE	Italian	1696-1743	
4760. Santa Maria della Salute	20 x 30	CFA	15.00
MARGOTTI, FRANCESCO	Italian	c. 1868	
4761. Jesus Sleeping	11 x 13	IA	3.00
MARGOTTON, RENE			
4762. La Pecheuse	26 x 19	RL	15.00
4763. Vase of Canna	30 x 15	RL	15.00
MARGULES, DE HIRSCH	American	1899-	
4764. Fishing Boats	16 x 22-1/2	AR	7.50
MARIANA			
4765. Samplers (4)	9 x 7	AA	2.50 ea.
MARIANI, LEE	American	Contemporary	
4766. Columbus Circle	16 x 24	CFA	15.00
4767. Golden Gate	20 x 26	CAC	15.00
4768. Grand Army Plaza	16 x 24	CFA	15.00
4769. New York Harbour	20 x 24	CAC	15.00
MARIN, JOHN	American	1870-1953	
4770. Adirondacks along Ausable River	8 x 10	NYGS	2.00
4771. Boats and Sea, Deer Island, Maine	12 x 16	CAC	1.50
4772. Broadway Night	12 x 16	CAC	1.50
4773. Cape Split, Maine	15 x 20-1/2	NYGS	7.50
4774. Circus Elephants	19 x 24	NYGS	15.00
4775. Deer Isle Islets, Maine	17 x 20	NYGS	7.50
	12 x 14	NYGS	3.00
4776. Equestrians	8 x 10	NYGS	2.00
4777. Fishermen and Boats	8 x 23	NYGS	12.00
	7 x 23	CAC	16.00
4778. From the Bridge	18 x 21-1/2	PENN	1.00
4779. Going Through the Thoroughfare	8 x 10	NYGS	2.00
4780. Lions in the Ring	8 x 10	NYGS	2.00
4781. Lower Manhattan from the River	21-1/2 x 26	NYGS	15.00
	8 x 10	MMA	.35
4782. Maine Islands	16-1/2 x 19-1/2	NYGS	7.50
	12 x 16	CAC	1.50

	12 x 14	NYGS	3.00
4783. Movement: Boats and Objects, Blue Gray Sea	22 x 28	NYGS	15.00
4784. Movement on the Road	18 x 22	PENN	1.00
4785. Movement No. 2, Related to Down-town	12 x 16	CAC	1.50
4786. New Mexico No. 2, Area Near Taos	12 x 16	CAC	1.50
4787. Peach Trees in Blossom	8 x 10	NYGS	2.00
4788. Phippsburg, Maine	12 x 16	CAC	1.50
4789. Pine Tree	16 x 20	CFA	7.50
4790. Pine Trees, Small Pointe, Maine	16 x 20	IA	7.50
4791. Ramapo River near Suffern, New York	8 x 10	NYGS	2.00
4792. Sunset	15 x 17-1/2	NYGS	5.00
4793. Three-Master	8 x 10	NYGS	2.00
4794. Town in Maine	12 x 16	CAC	1.50
4795. Tunk Mountains, Autumn, Maine	25 x 30	NYGS	15.00
4796. Two-Masters Becalmed	12 x 16	CAC	1.50
4797. Women and Sea	8 x 10	NYGS	2.00
MARINI, MARINO	Italian	1901-	
4798. Cavallo	23 x 17	CFA	12.00
4799. Departure	24 x 16-1/2	NYGS	15.00
4800. Due Cavalieri	23 x 17	CFA	12.00
4801. Giocollieri	23 x 17	CFA	12.00
4802. Horse and Acrobat	22-1/2 x 16	ESH	10.00
4803. Horseman	24 x 18	NYGS	15.00
4804. Horse on Red Ground	28 x 21	CFA	25.00
4805. Red Rider	28 x 20	CFA	15.00
	27-1/2 x 19	IA	15.00
4806. Rider	22-1/2 x 18	E SH	10.00
MARIO DEI FIORI (NUZZI, MARIO) Italian		1603-1673	
4807. Flowers and Fruit	8 x 30	IA	10.00
4808. Fruit	8 x 30	IA	10.00
MARMA, R.			
4809. Florence, Mercato dell' Pulci	11 x 14	AL	5.00
4810. Florence, Mercato di S. Piero	11 x 14	AL	5.00
4811. Florence, Piazza S. Spirito	20 x 7	AL	5.00
4812. Florence, Ponte Vecchio	11 x 14	AL	5.00
4813. Florence, La Sinagoga	20 x 7	AL	5.00
4814. Florence, Via Alzani	11 x 14	AL	5.00

4815. Florence, Via Orivolo	20 x 7	AL	5.00
4816. Florence, Volta dei Tintori	11 x 14	AL	5.00
MARMION, SIMON	French	c. 1425-1489	
4817. Christ of Piety	10 x 8	ESH	1.00
4818. Virgin of Sorrows	10 x 8	ESH	1.00
MARQUET, ALBERT	French	1875-1947	
4819. Barques a La Rochelle	21-1/2 x 26	NYGS	15.00
4820. Beach at Les Sables D'Olonne	18 x 22-1/2	ESH	10.00
4821. Boat Scene	20 x 24	PENN	1.00
4822. Bridge at Michel	17 x 22	CAC	10.00
4823. Colours at Naples	18 x 23	ESH	10.00
4824. Ete, La Plage des Sables	19-1/2 x 24	PENN	1.00
4825. Harbour of Naples	8 x 10	ESH	1.00
4826. Ile de France	21 x 26	CFA	12.00
4827. Notre Dame	18 x 22-1/2	NYGS	10.00
	8 x 6	CFA	1.00
4828. Paris in Autumn	23 x 18	CAC	12.00
4829. Paris in Grey Weather	18 x 23	CAC	12.00
4830. Paris in Winter	18 x 23	CFA	12.00
4831. Paris, Pont Saint Michel	17 x 22	CAC	10.00
	8 x 10	ESH	1.00
4832. Plage de Fecamp	20 x 24	PENN	1.00
4833. Pont Neuf	19-1/2 x 24	NYGS	12.00
	18 x 22	CAC	7.50
4834. Pont Neuf au Soleil	17 x 23	NYGS	16.00
4835. Port D'Audierne	21 x 26	NYGS	15.00
4836. Port du Havre	15 x 18	CAC	5.00
4837. Port of Algiers	21 x 25-1/2	NYGS	12.00
4838. River Landscape	18 x 23	HNA	5.95
4839. Road to LaFrette	24 x 30	CAC	15.00
	8 x 10	ESH	1.00
4840. Sailboats at La Rochelle	13 x 13	CFA	5.00
4841. St. Gervais Church, Paris	19 x 23	CFA	15.00
4842. Seascape	19 x 25	CFA	10.00
4843. The Seine near Poissy	18 x 22-1/2	ESH	10.00
	8 x 10	ESH	1.00
MARSH, REGINALD	American	1898-1954	
4844. High Yaller	20 x 15	NYGS	7.50
4845. Wooden Horses	6 x 10	NYGS	.50
MARSHALL			
4846. Cocks (2) Peace War	21 x 15-1/2	AA	10.00 ea.
MARSHALL, G.			
4847. Spring	21 x 16	IA	3.50

MARSHALL, WILLIAM E.	American	1837-1906	
4848. Abraham Lincoln	21 x 15-1/2	NYGS	15.00
MARSTON, ST. CLAIR	English	1886-	
4849. Afternoon, Tuscany	19 x 22-1/2	RL	7.50
4850. Bluebell Time	20 x 24	CFA	10.00
4851. Corfe Castle	16 x 24	CAC	6.00
4852. Delphiniums	16 x 12	CAC	1.75
4853. Trossachs, Loc Achray	22-1/2 x 19	RL	6.00
MARTELLINI, GASPARE	Italian	1785-1857	
4854. Head of a Girl	15 x 11	IA	3.00
4855. Barges on the Seine	18 x 24	CAC	7.50
4856. View of the Seine	17 x 24	PENN	1.00
MARTIN, FLETCHER	American	1904-	
4857. Clown Act	11-1/2 x 15-1/2	NYGS	10.00
MARTIN, HOMER	American	1836-1897	
4858. Harp of the Winds	22 x 31	NYGS	12.00
	15-1/2 x 22	NYGS	7.50
	8 x 10	NYGS	.50
MARTINEZ, ALFREDO RAMOS	Mexican	1872-1946	
4859. Flower Vendors	11 x 18	AR	3.00
MARTINI, FRANCESCO See FRANCESCO DI GIORGIO MARTINI			
MARTINI, JOSEPH DE	American	1896-	
4860. Moonlight	11 x 20	NYGS	5.00
4861. The Road to Calvary	10 x 8	ESH	1.00
MARTINI, SIMONE	Italian	1284-1344	
4862. Angel	15 x 11	IA	3.00
4863. Angel	16 x 12	IA	3.00
4864. Annunciata	15 x 11	IA	3.00
4865. Annunciation	11 x 13	IA	3.00
4866. Angel--Detail of No. 4865	15 x 11	IA	3.00
4867. Crucifixion and Saints	16 x 8	IA	3.00
4868. Giudoriccio of Fogliano	6 x 16	IA	3.00
4869. Detail of No. 4868	11 x 15	IA	3.00
4870. Madonna	15 x 11	IA	3.00
4871. Madonna and Child	16 x 11	IA	3.00
4872. Madonna Enthroned and Saints	15 x 10	IA	3.00
4873. St. Clare	15 x 11	IA	3.00
4874. St. Dominic	15 x 12	IA	3.00
4875. St. Francis	15 x 10	IA	3.00
MASON, FRANK W.			
4876. Heading for Home	15 x 23	CFA	7.50
4877. Homeward Bound	15 x 23	CFA	7.50
MASON, ROY M.	American	1886-	
4878. Falcon's Nest	21-1/2 x 30	IA	12.00
4879. Fisherman's Hangout	14-1/2 x 20	IA	7.50
4880. Gleaners	21-1/2 x 30	IA	12.00
4881. Montezuma Marshes	21-1/2 x 30	IA	12.00

173 Masaccio (Guidi, Tommaso)

4882. Open Season	21-1/2 x 30	IA	12.00
4883. Piney Creek	21-1/2 x 30	IA	12.00
4884. Pintail Point	21-1/2 x 30	IA	12.00
4885. The Ritz	21-1/2 x 30	IA	12.00
4886. Three Mallards	13 x 18	PENN	1.00
MASACCIO (GUIDI, TOMMASO)	Italian	1401-1428	
4887. Crucifixion	10 x 7	NYGS	.50
4888. Expulsion from Paradise	15 x 8	IA	3.00
	10 x 4	NYGS	.50
4889. Head of St. John	15 x 10	IA	3.00
4890. St. Anne, Madonna and Child with Angels	15 x 9	IA	3.00
4891. St. Peter and St. John Almsgiving	15 x 10	IA	3.00
4892. Woman and Child-- Detail of No. 4891.	15 x 9	IA	3.00
4893. St. Peter Healing the Sick	15 x 10	IA	3.00
4894. Tribute Money	19 x 25	AA	10.00
	15 x 22	NYGS	4.00
	10 x 15	IA	3.00
	4 x 10	NYGS	.50

MASSI, GENTILE   See   GENTILE DA FABRIANO

MASSON, ANDRÉ	French	1896-	
4895. House of the Vestals	22 x 26-1/2	ESH	12.00
MASSON, HENRI	Belgian (Res. Canada)	1907-	
4896. Gaspé Village	23 x 31	CFA	18.00
MASSYS, CORNELIS	Flemish	1508-1575	
4897. Arrival in Bethlehem	21 x 29-1/2	NYGS	15.00
	15-1/2 x 22	NYGS	7.50
	5-1/2 x 7-1/2	NYGS	.50
MASSYS, JAN	Flemish	1505-1575	
4898. Portrait of Andrea Doria	15 x 10	IA	3.00

MASSYS, QUENTIN See METSYS, QUENTIN

MASTER OF COLOGNE			
4899. Madonna with Sweet Pea	21 x 13-1/2	NYGS	18.00
MASTER OF THE FEMALE HALF-LENGTH			
4900. Portrait of a Lady	20 x 15	NYGS	7.50
MASTER OF THE HALF-LENGTH			
4901. Three Musical Ladies	21 x 19	IA	15.00
MASTER OF THE LIFE OF MARY			
4902. Annunciation	29 x 35	NYGS	24.00
	18 x 23	HNA	5.95
	16-1/2 x 20	IA	4.00
MATHIEU, PAUL	Belgian	1872-1932	
4903. Les Capetiens Partout	15 x 30	ESH	15.00
MATISSE, HENRI	French	1859-1954	
4904. Amber Necklace	10 x 8	ESH	1.00

4905.	Anemones	25 x 31-1/2	NYGS	18.00
4906.	Anemones by the Window	22 x 18	CAC	10.00
4907.	Apples on a Pink Tablecloth	23 x 28	NYGS	12.00
		22 x 28	AA	15.00
		22-1/2 x 27	PENN	1.00
4908.	Asphodeles	30 x 23	NYGS	18.00
		10 x 8	ESH	1.00
4909.	Blossoming Garden	19 x 24	CFA	12.00
4910.	La Blouse Roumaine	24 x 18-1/2	PENN	1.00
4911.	Blue Nude	13 x 20	PENN	1.00
4912.	Blue Room	21-1/2 x 18	NYGS	15.00
4913.	Blue Window	25-1/2 x 17	MMA	10.00
4914.	Les Capucines a la Danse	8 x 10	ESH	1.00
4915.	Carnival in Nice	15 x 23	CFA	12.00
4916.	Coffee	11 x 7	NYGS	.50
4917.	Conversation Piece	18-1/2 x 22	ESH	10.00
4918.	Corner of the Studio	8 x 10	ESH	1.00
4919.	La Danse	18 x 12	NYGS	8.00
4920.	Fauve Landscape	8 x 10	ESH	1.00
4921.	Femme aux Anemones	14-1/2 x 20-1/2	NYGS	10.00
4922.	Flower Petals	11 x 47	NYGS	20.00
4923.	Flowers and Fruits	24 x 19	CFA	15.00
4924.	Girl Reading	20 x 24	CFA	15.00
4925.	Girl with Anemones	24 x 30	DAC	8.00
		20 x 24	PENN	1.00
		11 x 14	DAC	2.80
4926.	Girl with Anemones	24 x 20	CFA	15.00
		10 x 8	ESH	1.00
4927.	Goldfish	17 x 14	CAC	10.00
4928.	Le Grand Atelier	20 x 24	NYGS	10.00
		8 x 10	ESH	1.00
4929.	Grand Interieur Rouge	22 x 14-1/2	NYGS	12.00
4930.	Green Pumpkin	32 x 26	CAC	18.00
4931.	Idol	20 x 24	DAC	6.00
		19 x 24	CAC	15.00
4932.	Interior in Nice	6 x 8	CFA	1.00
4933.	Interior with Black Fern	22-1/2 x 17	ESH	10.00
4934.	Interior with Egyptian Curtain	22-1/2 x 17	ESH	10.00
4935.	Interior with Flowers	24 x 15	PENN	1.00
4936.	Large Studio	8 x 10	ESH	1.00
4937.	Marguerite Reading	18 x 23	HNA	5.95
4938.	La Nappe Rose	19 x 26	NYGS	15.00
4939.	Narcissi and Fruit	24 x 19-1/2	NYGS	12.00
4940.	Odalisque	21 x 14	NYGS	18.00
4941.	Open Window, Collioure	10 x 8	ESH	1.00
4942.	Piano Lesson	8 x 10	MMA	.35

4943.	Pineapple and Anemones	8 x 10	MMA	.35
4944.	Plum Blossoms' Green	26 x 20	DAC	6.00
4945.	Portfolio (23)		NYGS	7.50 set
			or	.50 ea

Amber Necklace	8 x 6	
Blue Dress in Ochre Armchair	8 x 6	
Cap D'Antibes Road	6 x 8	
Conversation Piece	6 x 8	
Decoration Figure	8 x 6	
Embroidered Blouse	8 x 6	
Luxury, Calm and Delight	8 x 5	
Mandolin Player	7 x 6	
My Room in Ajaccio	6 x 8	
Odalisque with Red Coffer	6 x 8	
The Piano	7 x 6	
Purple Dress	8 x 5	
Recumbent Nude	6 x 8	
Recumbent Odalisque	6 x 7	
Spanish Girl	8 x 3	
Still Life, Green Buffet	6 x 8	
Still Life with Oranges	7 x 6	
Studio Interior	7 x 6	
Three Sisters	8 x 6	
Window in Nice	8 x 6	
Young Girl with Anemones	8 x 6	
Yellow Hat	8 x 6	
Young Sailor with Cap	8 x 6	

4946.	Purple Robe	20 x 16	PENN	1.00
4947.	Red Studio	8 x 10	MMA	.35
4948.	Reverie	25 x 20	CFA	15.00
4949.	Still Life	27-1/2 x 34	IA	20.00
4950.	Still Life	20 x 24	PENN	1.00
				1.98 (Pr.)
4951.	Still Life by the Window	22 x 18-1/2	ESH	10.00
4952.	Still Life, Flowers and Fruit	18 x 23	HNA	5.95
4953.	Still Life with Asphodels	8 x 10	ESH	1.00

4954. Still Life with Dahlias	19 x 24	PENN	1.00
	8 x 10	ESH	1.00
4955. Still Life with Goldfish	24 x 15	NYGS	10.00
4956. Still Life with Green Carpet	17-1/2 x 22-1/2	ESH	10.00
4957. Still Life with Lemons	16 x 19	NYGS	7.50
4958. Still Life with Magnolia	20 x 28	CFA	15.00
4959. Still Life with Oysters	18 x 23	HNA	5.95
4960. Still Life with Peaches	18 x 23	CAC	15.00
4961. Still Life with Pineapple	22 x 28	AA	15.00
4962. Studio with La Danse	10 x 8	ESH	1.00
4963. Tabac Royal	24 x 30	DAC	8.00
	21 x 26	HNA	5.95
	11 x 14	DAC	2.80
4964. Two Young Girls	24 x 20	PENN	1.00
4965. White Dress	15 x 19	CFA	7.50
4966. Woman and Aquarium	8 x 10	CAC	1.50
4967. Yellow Chair	19 x 23	CAC	15.00
4968. Young Sailor with Cap	10 x 8	ESH	1.00
MATTA, ROBERTO	Chilean (Res. U.S.)	1912-	
4969. Listen to Living	8 x 10	MMA	.35
4970. Who's Who	23 x 29-1/2	NYGS	15.00
MATTEO DI GIOVANNI	Italian	1435-1495	
4971. St. Barbara	15 x 11	IA	3.00
4972. St. Magdalene	16 x 12	IA	3.00
MATTHEW, K.			
4973. Autumn Glory	23 x 32	NYGS	7.50
4974. Spring Idyll	23 x 32	NYGS	7.50
4975. Summer Vista	23 x 32	NYGS	7.50
4976. Winter's Dreamland	23 x 32	NYGS	7.50
MATTHEWS			
4977. Abraham Lincoln	10 x 8	NYGS	.50
MAURER, ALFRED HENRY	American	1868-1932	
4978. Outside the Town	18 x 23	CAC	7.50
4979. Still Life with Doily	17-1/2 x 21	NYGS	12.00
MAUVE, ANTON RUDOLF	Dutch	1838-1888	
4980. Spring	9 x 14	CAC	2.50
MAX, GABRIEL	Austrian	1840-1915	
4981. Christ Healing the Sick Child	13 x 8	CAC	1.50
4982. St. Veronica's Veil	22 x 17-1/2	IA	7.50
	20 x 16	IA	5.00
	12 x 9	AL	1.00
	11 x 9	IA	1.75
MAYNO, FARY JUAN	Spanish	1569-1649	
4983. Adoration of the Magi	8 x 10	NYGS	.50
MAZETTI			
4984. Austria	8 x 12	CAC	1.50
4985. Chillon	12 x 16	CAC	2.00
4986. Glerolles	12 x 16	CAC	2.00
4987. Matterhorn	12 x 16	CAC	2.00
4988. Monte Rosa	12 x 16	CAC	2.00

4989. Zermatt	12 x 8	CAC	1.50

MAZZOLA, FRANCESCO See PARMIGIANINO
MAZZONOVITCH

4990. April the 20th	16 x 16	CAC	6.00

MC EWEN

4991. Judgement of Paris	8 x 10	NYGS	.50
4992. With Grandma	8 x 10	NYGS	.50

MC FEE, HENRY LEE   American   1886-1953

4993. Still Life: Apples	20 x 15	NYGS	5.00

MC GILL

4994. Blue Bonnets	22 x 28	CAC	7.50

MC GINNIS, EVELYN

4995. Desert Calm	18 x 36	AA	12.00
4996. Desert Mood (2)	24 x 8	AA	3.00 ea.
4997. Desert Mood (2)	8 x 24	AA	3.00 ea.
4998. Desert Peace	18 x 36	AA	12.00
4999. Heart of the Desert	15 x 30	AA	7.50
5000. Palo Verde Tree in the Desert	18 x 36	AA	12.00
5001. Smoke Tree in the Desert	18 x 36	AA	12.00
5002. Sunlight and Shadows in the Desert	15 x 30	AA	7.50

MC GONIGAL, M.

5003. Sunlit Waters	16 x 20-1/2	RL	3.50
5004. Waiting for the Tide	16 x 20-1/2	RL	3.50

MC GREGOR, WILLIAM   English   Contemporary

5005. Ben Lomond from Loch Ard	15 x 28	RL	6.00
5006. Loch Leven	18 x 24	RL	6.00
5007. Loch Long	18 x 24	RL	6.00
5008. Off the Coast of Arran	15 x 28	RL	6.00

MC KNIGHT, DODGE   American   1860-1950

5009. Winter Landscape	14 x 18	CFA	6.00

MEDICI

5010. Agate Cup	10 x 8	NYGS	1.50
5011. Cosimo II de Medici	10 x 8	NYGS	1.50
5012. Cup with Hercules	10 x 8	NYGS	1.50
5013. Gold Flask	10 x 8	NYGS	1.50
5014. Jewel Case	10 x 8	NYGS	1.50
5015. Lapis Lazuli Vase	10 x 8	NYGS	1.50
5016. Red Jaspar	10 x 8	NYGS	1.50
5017. Rock Crystal	10 x 8	NYGS	1.50
5018. Silver Ewer	10 x 8	NYGS	1.50
5019. Tiberio	10 x 8	NYGS	1.50
5020. Venus and Cupid	10 x 8	NYGS	1.50

MEEK, THOMAS

5021. Column Marcus Aurelius	22-1/2 x 16-1/2	AL	10.00
5022. Forum of Trajan and Church of S. Maria	22-1/2 x 16-1/2	AL	10.00
5023. Grand Central, N. Y.	17 x 26	AL	10.00

5024. Madison Square Park	26 x 17	AL	10.00
5025. Piazza San Pietro	22-1/2 x 16-1/2	AL	10.00
5026. Public Library	26 x 17	AL	10.00
5027. S. Maria Trastavere	22-1/2 x 16-1/2	AL	10.00
MEGARGEE, LON	American	1886-	
5028. Cowboy and his Lady	13 x 16	NYGS	3.00
5029. Desert Song	13 x 16	NYGS	3.00
5030. Donkey Business	12 x 18	NYGS	3.00
5031. Home on the Ranch	16 x 20	NYGS	5.00
	12 x 15	NYGS	3.00
5032. Saturday Night on the Ranch	16 x 20	NYGS	5.00
	12 x 15	NYGS	3.00
5033. What's Up	12 x 18	NYGS	3.00
MELOZZO DA FORLI	Italian	1438-1494	
5034. Angel Announcing	15 x 8	IA	3.00
5035. Arch Angel Gabriel	27 x 14	CFA	12.00
5036. Sixtus IV Appoints Platina his Librarian	15 x 11	IA	3.00
5037. Il Cardinale Giuliano della Rovere--Detail of No. 5036	15 x 11	IA	3.00
5038. The Platina--Detail of No. 5036	15 x 11	IA	3.00
MEISSONIER, JEAN LOUIS ERNEST French		1815-1891	
5039. Halting at an Inn	8 x 10	CAC	1.00
5040. Soldiers Gambling	8 x 10	CAC	1.00
MELLIN			
5041. Western Horses (4)	8 x 10	DAC	.60 ea.
MEMLING, HANS	Flemish	1433-1494	
5042. Adoration of the Magi	8 x 8	NYGS	.50
5043. Barbara van Vlanderbergh	9 x 7	NYGS	.50
5044. Crucifixion	14 x 11	IA	3.00
5045. Madonna and Child	10 x 8	NYGS	.50
5046. Madonna and Child Enthroned	26-1/2 x 18	NYGS	20.00
5047. Madonna and Child with Angels	20 x 16	NYGS	10.00
	10 x 8	NYGS	.50
5048. Portrait of a Man	10 x 7	NYGS	.50
5049. Portrait of Unknown Man	13 x 9	IA	3.00
5050. Portrait of Unknown Man	10 x 7	IA	3.00
5051. Portrait of a Young Man	15 x 10-1/2	NYGS	7.50
5052. Saint Benedict	15 x 11	IA	3.00
5053. Virgin Enthroned and Two Angels	15 x 11	IA	3.00
5054. Young Man at Prayer	10 x 8	NYGS	.50

MEMMI, LIPPO	Italian	1317-1347	
5055. Crucifixion and Saints	16 x 8	IA	3.00
5056. Madonna Enthroned and Saints	10 x 15	IA	3.00
5057. St. Dominic	15 x 12	IA	3.00
MENABONI, ATHOS	American	Ac. 1959	
5058. Cardinal	18 x 14	CAC	12.00
5059. Red-Winged Blackbird	18 x 14	CAC	12.00
MENGS, ANTON RAPHAEL	German	1728-1774	
5060. Rest on the Flight to Egypt	19 x 25-1/2	IA	10.00
MENZ			
5061. Commerce	19 x 23	CFA	7.50
MENZEL, ADOLPH VON	German	1815-1905	
5062. Flute Concert	20 x 29	CFA	12.00
5063. Garden of Ministry	13 x 21	AR	10.00
5064. Round Table	24 x 20	NYGS	7.50
MEO DE SIENA	Italian	1345-1370	
5065. Madonna and Child	15 x 9	IA	3.00
MERCKER, ERICH	German	1891-	
5066. Furnace	25 x 34	CFA	15.00
5067. Industry	26 x 34	CFA	15.00
MERISI, MICHELANGELO See CARAVAGGIO			
MERILL, WILLIAM			
5068. Moppets (4)	12 x 30	DAC	4.00 ea.
	6 x 15	DAC	1.20 ea.
MERTE, OSCAR			
5069. Across the Field	23-1/2 x 37	NYGS	12.00
MERYON			
5070. San Francisco	7 x 37	CAC	15.00
METCALF, WILLARD	American	1858-1925	
5071. Golden Carnival	28 x 31	NYGS	12.00
5072. Icebound	8 x 10	NYGS	.50
METELLI, ORNEURE	Italian	1872-1938	
5073. Public Gardens at Terni	18 x 27	CFA	12.00
METLI			
5074. Calla Lilies	22 x 18	CAC	12.00
METSU, GABRIEL	Dutch	1629-1667	
5075. Letter Reader	20-1/2 x 16	NYGS	10.00
5076. Letter Writer	20-1/2 x 16	NYGS	10.00
5077. Violoncello Player	22 x 17	CAC	15.00
METSYS, JAN See MASSYS, JAN			
METSYS, QUENTIN	Flemish	1466-1530	
5078. Pawn-Broker and his Wife	11 x 11	IA	3.00
5079. Portrait of Erasmus	15 x 11	IA	3.00
5080. Portrait of Pierre Gilles	15 x 11	IA	3.00
5081. Virgin and Child	15 x 10	IA	3.00
MEULEN, PIETER VANDER			
5082. Royal Hunt	30 x 35-1/2	NYGS	10.00

MEUNIER, CONSTANTIN	Belgian	1831-1905	
5083. Courting Days	19 x 16	CAC	5.00
5084. Wedding Bells	19 x 16	CAC	5.00
MEYER-EBERHARDT, CURT	German	1895-	
5085. Fawn Standing	15 x 11-1/2	IA	10.00
5086. Winter Worries	18 x 17	CAC	10.00
5087. Young Foal	12 x 10	IA	10.00
MICHELANGELO BUONARROTI	Italian	1475-1564	
5088. Adam et Eve	11 x 7-1/2	NYGS	4.00
5089. Creation of Adam			
(or Man)	22 x 46	IA	18.00
	5 x 11	IA	1.75
5090. Cumean Sibylle	11 x 8	IA	1.75
5091. Daniel, Prophet (Head)	11 x 8	IA	1.75
5092. David (Marble)	15 x 11	IA	3.00
5093. Delphic Sibylle	24 x 17-1/2	IA	12.00
	10 x 8	IA	1.75
5094. Head--Detail of No.			
5093	11 x 8	IA	1.75
	10 x 8	NYGS	.50
5095. Eritrian Sibylle			
(Head)	11 x 8	IA	1.75
5096. Ezekiel, Prophet			
(Head)	11 x 8	IA	1.75
5097. Holy Family	11" circle	IA	3.00
	8 x 10	NYGS	.50
5098. Isaiah, Prophet	24 x 17-1/2	IA	12.00
	11 x 8	IA	1.75
5099. Head--Detail of No.			
5098	10 x 7-1/2	IA	1.75
5100. Jeremiah, Prophet			
(Head)	11 x 8	IA	1.75
	10 x 8	NYGS	.50
5101. Libyan Sibylle	11 x 8	IA	1.75
5102. Male Torso	15 x 11	AR	4.00
5103. Mater Dolorosa	20 x 16	NYGS	7.50
5104. Pieta	28 x 22	NYGS	12.00
	14 x 11	NYGS	3.00
	9 x 11	CFA	3.50
5105. Sixtine Chapel			
(Central Part of			
Ceiling)	15 x 11	IA	3.00
5106. Study	16 x 9	AR	4.00
MICHELINO DI BESOZZO	Italian	15th Century	
5107. Marriage of St.			
Catherine	15 x 11	IA	3.00
MIERIS, FRANZ VAN	Dutch	1635-1681	
5108. Charlatan	14 x 10	IA	3.00
5109. Repast of Two Old			
People	13 x 11	IA	3.00
MIGNARD, PIERRE	French	1612-1695	
5110. Madonna of the Grapes	24 x 18	IA	7.50
	14 x 11	IA	3.00

	10-1/2 x 9	IA	1.75
	10 x 8	ESH	1.00
MILBOURNE, CHARLES			
5111. Government House	17 x 22	PENN	1.00
MILLAIS, JOHN FRANCOIS	French	1815-1875	
5112. Boyhood of Raleigh	8 x 9	NYGS	.50
MILLER, MARY			
5113. Peace Rose	20 x 16	IA	4.00
5114. Quiet Moment	30 x 24	IA	15.00
5115. Rose Bouquet	20 x 16	IA	4.00
	12 x 9	IA	1.50
MILLET, JEAN FRANCOIS	French	1814-1875	
5116. Angelus	20 x 24	IA	7.50
	11 x 14	IA	3.00
	10-1/2 x 14	NYGS	3.00
	8-1/2 x 11	IA	1.75
	7-1/2 x 9	IA	.50
5117. La Becqueé	10-1/2 x 8	NYGS	4.00
5118. Bringing Home the Newborn Calf	8 x 10	NYGS	.50
5119. Bundlers	11 x 13	IA	3.00
5120. Feeding her Birds	8 x 10	NYGS	.50
5121. First Steps	8 x 10	NYGS	.50
5122. Girl Gleaner	15-1/2 x 12	AR	4.00
5123. Gleaner	16 x 12	CFA	4.00
5124. Gleaners	17-1/2 x 23-1/2	IA	7.50
	11 x 14	IA	3.00
	10-1/2 x 14	NYGS	3.00
	8-1/2 x 11	IA	1.75
	8 x 10	IA	.50
5125. Guardian of the Flock	8 x 10	NYGS	.50
5126. Knitting Lesson	8 x 10	NYGS	.50
5127. Man with a Hoe	14-1/2 x 18	IA	3.00
5128. Shepherdess with her Sheep	11 x 14	IA	3.00
5129. Sower	8 x 10	NYGS	.50
5130. Spinner: Goat-Herdess of the Auvergne	14 x 11	IA	3.00
5131. Woman Churning	8 x 10	NYGS	.50
MILNE, MAC LAUGHLAN	Scotch	Contemporary	
5132. Sannox Bay, Arran	18 x 21-1/2	RL	6.00
MINAMI, KUNZO	Japanese	1883-1950	
5133. Crane and Fancy	24 x 18	PENN	1.00
5134. Odd Birds Bathing	24 x 18	PENN	1.00
5135. Odd Birds in a Tree	24 x 18	PENN	1.00
5136. Weathervane Crane	24 x 18	PENN	1.00
MINAUX, ANDRÉ	French	1923-	
5137. Landscape, Ile de France	22-1/2 x 18	ESH	10.00
5138. Pastry Cook	22-1/2 x 16	ESH	10.00
MIRIMAO			
5139. Fleurs des Champs	18-1/2 x 15	NYGS	12.00

MIRO, JOAN	Spanish	1893-	
5140. Birds' Wings Glide over the Moon	10 x 8	ESH	1.00
5141. Catalan Landscape	8 x 10	MMA	.35
5142. Comets	10 x 31-1/2	PENN	1.00
5143. Composition	19-1/2 x 14	ESH	10.00
5144. Composition, 1933	20 x 22	AR	12.00
5145. Composition, 1950	13-1/2 x 18	AR	12.00
5146. Dog Barking at the Moon	18 x 23	HNA	5.95
	16 x 20	MMA	6.00
	8 x 10	AR	2.00
5147. Femmes, Oiseau au Claire de Lune	23 x 18-1/2	NYGS	12.00
5148. Fighting Cock	16 x 12	AR	5.00
	10 x 8	AR	2.00
5149. Figures under the Moon	20 x 16	AR	5.00
5150. Fragment	9 x 29-1/2	PENN	1.00
5151. Fragment of a Triptych	26 x 20	PENN	1.00
5152. Fresco, 1951	10 x 31	AR	12.00
5153. Harlequin's Carnival	16 x 22-1/2	ESH	10.00
	8 x 10	MMA	.35
5154. Man, Woman and Child	23 x 30	NYGS	15.00
5155. Maternity	24 x 19	AR	10.00
5156. Menagerie	20 x 28	CFA	15.00
5157. Moon	12 x 16	AR	5.00
	8 x 10	AR	2.00
5158. Mural	8 x 39	CAC	15.00
5159. Nursery Decorations	6 x 24	AR	5.00
5160. Personage Throwing a Stone at a Bird	8 x 10	MMA	.35
5161. Personnages and Blue Moon	16 x 20	CFA	7.50
5162. Personnages Orageux	18 x 22-1/2	ESH	10.00
5163. Portrait 1	23-2/2 x 18-1/2	PENN	1.00
5164. Potato	8 x 10	MMA	.35
5165. Rays of the Sun	18 x 25	CAC	7.50
5166. Rooster	17 x 12	CAC	6.00
5167. Le Soleil	25 x 19	CAC	12.00
5168. Sun	12 x 16	AR	5.00
	8 x 10	AR	2.00
5169. Woman and Birds in Front of the Sun	21 x 15	IA	7.50
5170. Woman and Bird in the Night	6 x 24	AR	5.00
5171. Woman, Birds and Moon	21 x 17	CFA	12.00
5172. Woman, Birds and Stars	21 x 30	NYGS	16.00

MITCHELL, BRUCE	American	1908-	
5173. Fire Island Landing	12-1/2 x 19	NYGS	5.00
5174. My Hideaway	24 x 30	AA	10.00
5175. Spring Breakup in			
the Laurentians	24 x 30	AA	10.00
MITCHELL, JAMES	English	1902-	
5176. Close Ashore	15 x 30	DAC	4.00
5177. Land's End	24 x 48	DAC	10.00
5178. Off the Highlands	15 x 30	DAC	4.00
5179. Out Islands Schooner	15 x 30	DAC	4.00
5180. Tropic Landfall	15 x 30	DAC	4.00
MIXER			
5181. Palomino	21 x 16	CFA	7.50
5182. Quarter Horse	21 x 16	CFA	7.50
MODERSOHN-BECKER			
5183. Still Life	18 x 23	HNA	5.95
MODIGLIANI, AMADEO	Italian	1884-1920	
5184. Algerian	22 x 13	CFA	12.00
5185. Boy in Blue	23 x 14	AA	10.00
5186. Caryatid	21 x 17	ESH	10.00
	10 x 8	ESH	1.00
5187. Girl in Pink	21 x 15-1/2	AA	7.50
5188. Girl with Black Tie	22-1/2 x 17	ESH	10.00
5189. Girl with Braids	26 x 21	HNA	5.95
5190. Grocer's Daughter	7 x 6	CFA	1.00
5191. Gypsy Woman and			
Child	24 x 15	NYGS	10.00
	23 x 18	HNA	5.95
5192. Jeanne	26 x 16	CAC	12.00
5193. Lolotte	24 x 15	PENN	1.00
5194. Madame Zboroski	21 x 16	NYGS	7.50
5195. Peasant Boy	16 x 10	AR	3.00
5196. Portfolio (4)	16 x 10	PENN	2.98 set
Mme. Amedee			
Mme. Kisling			
Woman with Baby			
Woman with Red Hair			
5197. Portrait	18 x 12-1/2	NYGS	8.00
5198. Portrait of a Woman	9 x 7	NYGS	.50
5199. Portrait of a Young			
Woman	23 x 18	HNA	5.95
5200. Portrait of Jeanne			
Hebuterne	26-1/2 x 17-1/2	NYGS	18.00
5201. Portrait of Mme.			
Hebuterne	23 x 14	ESH	10.00
5202. Reclining Nude	21-1/2 x 32	NYGS	15.00
	20 x 30	ESH	15.00
	17 x 26	CAC	15.00
	17 x 23	IA	12.00
5203. Seated Nude	22-1/2 x 14-1/2	ESH	10.00
	10 x 8	ESH	1.00
5204. Self-Portrait	10 x 8	ESH	1.00
5205. Two Lovers	24 x 19	PENN	1.00

5206.	Woman with a Baby	24 x 15	PENN	1.00
				1.98 (Pr.)
5207.	Woman with a Collar	22-1/2 x 15	ESH	10.00
5208.	Woman with Red Hair	24 x 15	PENN	1.00
				1.98 (Pr.)
5209.	Young Woman of Montmartre	14 x 11	DAC	2.80
5210.	Young Woman with Earrings	10 x 8	ESH	1.00

MOESLER

| 5211. | Birth of the Flag | 30 x 40 | CFA | 15.00 |

MOLLENHAUER, ERNST

| 5212. | Harbour at East Lake | 27 x 23 | ESH | 10.00 |
| 5213. | Landscape North Sea | 27 x 22 | ESH | 12.00 |

MONACO, LORENZO (FRA LORENZO DEGLI ANGELI) See
LORENZO MONACO

MONAHAN, HUGH C.

5214.	Evening Glow	20 x 24	RL	7.50
5215.	Greylag on the Loch	16 x 24	RL	7.50
5216.	Mallard, Anglesay	16 x 24	RL	7.50
5217.	Pink Feet near Griffel	16x 24	RL	7.50

MONDRIAN, PIET   Dutch   1872-1944

5218.	Broadway Boogie Woogie	8 x 10	MMA	.35
5219.	Composition in Grey, Blue, Red and Yellow	8 x 10	MMA	.35
5220.	Opposition of Lines, Red and Yellow	17 x 13	NYGS	10.00
5221.	Painting 1, 1921	19 x 12	AR	7.50
5222.	Trafalgar Square	21 x 17	MMA	6.00

MONET, CLAUDE   French   1840-1926

5223.	Anemones	10 x 8	ESH	1.00
5224.	Argenteuil	12 x 16	AA	3.00
5225.	Autumn at Argenteuil	20 x 27	NYGS	18.00
5226.	Banks of the Seine, Vetheuil	22 x 30	NYGS	16.00
5227.	Le Bassin d'Argenteuil	22 x 29	CFA	12.00
		18 x 26	DAC	6.00
		16 x 22-1/2	ESH	10.00
		8 x 10	ESH	1.00
5228.	Beach at Saint-Adresse	22 x 30	AA	15.00
		15 x 20	IA	5.00
5229.	Boat Races at Argenteuil	22 x 29	CFA	12.00
5230.	Beach at Trouville	22 x 26	CFA	12.00
		18 x 22	PENN	1.00
5231.	Boating on the Epte	11 x 12	IA	3.00
5232.	Boats and Regatta at Argenteuil	18 x 30	ESH	15.00

5233.	Boats at Argenteuil	23-1/2 x 31	NYGS	15.00
5234.	Boats at Etretat	21-1/2 x 27	NYGS	18.00
5235.	Boats on the Seine	6 x 9	NYGS	.50
5236.	Bordighera	18-1/2 x 21-1/2	ESH	10.00
		8 x 10	ESH	1.00
5237.	Blue Barque	21 x 25	CFA	15.00
5238.	Bridge at Argenteuil	21 x 28	CFA	15.00
		16-1/2 x 22-1/2	ESH	10.00
		8 x 10	ESH	1.00
5239.	Camille Monet with Son and Nurse in the Garden	18 x 23	HNA	5.95
5240.	Cap D'Antibes	25 x 38-1/2	NYGS	18.00
		21 x 28-1/2	AR	12.00
5241.	Cape Martin	19-1/2 x 24-1/2	PENN	1.00
5242.	Chateau--Gaillard	17 x 22-1/2	ESH	10.00
5243.	Chrysanthemums	16 x 20	PENN	1.00
5244.	Cliff Walk	25 x 30-1/2	NYGS	15.00
5245.	Corn Poppies	18 x 23	HNA	5.95
		6 x 8	CFA	1.00
5246.	Corniche de Monaco	24 x 30	DAC	8.00
5247.	Fisherman's Cottage on Cliffs	18 x 23	HNA	5.95
5248.	Fishing on the Seine	23 x 31-1/2	IA	15.00
5249.	Haystack at Sunset	18 x 23	HNA	5.95
5250.	In the Garden	10 x 8	ESH	1.00
5251.	Jean Monet on a Mechanical Horse	19 x 23	NYGS	12.00
		8 x 10	ESH	1.00
5252.	Landscape near Vetheuil	22 x 27	NYGS	12.00
5253.	Madame Monet in her Garden at Giverny	22-1/2 x 16-1/2	IA	6.00
5254.	Mill at Zaandam	6 x 9	NYGS	.50
5255.	Mistral: Cap D'Antibes	21-1/2 x 27	NYGS	18.00
5256.	Monet's House at Argenteuil	25 x 20-1/2	NYGS	18.00
5257.	On the Seine	20 x 33	CFA	15.00
5258.	Pond at Argenteuil	14 x 19	CFA	4.00
5259.	Pool with Nympheas	13 x 14	CFA	5.00
5260.	Poplar Trees	8 x 10	MMA	.35
5261.	Poplars	23 x 18	HNA	5.95
5262.	Poppies	17-1/2 x 22-1/2	NYGS	10.00
5263.	Poppy Field	18-1/2 x 22-1/2	ESH	10.00
		8 x 10	ESH	1.00
5264.	Poppy Field near Giverny	18 x 23	HNA	5.95
5265.	Regatta	19 x 29	NYGS	22.00
5266.	Regatta at Argenteuil	14 x 22-1/2	ESH	10.00
		8 x 10	ESH	1.00
5267.	The River	21 x 26	NYGS	15.00
		20 x 24	DAC	6.00

5268. Road in Snow at Honfleur	5 x 8	CFA	1.00
5269. Rocks of Belle Isle	8 x 10	NYGS	.50
5270. Rouen Cathedral	10 x 8	ESH	1.00
5271. Sailing Boats at Argenteuil	17 x 22-1/2	ESH	10.00
	8 x 10	ESH	1.00
5272. Sailor at Argenteuil	8 x 10	ESH	1.00
5273. Sea at Etretat	8 x 10	ESH	1.00
5274. Seacoast at Trouville	18 x 24	PENN	1.00
5275. Seine at Argenteuil	21 x 28-1/2	NYGS	22.00
	11 x 19	CFA	5.00
	7 x 9	NYGS	.50
5276. Seine at Bougival	16 x 22-1/2	ESH	10.00
	8 x 10	ESH	1.00
5277. Seine at Vetheuil	20 x 33-1/2	NYGS	18.00
	17-1/2 x 30	RL	10.00
5278. Snow at Argenteuil	11 x 13	IA	3.00
	7 x 8	NYGS	.50
5279. Still Life	20 x 28	NYGS	16.00
5280. Still Life: Apples and Grapes	21-1/2 x 26-1/2	NYGS	12.00
5281. Still Life: Fruit	23-1/2 x 29	NYGS	18.00
5282. Stone Pines, Antibes	26 x 32	CFA	15.00
5283. Summer	28 x 35	NYGS	18.00
	18 x 22-1/2	NYGS	10.00
	6 x 7	NYGS	.50
5284. Sunflowers	10 x 8	ESH	1.00
5285. Train Station, St. Lazare	8 x 10	NYGS	.50
5286. Tulip Field	18 x 22-1/2	ESH	10.00
	8 x 10	ESH	1.00
5287. Tulips in Holland	19 x 24	PENN	1.00
5288. Venice, Palazzo da Mula	18 x 23	HNA	5.95
5289. Venice, San Giorgio Maggiore	18 x 22-1/2	ESH	10.00
5290. Vetheuil	19 x 26	NYGS	15.00
5291. Vetheuil, 1880	8 x 10	ESH	1.00
5292. View of Amsterdam, West Church Tower	19-1/2 x 24	NYGS	7.50
5293. Water Lilies	23 x 18	HNA	5.95
	14 x 13	PENN	1.00
5294. Water Lilies	16 x 16-1/2	IA	6.00
	13 x 14	CFA	5.00
5295. Water Lilies--Detail of	13-1/2 x 30-1/2	ESH	15.00
5296. Woman with a Parasol	10 x 8	ESH	1.00
5297. Zaandam	17 x 26-1/2	NYGS	10.00

MONETTI

5298. Alpine Slope	15 x 40	DAC	8.00
5299. Alpine Stream	15 x 40	DAC	8.00
5300. Serene Setting	24 x 48	DAC	10.00

MONIER, MADELEINE
| 5301. Bouquet (2) | 27-1/2 x 21 | IA | 10.00 ea. |

MONNOYER
| 5302. Basket of Flowers 1 | 22 x 18 | CFA | 12.00 |
| 5303. Basket of Flowers 2 | 22 x 18 | CFA | 12.00 |

MONREALESE, IL See NOVELLI, PIETRO
MONTAGU, RODERIC
5304. Ascole Piceno	11 x 14	AL	5.00
5305. Barcarolle, Venezia	7 x 18	AL	5.00
5306. Camp Vaccinio	14 x 11	CAC	5.00
5307. Capricio, Venezia	20 x 16	AL	8.00
5308. Carriage of Love	14 x 11	CAC	5.00
5309. Castel del Monte	11 x 14	AL	5.00
5310. Castle San Angelo	30 x 40	CAC	120.00
5311. Della Fortuna	18 x 28	CAC	12.00
5312. Flower Girl	18 x 7	CAC	5.00
5313. Garden of Flowers	28 x 11	CAC	10.00
5314. Garden of Love	28 x 11	CAC	10.00
5315. Garden of Rommance	28 x 11	CAC	10.00
5316. Garden of Secret Love	28 x 11	CAC	10.00
5317. Isle of Istria	18 x 28	CAC	12.00
5318. Lido, Venezia	7 x 18	AL	5.00
5319. Marina di Giorgio, Venezia	20 x 16	AL	8.00
5320. Piazza Palladino	30 x 40	AL	24.00
5321. The Prince	14 x 11	CAC	5.00
5322. Tarquina	11 x 14	AL	5.00
5323. Urbino	11 x 14	AL	5.00
5324. Villa della Rose	18 x 7	CAC	5.00
5325. Villa Umberto	18 x 7	CAC	5.00

MONTE DEL FORE
| 5326. Choral Page | 15 x 10 | IA | 3.00 |

MONTICELLI, ADOLPHE | French | 1824-1886 |
| 5327. Les Martigues | 9 x 14 | IA | 3.00 |

MONTJOIE
5328. Le Carousel	8 x 10	CFA	6.00
5329. Le Lapin Agile	8 x 10	CFA	6.00
5330. Moulin Rouge	8 x 10	CFA	6.00
5331. Place de la Concorde	8 x 10	CFA	6.00
5332. Rue de L'Abrevoir	8 x 10	CFA	6.00
5333. Rue Norvins	8 x 10	CFA	6.00

MONTLACK
| 5334. Spring Idyll | 30 x 25 | CAC | 10.00 |
| 5335. Stillness of Eternity | 30 x 25 | CAC | 10.00 |

MOORE, HENRY | English | 1898- |
5336. Family Group	20 x 24	PENN	1.00
5337. Ideas for Metal Sculpture, 1937	15-1/2 x 22	NYGS	18.00
5338. Ideas for Two-Figure Sculpture	8 x 10	MMA	.35
5339. Standing Figures	18-1/2 x 10-1/2	NYGS	10.00
5340. Two Women Seated	24 x 22	NYGS	12.00
	23 x 22	AR	15.00

MOORE, NELSON
  5341. West Springfield   18 x 26   DAC   6.00
MOPP, MAXIMILIAN   Austrian   1885-
  5342. Chess with Emanuel
          Lasker   16 x 20   AR   7.50
                                    8 x 10   AR   1.50
  5343. String Quartet   16 x 20   AR   7.50
                                    8 x 10   AR   1.50
  5344. Symphony   21 x 31   NYGS   12.00
MORALES, LUIS DE   Spanish   1500-1586
  5345. Virgin and Child   22 x 17   IA   10.00
MORAN, THOMAS
  5346. Dream City   20 x 24   AA   10.00
  5347. Gen. Wayne at
          Stony Point   18 x 30   CAC   10.00
  5348. Grand Canyon   20 x 30   CAC   10.00
MORANDO, PAOLO (IL CAVAZZOLA) Italian   1486-1522
  5349. Madonna and Child   7 x 6   IA   1.50
MOREAU, LUC ALBERT   French   1882-1948
  5350. Knockout   17-1/2 x 24   PENN   1.00
MOREAU, JEAN MICHEL, THE YOUNGER   French 1741-1814
  5351. French Park   9 x 14   AR   4.00
                                    7 x 11   CAC   3.00
MORELLI, DOMENICO   Italian   1826-1901
  5352. Mater Purissima   20 x 28   IA   10.00
                                    20 x 27   IA   7.50
  5353. Sacred Heart of Jesus   10 x 8   NYGS   .50
MORGAN, ALFRED K.   English   1868-1928
  5354. Little Hostess   26-1/2 x 35-1/2 NYGS   10.00
MORGA THULER
  5355. Winter   25 x 31   CFA   15.00
MORISOT, BERTHE   French   1841-1895
  5356. Children of Gabriel
          Thomas   22 x 17   CAC   10.00
  5357. Cradle   20 x 16   PENN   1.00
                                                               1.98 (Pr.)
                                    10 x 8   ESH   1.00
  5358. Farm in Normandy   10 x 12   IA   3.00
  5359. Girl Writing a Letter   10 x 8   ESH   1.00
  5360. Jour d'Ete   16 x 26   NYGS   15.00
  5361. On the Terrace   20 x 16   CFA   12.00
                                    7 x 6   CFA   1.00
  5362. Portrait of a Young
          Girl   23 x 18   HNA   5.95
  5363. Skating in the Bois   20 x 16   PENN   1.00
  5364. Swans   11 x 14-1/2   ESH   8.00
  5365. Thames Estuary   10 x 8   ESH   1.00
  5366. Two Children   22-1/2 x 18   ESH   10.00
  5367. Young Girl Waiting   10 x 8   ESH   1.00
MORLAND, GEORGE   English   1763-1804
  5368. End of the Hunt   23-1/2 x 31   NYGS   15.00
  5369. Inside of a Stable   12-1/2 x 18-1/2 NYGS   5.00
  5370. Shepherds Reposing   22 x 17   CAC   12.00

5371. Weary Sportsman	22 x 17	CAC	12.00
MORO, GIUSEPPE	Italian	1888-	
5372. Jungfrau	22 x 33	CAC	12.00
5373. Princess Isabella	26 x 20	PENN	1.00
MORONE, FRANCESCO	Italian	1473-1529	
5374. St. John, the Baptist	11 x 7-1/2	AR	3.00
MORONI, GIOVAN BATTISTA	Italian	1525-1578	
5375. Count P. Secco Suardi	16 x 8	IA	3.00
5376. Gentleman in Adoration before the Madonna	20 x 21-1/2	NYGS	12.00
5377. Tailor	23 x 17-1/2	NYGS	12.00
	7 x 5	NYGS	.50
MOROT, PIERRE			
5378. Paris (6)			
Arc de Triomphe	24 x 10	AA	8.00
Notre Dame	12 x 27	AA	10.00
Petite Rue	24 x 10	AA	8.00
Place Furstenberg	18 x 24	AA	12.00
Place du Tertre	18 x 24	AA	12.00
Sacre Coeur	12 x 27	AA	10.00
MORRIS, GEORGE FORD	American	1873-	
5379. Man O'War	9-1/2 x 12-1/2	NYGS	2.00
5380. Man O'War (A Study)	17 x 13	NYGS	4.00
5381. Whirlaway	9-1/2 x 12-1/2	NYGS	2.00
5382. Whirlaway (A Study)	17 x 13	NYGS	4.00
MORSE, SAMUEL F. B.	American	1791-1872	
5383. General Lafayette	24 x 16-1/2	NYGS	12.00
MOSES, (GRANDMA), ANNA MARY ROBERTSON			
	American	1860-1961	
5384. Apple Butter Making	11 x 13	CFA	2.00
5385. Christmas at Home	10 x 13	CFA	2.00
5386. Dead Tree	16 x 20	CFA	7.50
5387. Old Checkered House	18 x 22	CAC	10.00
5388. Old Homestead	23 x 27	CAC	18.00
5389. Portfolio (6)	12 x 16	CFA	15.00 set
MOULY, MARCEL	French	1918-	
5390. Festival of Ships	23 x 28	RL	15.00
5391. Spanish Balcony	23 x 30	RL	12.50
5392. Street in Spain	23 x 29	RL	12.50
5393. Venice in Blue Light	23 x 28	RL	15.00
5394. Venice Vert et Gris	23 x 29	RL	12.50
MOUNT, WILLIAM S.	American	1807-1868	
5395. Bargaining for a Horse	19 x 24	NYGS	12.00
MUCHA			
5396. Collioure	19 x 14-1/2	NYGS	12.00
MU CH'I			
5397. Wild Goose, Flying	28-1/2 x 11	NYGS	15.00
5398. Wild Goose, Resting	28-1/2 x 11	NYGS	15.00
MUHLENWEG, ELIZABETH			
5399. Madonna	22 x 16	ESH	10.00

MULLER
5400. Flowers	23-1/2 x 31-1/2	ESH	10.00 (Pr.)

MULLER, ERICH MARTIN — German — 1888-
5401. Lake in Bavaria	21 x 30	CAC	10.00
5402. Majesty of the Mountains	21 x 28-1/2	ESH	10.00

MUNCH, ANNA — Danish — 1876-
5403. Anette	12-1/2 x 5	ESH	3.00 (Pr.)
5404. Jackie	12-1/2 x 5	ESH	3.00 (Pr.)
5405. Madleine	12-1/2 x 5	ESH	3.00 (Pr.)
5406. Marika	12-1/2 x 5	ESH	3.00 (Pr.)
5407. Marilyn	12-1/2 x 5	ESH	3.00 (Pr.)
5408. Yvonne	12-1/2 x 5	ESH	3.00 (Pr.)

MUNCH, EDVARD — Norwegian — 1863-1944
5409. Bridge	24 x 24	NYGS	12.00
5410. Farmyard	26 x 34	NYGS	18.00
5411. Manor House	16 x 22	CFA	6.00
5412. Park in Kosen	23 x 26-1/2	AR	15.00
	23 x 26	CFA	15.00

MUNCHHAUSEN, AUGUST VON
5413. American Sports (6) Baseball (2) Fencing (2) Football (2)	12 x 16	IA	2.50 ea.
5414. Allegro--Swan Lake	20 x 16	NYGS	6.00
	14 x 11	NYGS	3.00
	7-1/2 x 6	NYGS	1.00
5415. Andante--Swan Lake	20 x 16	NYGS	6.00
	14 x 11	NYGS	3.00
	7-1/2 x 6	NYGS	1.00
5416. L'Arabesque Romantique	20 x 16	NYGS	6.00
5417. L'Attitude Romantique	20 x 16	NYGS	6.00
5418. Corps du Ballet Russe	21-1/2 x 28	NYGS	7.50
	13 x 16	NYGS	3.00
5419. En Presentation	20 x 16	NYGS	6.00
5420. Finale	20 x 16	NYGS	6.00
	16 x 13	NYGS	3.00
5421. Interlude	20 x 16	NYGS	6.00
	16 x 13	NYGS	3.00
5422. Pas de Deux--Swan Lake	16 x 13	NYGS	3.00
5423. Pas de Trois	21-1/2 x 28	NYGS	7.50
	13 x 16	NYGS	3.00
5424. Pose Classique	20 x 16	NYGS	6.00
	16 x 13	NYGS	3.00
5425. Sur La Pointe	20 x 16	NYGS	6.00
5426. Variation Classique	20 x 16	NYGS	6.00
	16 x 13	NYGS	3.00
5427. Variation--Swan Lake	16 x 13	NYGS	3.00

MUNDING
5428. Black Forest	19-1/2 x 27-1/2	ESH	8.00 (Pr.)
5429. Fir Forest	12 x 16	ESH	3.00 (Pr.)

MUNKACSY, MIHALY	Hungarian	1844-1900	
5430. The Saviour	32 x 23-1/2	IA	12.00
	24 x 18	NYGS	7.50
	14 x 10	NYGS	3.00
MUNNINGS, (SIR) ALFRED J.	English	1878-	
5431. After the Race	19 x 25	RL	10.00
5432. Before the Start	16 x 23	RL	10.00
5433. Belvoir Hounds Exercising in the Park	20 x 24	RL	15.00
5434. Black Knight	17 x 12	RL	6.00
5435. Full River	18-1/2 x 24	RL	10.00
5436. Gypsy Life	19 x 24	RL	10.00
5437. Major T. Bouch, MFH, with the Belvoir Hounds	20 x 24	RL	15.00
5438. October Meeting	16 x 29	RL	15.00
5439. Our Mutual Friend	20 x 25	RL	10.00
5440. Saddling Paddock, Cheltenham, March Meeting	16 x 25	RL	10.00
5441. Studies of Pixie, an Exmoor Foal	15-1/2 x 15	RL	5.00
5442. Warren Hill	16 x 23	RL	10.00
MUNTER, GABRIELE	German	1877-	
5443. Mountain View	17 x 20	CFA	6.00
MURILLO, BARTOLOME ESTEBAN Spanish		1618-1682	
5444. Boys Eating	23 x 18	HNA	5.95
5445. The Divine Shepherd	16 x 12	IA	5.00
5446. The Infant Jesus-- Detail of No. 5445	14 x 11	IA	1.50
5447. Ecce Homo	13 x 11	IA	3.00
	10 x 7	NYGS	.50
5448. Girl and her Duenna	29 x 24	NYGS	16.00
5449. Immaculata	26 x 18	IA	5.00
5450. The Immaculate Conception	35-1/2 x 24	IA	15.00
	23-1/2 x 16	IA	7.50
	20 x 10-1/2	IA	5.00
	20 x 10	NYGS	5.00
	13 x 10	IA	3.00
	11 x 8	IA	1.75
	8 x 6	NYGS	.50
5451. Jesus and St. John	6 x 7	NYGS	.50
5452. Jesus Feeding the Five Thousand	16 x 39	IA	12.00
5453. Madonna and Child	24 x 18	DAC	6.00
	24-1/2 x 17	IA	7.50
	16 x 12	DAC	2.00
	15 x 11	IA	3.00
5454. Detail of No. 5453	15 x 11-1/2	IA	3.50
	15 x 11	IA	3.00
	10 x 7	IA	1.75

5455. Moses Striking the Rock	16 x 39	IA	12.00
5456. Pastry Eaters	22 x 18	DAC	6.00
5457. St. John and the Lamb	23 x 18	HNA	5.95
	19 x 14-1/2	IA	5.00
5458. St. Joseph and the Holy Child	24 x 20	IA	7.50
	24 x 18	NYGS	7.50
5459. Santiago Madonna	24 x 17	AA	7.50
5460. Urchins	20 x 15-1/2	NYGS	7.50
5461. Young Beggar	12 x 9	CFA	2.50
MURIS			
5462. Down to the Sea	18 x 22	CAC	7.50
5463. Flower Shop	18 x 22	CAC	7.50
5464. Mediterranean Harbour	18 x 22	CAC	7.50
MURPHY, H. DUDLEY	American	1867-1945	
5465. Silver Bowl	25 x 30	CFA	12.00
MURRAY, ALBERT K.	American	1906-	
5466. Aligning	14 x 21	NYGS	3.00
5467. Georgetown, Great Exuma, B.W.I.	12 x 18	NYGS	3.00
5468. Landscapes (4)	12 x 30	DAC	4.00 ea.
	6 x 15	DAC	1.20 ea.
MUSIC, ANTONIO ZORAN	Austrian (Res. France)	1909-	
5469. Suite Byzantine	23-1/2 x 28-1/2	NYGS	15.00
MYERS, FRANK H.	American	1899-	
5470. Early Moonlight	24 x 30	IA	10.00

N

NASH, PAUL	English	1889-	
5471. Aylesbury Plain	19 x 24	CAC	10.00
5472. Pond in the Field	20 x 28	CFA	12.00
5473. Sussex Landscape	15 x 21	AP	5.00
5474. Threshing	8 x 10	AP	.50
5475. Wood on the Downs	16 x 20	CAC	12.00
NATOIRE, CHARLES JOSEPH	French	1700-1777	
5476. Girl with Tambourine	11 x 8	CFA	8.50
NATTIER, JEAN MARC	French	1685-1766	
5477. Anne Henriette	11 x 15	IA	3.00
5478. Madame Decaumartin as Hebe	28 x 22	NYGS	12.00
5479. Madame Sophie de France	30 x 24	IA	12.00
	20 x 16	IA	6.00
	14 x 11	IA	3.00
	10 x 8	NYGS	.50
5480. Madame Victoire de France	20 x 16	IA	6.00
	14 x 11	IA	3.00
	10 x 8	NYGS	.50

5481. Marie Adelaide	11 x 15	IA	3.00
	8 x 11	IA	1.75
	8 x 10	NYGS	.50
5482. Marie Zephirine	12 x 15	IA	3.00
5483. Princess Mary Anne	11 x 15	CFA	3.00
5484. Portrait de Jeune			
Femme	9 x 8	CFA	6.00

NAUJOKS, CURT German 1898-1927

5485. St. Cecelia	10 x 7-1/2	IA	10.00
	9 x 7	CAC	5.00

NAY, ERNST WILHELM German 1902-

5486. Blue-Umber	17 x 24	NYGS	18.00
5487. Green Planes	21 x 33-1/2	NYGS	18.00
5488. Green Slices	21 x 33	CFA	18.00
5489. Motion	33-1/2 x 25	NYGS	28.00
5490. Red and Blue	31-1/2 x 24	NYGS	18.00
5491. Yellow Vermilion	16-1/2 x 23-1/2	NYGS	18.00

NEGRETE, EZEQUIEL Mexican 1902-

5492. Labor in the Fields	8 x 10	AP	.60

NEGRETTI, JACOPO See PALMA IL VECCHIO

NELSON, GEORGE LAURENCE American 1887

5493. Delft Bowl	16 x 20	CAC	35.00
5494. Oriental Splendor	24 x 30	CAC	7.50
5495. Purple Symphony	20 x 16	CAC	3.50

NEROCCIO DI BARTOLOMMEO LANDI Italian 1447-1500

5496. Madonna and Child	16 x 8	IA	3.00

NEVILLE

5497. Long Crendon	16 x 20	CAC	4.00
5498. Polperro	16 x 20	CAC	4.00
5499. Wickham	12 x 16	CAC	2.00
5500. Wiltshire Lane	12 x 16	CAC	2.00

NEWTON, ALGERNON H. English 1881-

5501. Dawn	17 x 26	RL	7.50
5502. Whispering Breeze	18-1/2 x 28	RL	10.00

NEWTON, RICHARD

5503. Favorites	24 x 32	AA	10.00
5504. Grand Parade	24 x 20	AA	7.50
5505. Hail Victory	24 x 20	AA	7.50
5506. Morning of the Hunt	25 x 30	AA	10.00
5507. Stable of Champions	20 x 24	AA	7.50

NICHOLS, DALE American 1904-

5508. Company for Supper	27 x 36	NYGS	12.00
	19-1/2 x 26	NYGS	7.50
	6 x 8	NYGS	.50
5509. End of the Hunt	19-1/2 x 26	NYGS	7.50
5510. Evening in the			
Country	20 x 26	NYGS	7.50
5511. Grains of Wheat	6 x 10	NYGS	.50
5512. Summer Bounty	20 x 26	NYGS	7.50

NICHOLSON, JOHN M. English 1901-

5513. In Old England	26 x 36	CFA	15.00

NICHOLSON, WINIFRED ROBERTS English Contemporary

5514. Crete	18 x 23	HNA	5.95

5515. Flowers in a Jug	21 x 15	CFA	10.00
NICHOLLS, BERTRAM	English	1883-	
5516. On the Wye (Near			
Goodrich Castle)	18 x 23	RL	6.00
NICOL, FRANCOIS PAUL	French	1879-	
5517. Bambina	18 x 15	IA	6.00
5518. Lapland Boy	18 x 15	IA	6.00
5519. Mimosa	20 x 16-1/2	IA	10.00
5520. Serenata	18 x 15	IA	6.00
5521. Sorrentina	26-1/2 x 20-1/2	IA	15.00
NIEUSDNHOVEN, WILLEM VON			
5522. Vocations, Early (4)	10 x 8	DAC	1.00 ea.
Alchemist			
Cobbler			
Coppersmith			
Violin Maker			
NIGG, JOSEPH	Austrian	1782-1885	
5523. Floral and Fruit	26 x 21	CAC	20.00
5524. Floral and Fruit (4)	25 x 20	CAC	20.00 ea.
5525. Floral and Fruit	24 x 19	CAC	20.00
5526. Grandmother's			
Bouquet I	21 x 15-1/2	IA	7.50
5527. Grandmother's			
Bouquet II	21 x 15-1/2	IA	7.50
NIKKELIN, J. M. VAN	Dutch	1690-	
5528. June Blossoms	20 x 16	NYGS	7.50
NINETTA			
5529. Farm Scenes (4)	16 x 20	DAC	4.00 ea.
	8 x 10	DAC	1.00 ea.
Apple Time			
Corral			
Fall Pasture			
Spring Willow			
5530. Flowers (4)	24 x 8	DAC	2.00 ea.
	21 x 7	DAC	1.40 ea.
	12 x 4	DAC	.60 ea.
NINO			
5531. La Dore	12 x 16	CAC	2.00
5532. Lallier	12 x 16	CAC	2.00
NOBLE, JAMES			
5533. Camelias	17 x 13	CFA	5.00
5534. Delft Vase	17 x 13	CFA	5.00
5535. Spring Blossoms	17 x 13	CFA	5.00
5536. White and Blue	17 x 13	CFA	5.00
NOIREAUT, L.			
5527. Humorist	12 x 9	CFA	1.50
5538. Old Salt	12 x 9	CFA	1.50
NOLDE, EMIL	German	1867-1956	
5539. Flowers	16 x 11	AP	5.00
5540. Heavy Seas at Sunset	13-1/2 x 18	NYGS	10.00
NORO KAISEKI	Japanese	1747-1828	
5541. Summer Landscape	24 x 10-1/2	IA	12.00

NOVELLI, PIETRO (IL MONREALESE)	Italian	1603-1644	
5542. Portrait of a Child	15 x 11	IA	3.00
NOURSE, ELIZABETH	American	1859-1938	
5543. Mother and Children	20 x 13	CAC	7.50
NOWAK, HEINZ	German		
5544. Red Bridge	13 x 35-1/2	IA	8.00
NUVOLONE			
5545. Virgin and Child	8 x 10	AP	.50

O

OBSTNER			
5546. Orange Girl	16 x 20	ESH	5.00 (Pr.)
OCHTERVELT, JACOBUS	Dutch	1635-1709	
5547. Musicians	30 x 24	CFA	18.00
	25 x 20	NYGS	10.00
	24 x 20	DAC	6.00
	16 x 12	DAC	2.00
O'CONNELL, DAVID			
5548. Last Supper	18 x 24	CAC	10.00
5549. Our Lady of Walsingham	21 x 21	IA	10.00
5550. Sacred Heart of Jesus	19-1/2 x 15	IA	8.50
5551. Sacred Heart of Mary	19-1/2 x 15	IA	8.50
5552. Transfiguration	21 x 21	IA	10.00
O'CONNOR, JOHN	English	1913-	
5553. Lake in Autumn	19 x 26	RL	10.00
OERDER, FRANS	Dutch	1876-	
5554. Blossom Time	28 x 34	NYGS	10.00
	17 x 21	NYGS	3.00
5555. Magnolias	28 x 34	NYGS	10.00
	20 x 24	NYGS	5.00
OGDEN			
5556. Silvery Night	24 x 29	CAC	6.00
	16 x 20	CAC	3.00
5557. Winter Silence	24 x 29	CAC	6.00
	16 x 20	CAC	3.00
OKADA, KENZO	Japanese	Contemporary	
5558. Eventails	22 x 27-1/2	NYGS	15.00
O'KEEFFE, GEORGIA	American	1887-	
5559. Autumn Leaves	20 x 15-1/2	NYGS	5.00
5560. Pelvis with Distance	8 x 10	MMA	.35
5561. Ram's Head with Holly-hock and Little Hills	25 x 30	NYGS	15.00
5562. White Flower	25 x 30	NYGS	15.00
OKAMURA, ARTHUR	Japanese-American	1932-	
5563. Puppet Show Woman	26 x 12	PENN	1.00
OLSSON, JULIUS	English	d. 1942	
5564. Off the Western Land	19 x 25	CAC	5.00
OLSZEWSKI, KARL EWALD	Austrian	1884-	
5565. After the Storm	22 x 31-1/2	NYGS	15.00
5566. Coming Storm	16 x 22	CFA	7.50
5567. Flying Swans	22 x 32	CFA	15.00
5568. Heading South	17 x 24	NYGS	8.00
5569. Homeward	22 x 30	CFA	12.00

5570. Quiet Lake	26 x 33	NYGS	10.00
5571. Sea Gulls	22 x 30	CFA	12.00
5572. Wild Geese before Storm	25 x 35-1/2	NYGS	15.00
OOMELING, F.	Dutch		
5573. Wedding Feast in Holland	22 x 31	CAC	7.50
OPPER, E.	American	1880-	
5574. Fire Engine	23 x 30-1/2	NYGS	12.00
	11 x 14	NYGS	3.00
	5-1/2 x 7-1/2	NYGS	.50
ORLANDINI, ORLANDO PALADINO	Italian	1905-	
5575. Chrysanthemums	20 x 25	CFA	10.00
OROZCO, JOSÉ CLEMENTE	Mexican	1883-1949	
5576. Hispano-American Mural	8 x 8	NYGS	.50
5577. Mexican Pueblo	20 x 24-1/2	NYGS	12.00
5578. Zapatistas	23 x 28	NYGS	18.00
	8 x 10	MMA	.35
	6 x 7-1/2	NYGS	.50
OSSWALD-TOPPI, MARGHERITA	Italian-Swiss	1897-	
5579. Red and White Flowers	23 x 16	CAC	8.00
OSTADE, ADRIAEN VAN	Dutch	1610-1685	
5580. Backgammon Players	9 x 7-1/2	AR	3.50
5581. Country Inn	21-1/2 x 16	NYGS	10.00
5582. Dutch Tavern	9 x 7-1/2	AR	3.50
OSTHAUS, EDMUND HENRY	American	1858-1928	
5583. In Action	20 x 26	IA	7.50
OSWALD, CARLOS	Italian-Brazilian	1882-	
5584. Last Supper	16-1/2 x 28-1/2	IA	8.00
5585. Sacred Heart of Jesus	23 x 17	IA	6.00
	18 x 13	IA	4.50
OTT, THERESE	French	Contemporary	
5586. Incoming Tide	20 x 25	RL	7.50
5587. Pornic	20 x 25	RL	7.50
OTTEMA			
5588. Blossom Time	24 x 30	CAC	10.00
5589. Summer Idyl	22 x 18	CAC	6.00
OTTO, WALT	American		
5590. Summer Idyll	22 x 18	NYGS	6.00
OUDOT, ROLAND	French	1897-	
5591. Church of Magagnose	12 x 17	CAC	6.00
5592. Gladiolus	23 x 17	CFA	10.00
5593. Harvest	21 x 29	CAC	12.00
5594. Village near Houdan	10 x 15	CAC	5.00
OUTIN, Pierre	French	1840-1899	
5595. The Toast	24-1/2 x 20	NYGS	10.00
OWEN, R. EMMETT			
5596. Big Maples	24 x 36	NYGS	12.00
OWENS			
5597. Custom House	7 x 10	CFA	6.00
5598. Gravesend	7 x 10	CFA	6.00
5599. Sheerness	7 x 10	CFA	6.00

P

PACCHIA, GIROLAMO DEL	Italian		1477-1535
5600. Madonna and Child			
with St. John	12" circle	IA	3.00

PADOVANINO, IL (ALESSANDRO VAROTARI)   Italian   1580-1650

5601. Portrait of a Woman	14 x 11	IA	3.00

PADUA, PAUL M.

5602. Before the Mirror	19 x 15	ESH	6.00
5603. Brother and Sister	17 x 13	ESH	6.00
5604. Hollywood Swing	27 x 22	IA	12.00
5605. Lady in Front of a			
Mirror	23 x 17	CFA	10.00
5606. Love Letter	28 x 24	CFA	15.00
	23 x 19	CFA	10.00
5607. Old Farmer	10-1/2 x 8	ESH	4.00
5608. Reading Lady	22 x 18	CFA	10.00
5609. Sea Coast	29 x 24	NYGS	15.00
5610. Sunshine Lady	22-1/2 x 17	IA	10.00

PAGHOLO, (FRA) BARTOLOMMEO DI (FRA BARTOLOMMEO
DELLA PORTA, KNOWN AS BACCIO)   Italian   1475-1517

5611. Angel, Figure of	12 x 8	CFA	3.00
5612. Angel Musician (Detail			
from "The Virgin			
Enthroned")	15 x 11	IA	3.00
5613. Deposition from the			
Cross	11 x 14	IA	3.00
5614. Holy Family	12 x 11	IA	3.00
5615. St. Catherine (Detail			
from "God in Glory")	15 x 11	IA	3.00
5616. Savonarola, Portrait of	15 x 10	IA	3.00

PAILES, ISSAAK   Russian-French   1895-

5617. Nature Morte	16 x 20	PENN	1.00

PALMA IL VECCHIO, JACOPO (OR GIACOMO) (NEGRETTI,
JACOPO)   Italian   1480-1528

5618. Christ on the Mount			
of Olives	11 x 8	AR	3.00
5619. St. Barbara	15 x 7	IA	3.00

PALMEIRO, JOSE   Spanish   1908-

5620. Little Harbour	19 x 26	RL	10.00

PALMER, ROD

5621. After the Rain	24 x 40	DAC	8.00
	12 x 20	DAC	2.00
5622. Bright Cloud	9 x 12	NYGS	15.00
5623. Carriage Drive	24 x 40	DAC	8.00
	12 x 20	DAC	2.00
5624. Crystal Lake	24 x 40	DAC	8.00
	12 x 20	DAC	2.00
5625. Distant View	24 x 40	DAC	8.00
	12 x 20	DAC	2.00
5626. Flower Market	24 x 40	DAC	8.00
	12 x 20	DAC	2.00

5627. Foothills in Flower	24 x 40	DAC	8.00
	12 x 20	DAC	2.00
5628. Green Pasture	24 x 40	DAC	8.00
	12 x 20	DAC	2.00
5629. Quiet Water	24 x 40	DAC	8.00
	12 x 20	DAC	2.00
5630. Reaping the Harvest	24 x 40	DAC	8.00
	12 x 20	DAC	2.00
5631. Turning Leaves	24 x 40	DAC	8.00
	12 x 20	DAC	2.00

PALUE

5632. Approaching Twilight	20-1/2 x 30	NYGS	12.00
5633. Coastline at Arcachon	20-1/2 x 30	NYGS	12.00

PAN, ARTHUR   Hungarian (Res. England)
                                                        Contemporary

5634. H. M. the Queen in Coronation Robes	26 x 18	RL	12.50
5635. Sir Winston Churchill	17-1/2 x 22	RL	7.50

PANET, ANDRE

5636. Souvenir de Paris	15-1/2 x 36	NYGS	15.00

PANNINI, GIOVANNI PAOLO   Italian   1691-1764

5637. Interior of St. Peters	9 x 14	CFA	1.50
5638. Marcus Aurelius	33-1/2 x 26-1/2	AL	18.00
5639. Piazza del Quirinale	26 x 25	CFA	18.00
5640. Piazza de S. Maria Maggiore	26 x 25	CFA	18.00
5641. Roman Ruins	22 x 18	CFA	12.00
5642. Roman Ruins	11 x 15	IA	3.00
5643. Roman Ruins I	27 x 20	CFA	7.50
5644. Roman Ruins II	27 x 20	CFA	7.50
5645. Roman Ruins with Pyramid	22 x 18	CFA	12.00

PARADISE, PHIL   American   1905-

5646. Beach at Cortez	6-1/2 x 10	AR	1.00
5647. Fisher Folk at Guayamas	6-1/2 x 10	AR	1.00
5648. Flower Vendor	20 x 13	AR	5.00
	10 x 6-1/2	AR	1.00
5649. Maria	20 x 12	AR	5.00
	10 x 6	AR	1.00
5650. Marimba Players	25 x 18	AR	10.00
	24 x 18	AP	10.00
5651. Sunday Morning	20 x 13	AR	5.00
	10 x 6-1/2	AR	1.00
5652. Tomas	20 x 12	AR	5.00
	10 x 6	AR	1.00

PAREDES, V. DE

5653. Favorite Party of Louis XV	20 x 30	CFA	30.00
5654. Handel	20 x 30	CFA	30.00
5655. Mozart	20 x 30	CFA	30.00

5656.	Royal Visitors in			
	Watteau's Studio	20 x 30	CFA	30.00
PARIZOT, L.				
5657.	Notre Dame	8 x 12	CFA	5.00
5658.	Le Quai Conti	8 x 12	CFA	5.00
5659.	Le Quai de Tournelle	8 x 12	CFA	5.00
PARK, JOHN ANTHONY		English	1880-	
5660.	Church in the Fields	17 x 21	CAC	7.50
PARKER, SYBIL C.		English	1860-	
5661.	Door of the Fold	10 x 7	NYGS	.50
PARMIGIANINO, IL (MAZZOLA, FRANCESCO)			Italian	1503-1540
5662.	Marriage of			
	St. Catherine	9 x 15	IA	3.00
5663.	Portrait of a Woman			
	called "The Fair"	15 x 9	IA	3.00
PARRI DI SPINELLO ARETINO		Italian	1387-1453	
5664.	Virgin of the			
	Misericordia	11 x 11	IA	3.00
PARRISH, MAXFIELD		American	1870-	
5665.	Canyon	15 x 12	NYGS	2.00
		10 x 6	NYGS	1.00
5666.	Cleopatra	24 x 28	NYGS	12.00
		14 x 16	NYGS	6.00
		6 x 10	NYGS	1.00
5667.	Daybreak	18 x 30	NYGS	12.00
		10-1/2 x 18	NYGS	6.00
		6 x 10	NYGS	1.00
5668.	Dreaming	18 x 30	NYGS	12.00
		10 x 18	NYGS	6.00
5669.	Evening	15 x 12	NYGS	2.00
		10 x 6	NYGS	1.00
5670.	Garden of Allah	15 x 30	NYGS	12.00
		9 x 18	NYGS	6.00
5671.	Hilltop	30 x 18-1/2	NYGS	12.00
		20 x 12	NYGS	6.00
		10 x 6	NYGS	1.00
5672.	Lute Players	18 x 30	NYGS	12.00
		10 x 18	NYGS	6.00
		12 x 15	NYGS	2.00
		6-1/2 x 10	NYGS	1.00
5673.	Morning	15 x 12	NYGS	2.00
		10 x 6	NYGS	1.00
5674.	Page	12 x 10	NYGS	2.00
5675.	Reveries	16 x 12	NYGS	2.00
5676.	Prince	12 x 9-1/2	NYGS	2.00
5677.	Romance	14-1/2 x 24	NYGS	8.00
5678.	Rubaiyat	8 x 30	NYGS	9.00
		4 x 15	NYGS	2.00
		2 x 8-1/2	NYGS	1.00
5679.	Stars	30 x 18-1/2	NYGS	12.00
		20 x 12	NYGS	6.00

5680. Tranquility	29-1/2 x 24	NYGS	12.00
	17 x 13-1/2	NYGS	6.00
	11-1/2 x 9	NYGS	2.00
5681. Twilight	22-1/2 x 18	NYGS	12.00
5682. White Birch	11 x 9	NYGS	2.00
5683. Wild Geese	15 x 12	NYGS	2.00
PARSONS, ALFRED	English	1847-1920	
5684. Bredon-on-the-Avon	24 x 36	NYGS	15.00
	16 x 24	NYGS	10.00
PARTIKEL, ALFRED	German	1888-1946	
5685. In the Valley	26 x 35	CFA	15.00
PASCIN, JULES	American	1885-1930	
5686. Woman in Red	24-1/2 x 20	PENN	1.00
PASMORE, VICTOR	English	1908-	
5687. Quiet River	15 x 20	AP	6.00
PATENIER (OR PATINIR); JOACHIM Flemish		1480-1524	
5688. Flight into Egypt	18 x 23	HNA	5.95
5689. St. Jerome in a Rocky			
Landscape	14 x 13	CFA	4.00
PATER, JEAN BAPTISTE JOSEPH French		1695-1736	
5690. Arlequin et Pierrot	9 x 12	IA	10.00
			(Grav.)
5691. Blind Man's Buff	20 x 25-1/2	NYGS	12.00
5692. Dance	25 x 33-1/2	NYGS	15.00
5693. La Danse	12 x 10	IA	10.00
5694. L'Escarpolette	12 x 10	IA	10.00
5695. Fete Champetre	9 x 12	IA	10.00
			(Grav.)
5696. Meeting in a Park	11 x 13	IA	3.00
5697. Toilette	13 x 11	IA	3.00
PATRICK, JAMES MC INTOSH	Scotch	1907-	
5698. Autumn Idyll	27 x 36	NYGS	15.00
5699. Autumn in Kinnordy	16 x 22	CFA	10.00
5700. Early Spring in Scotland	19 x 27	NYGS	12.00
5701. Farm in Angus	16 x 22	CFA	10.00
5702. Late Summer in			
Scotland	19 x 27	NYGS	12.00
PAUL, RICHARD	American	1853-1900	
5703. Old Surrey	22 x 30	AA	10.00
PAULI, FRITZ	Swiss	1891-	
5704. Barbara	24 x 19	CFA	10.00
PEALE, JAMES	American	1749-1831	
5705. Fruit	17 x 27	NYGS	12.00
	9 x 14	NYGS	4.00
PEALE, REMBRANDT	American	1778-1860	
5706. Thomas Jefferson	18 x 15	NYGS	5.00
	17 x 14	IA	7.50
	9 x 7-1/2	NYGS	1.00
PEARS, CHARLES	English	1873-	
5707. In the Tropics	14 x 22	CFA	7.50
5708. Peaceful River	19-1/2 x 25	RL	7.50

PEARSON, MARGUERITE S.	English	1898-	
5709. Allegro	25 x 30	AA	10.00
5710. At the Melodeon	25 x 30	AA	10.00
5711. Blue Danube	25 x 30	AA	10.00
5712. Blue Kimono	25 x 30	AA	10.00
5713. Canterbury Bells	20 x 24	AA	5.00
5714. Hostess	28 x 23-1/2	AA	7.50
5715. Moment Musicale	25 x 30	AA	10.00
5716. Song	24 x 28	AA	7.50
5717. Zinnias	20 x 24	AA	5.00
PECHAUBES, EUGENE	French	1890-	
5718. Military Horsemen,			
French (6)	9-1/2 x 8-1/2	IA	5.00 ea.
First Empire--Carabineer			
First Empire--Imperial Guards			
First Empire--Officer of Artillery			
First Empire--Imperial Guards, Officer of			
Cuirasseers			
First Empire--Imperial Guards, Officer of Fifth			
Hussars			
Second Empire--Hussar			
PECHSTEIN, MAX	German	1881-1955	
5719. Blossoming Tree by			
the River	19 x 23-1/2	NYGS	12.00
5720. Boats at Sunrise	18 x 23	HNA	5.95
	17 x 19	CFA	6.00
5721. Boats on the Beach	25 x 29	CFA	18.00
5722. Fisherman	18 x 22	CFA	15.00
5723. Rising Sun	23-1/2 x 29-1/2	NYGS	18.00
5724. Stormy Ocean	23 x 27-1/2	ESH	10.00
5725. Sun on Baltic Beach	22 x 27-1/2	NYGS	12.00
5726. White Horse in Circus	25 x 18	PENN	1.00
PEDERSEN, CARL-HENNING	Danish	Contemporary	
5727. Blue Birds	31-1/2 x 26-1/2	NYGS	15.00
PEDRO, LUIS MARTINEZ	Cuban	Contemporary	
5728. Espacio Azul	24-1/2 x 29-1/2	NYGS	15.00
PEINER, WERNER	German	1897-	
5729. Good Earth	21 x 35-1/2	NYGS	12.00
5730. Village in the Snow	19-1/2 x 27-1/2	NYGS	12.00
PELHAM, GENE	American	1909-	
5731. Covered Bridge	11 x 14	NYGS	3.00
	6 x 7-1/2	NYGS	1.00
5732. Green Pastures	11 x 14	NYGS	3.00
	6 x 7-1/2	NYGS	1.00
5733. Hillside Stream	11 x 14	NYGS	3.00
	6 x 7-1/2	NYGS	1.00
5734. Peaceful Waters	25 x 31	NYGS	10.00
	17 x 21	NYGS	5.00
	9 x 12	NYGS	1.00
5735. Rolling Hills	24 x 36	NYGS	12.00
	17 x 21	NYGS	5.00
	9 x 12	NYGS	1.00

5736. Sunny Valley	24 x 36	NYGS	12.00
	17 x 21	NYGS	5.00
5737. Twin Pines	11 x 14	NYGS	3.00
	6 x 7-1/2	NYGS	1.00
5738. Valley Stream	24 x 36	NYGS	12.00
	17 x 21	NYGS	5.00
5739. Wayside Barn	11 x 14	NYGS	3.00
	6 x 7-1/2	NYGS	1.00
5740. Willow Pond	11 x 14	NYGS	3.00
	6 x 7-1/2	NYGS	1.00

PELLERANO, JOHN

5741. Jazz Musicians (8)	18 x 12	IA	2.50 ea.

       Baritone Sax
       Drummer
       Guitarist
       On the Vibes
       Playin the Slush Pump
       Rhythm Man
       Sax Man
       Swing Clarinet

PELLEW, JOHN (JACK)	English (Res. U. S.)		1903-
5742. Across the Harbor	11 x 14	DAC	2.00
	6 x 8	DAC	.60
5743. Antique Shop	11 x 14	DAC	2.00
	6 x 8	DAC	.60
5744. Romantic River	11 x 14	DAC	2.00
	6 x 8	DAC	.60
5745. Sailor's Retreat	11 x 14	DAC	2.00
	6 x 8	DAC	.60
5746. Signs of Spring	11 x 14	DAC	2.00
	6 x 8	DAC	.60
5747. Top of the Hill	11 x 14	DAC	2.00
	6 x 8	DAC	.60

PEN

5748. Clown Heads (4)	12 x 9	DAC	.80 ea.
5749. Clowns (8)	9 x 7	DAC	.60 ea.
5750. Me	14 x 9	CFA	3.00
5751. You	14 x 9	CFA	3.00
PENNACCHI, PIER MARIA	Italian		1464-1514
5752. Annunciation	11 x 10	IA	3.00
PERCY, SIDNEY			
5753. Lake Country	24 x 36	IA	12.00
PERFALL, ERICH VON	German		1881-
5754. Freight Ships on River	27-1/2 x 21	ESH	8.00
PERI, LUCIEN	English		1880-1949
5755. Landscape	12 x 20	ESH	4.00 (Pr.)
5756. Madonna della Serra	15 x 22	CFA	10.00
	7 x 10	CFA	1.00
5757. San Cipriano, Corsica	18-1/2 x 25	RL	7.50
5758. Still Waters	18-1/2 x 25	RL	7.50
PERRONNEAU, JEAN BAPTISTE	French 1715-1783		
5759. Girl with a Kitten	22-1/2 x 18-1/2	NYGS	18.00
	10 x 8	ESH	1.00

PERSIA--MURALS
5760.	Girl with a Drinking Cup	11 x 14	NYGS	4.00
5761.	In a Garden	11 x 14	NYGS	4.00
5762.	Lady in a Garden	11 x 14	NYGS	4.00
5763.	Persian Games	11 x 14	NYGS	4.00
5764.	Poem	18 x 18	NYGS	7.50
5765.	Resting under a Tree	18 x 18	NYGS	7.50
5766.	Summer's Day	11 x 14	NYGS	4.00
5767.	Time for Recreation	16 x 25	NYGS	12.00

PERUGINO (PIETRO VANNUCCI)   Italian   1445-1523
5768.	Baldassare Monaco	8 x 7	IA	1.50
5769.	Crucifixion	8 x 15	IA	3.00
5770.	Virgin and St. Bernard --Detail of No. 5769	15 x 11	IA	3.00
5771.	St. John and St. Benedict--Detail of No. 5769	15 x 10	IA	3.00
5772.	Crucifixion with the Virgin and St. John	24 x 13	IA	10.00
5773.	Don Biagio Milanesi	8 x 7	IA	1.50
5774.	Francesco delle Opere	13 x 11	IA	3.00
5775.	Lamentation of Christ	9 x 7-1/2	AR	3.00
5776.	Madonna	10 x 7	NYGS	.50
5777.	Madonna--Detail of No. 5776	10 x 8	NYGS	.50
5778.	Madonna and Angels	12 x 11	IA	3.00
5779.	Virgin--Detail of No. 5778	15 x 11	IA	3.00
5780.	Madonna and Child	20 x 15	CFA	7.50
5781.	Madonna and Child with Saints	20 x 15	NYGS	7.50
5782.	St. Mary Magdalene	15 x 11	IA	3.00
5783.	St. Michel	15 x 11	IA	3.00
5784.	Virgin Enthroned	13 x 11	IA	3.00
5785.	Virgin (Head)--Detail of No. 5784	15 x 11	IA	3.00
5786.	Virgin in Adoration	10 x 8	NYGS	.50
5787.	A Youth	15 x 10	IA	3.00

PESELLINO, FRANCESCO   Italian   1422-1457
5788.	Miracle of St. Anthony	9 x 15	IA	3.00

PETERSON
5789.	Autumn Bluebird	17 x 21	ESH	5.00
5790.	Baltimore Oriole	22 x 28	ESH	7.50
		17 x 21	ESH	5.00
5791.	Barn Swallow	17 x 21	ESH	5.00
5792.	Bluebird	22 x 28	ESH	7.50
5793.	Blue Jay	22 x 28	ESH	7.50
		17 x 21	ESH	5.00
5794.	Blue-Winged Teal	16 x 28	ESH	7.50
5795.	Bobolink	17 x 21	ESH	5.00
5796.	Bohemian Waxwing	17 x 21	ESH	5.00

5797.	Bufflehead	22 x 28	ESH	7.50
5798.	Cardinal	22 x 28	ESH	7.50
		17 x 21	ESH	5.00
5799.	Cedar Waxwing	22 x 28	ESH	7.50
		17 x 21	ESH	5.00
5800.	Cuckoo and Crimson			
	Mallow	17 x 21	ESH	5.00
5801.	Evening Grosbeak	17 x 21	ESH	5.00
5802.	Flamingoes	20 x 26	ESH	15.00
5803.	Golden Pheasant	25 x 32	ESH	15.00
5804.	Green-Winged Teal	22 x 28	ESH	7.50
5805.	Hooded Merganser	22 x 28	ESH	7.50
5806.	Hooded Warbler	17 x 21	ESH	5.00
5807.	Mocking Bird and			
	Magnolia	22 x 28	ESH	7.50
		17 x 21	ESH	5.00
5808.	Mountain Bluebird	17 x 21	ESH	5.00
5809.	Red-Bellied Woodpecker	17 x 21	ESH	5.00
5810.	Red Wing	22 x 28	ESH	7.50
		17 x 21	ESH	5.00
5811.	Ring-Necked Pheasant	25 x 32	ESH	15.00
5812.	Robin	17 x 21	ESH	5.00
5813.	Rose-Breasted Grosbeak	22 x 28	ESH	7.50
5814.	Scarlet Tanager	17 x 21	ESH	5.00
5815.	Sea Swallows	22 x 28	ESH	7.50
5816.	Shovellers on the Mud	22 x 28	ESH	7.50
5817.	Snowy Egrets	20 x 26	ESH	15.00
5818.	Summer Tanagers	22 x 28	ESH	7.50
		17 x 21	ESH	5.00
5819.	Teal and Willows	22 x 28	ESH	7.50
5820.	Towhee	17 x 21	ESH	5.00
5821.	Valley Quail	22 x 28	ESH	7.50
5822.	White-Winged Crossbill	17 x 21	ESH	5.00
5823.	Yellow-Billed Cuckoo	22 x 28	ESH	7.50
PETO, JOHN FREDERICK		American	1854-1907	
5824.	Books of Learning	9 x 12	CFA	3.00
5825.	Evening's Comfort	9 x 12	CFA	3.00
5826.	Letter Rack	25 x 21	CFA	15.00
5827.	Old Companions	23 x 31	NYGS	15.00
		11 x 14	NYGS	3.00
5828.	Old Cremona	18 x 23	HNA	5.95
5829.	Poor Man's Store	18 x 23	HNA	5.95
PETTENKOFEN, AUGUST		Austrian	1822-1889	
5830.	Children	10-1/2 x 12	NYGS	10.00
PHIDIAS		Greek	B.C. 490-	
5831.	Parthenon Rider	9 x 11	CFA	3.50
PHILIPP, ROBERT		American	1895-	
5832.	Cup of Chocolate	16 x 20	AR	6.00
5833.	Girl at the Piano	25 x 30	CFA	15.00
5834.	Girl in Blue	24 x 30	DAC	8.00
5835.	Rendezvous	17-1/2 x 21	NYGS	7.50
PHILIPP, WERNER				
5836.	Shelter Cove Ranch	16-1/2 x 21	IA	3.00

PHILIPPE, W.

5837. A la Mer	20 x 24	CFA	15.00
PHILPOT, LEONARD D.	English	1877-	
5838. Orchids	20 x 15	CFA	7.50
PIAZZETTA, GIOVANNI BATTISTA Italian		1682-1754	
5839. Country Girl	13 x 11	IA	3.00
5840. Fortune-Teller	15 x 11	IA	3.00
PICABIA, FRANCIS	Spanish	1878-1953	
5841. Amorous Display	26 x 19	AR	10.00
PICASSO, PABLO (RUIZ)	Spanish	1881-	
5842. Absinthe Drinker	27-1/2 x 20-1/2	IA	18.00
5843. Acrobat's Family	28 x 20	NYGS	12.00
	10 x 8	ESH	1.00
5844. Acrobate a la Boule	24 x 15	NYGS	10.00
Tr.-Acrobat on a Ball	20 x 12	PENN	1.00
5845. Aficionado	9 x 5	CFA	1.00
5846. Antique Bust	22 x 30	CFA	15.00
	6 x 8	CFA	1.00
5847. Arlequin	28-1/2 x 16	AR	12.00
5848. Arlequin au Cafe	22-1/2 x 16-1/2	ESH	10.00
5849. Artist's Son	21 x 15-1/2	NYGS	7.50
	15-1/2 x 11	NYGS	3.00
5850. Balcony	9 x 6	NYGS	.50
5851. Ballerina	8 x 6	CFA	1.00
5852. Before the Thrust	16 x 22	AP	10.00
5853. Blue Boy	24 x 13	NYGS	12.00
	14 x 11	NYGS	3.00
5854. Boats on the Beach	5 x 7	NYGS	.50
5855. Bouquet	23 x 15	AP	6.00
5856. Boy and Horse	24 x 16	PENN	1.00
5857. Boy in Red Harlequin Jacket	23 x 17	CAC	15.00
5858. Boy Leading a Horse	28 x 16-1/2	MMA	6.50
5859. Boy with Collar	7 x 5	CFA	1.00
5860. Boy with Pipe	26 x 21	HNA	5.95
5861. Bull Fight	18 x 21-1/2	ESH	10.00
	8 x 10	ESH	1.00
	5 x 7	NYGS	.50
5862. Bust of a Woman	8 x 10	ESH	1.00
5863. Cafe at Royan	20 x 27-1/2	IA	15.00
	8 x 10	ESH	1.00
5864. Candle, Vase and Blue Casserole	6 x 8	CFA	1.00
5865. Casserole Emaillee	19 x 24	PENN	1.00
			1.98 (Pr.)
	18 x 24	NYGS	10.00
5866. Chest of Drawers with Still Life	8 x 10	ESH	1.00
5867. Child with a Dove	28 x 20	NYGS	15.00
	18 x 13	AR	3.00
	17-1/2 x 13	AP	3.00
	14 x 10	NYGS	3.00

5868.	Children Reading	19-1/2 x 15	AR	7.50
5869.	La Chimese	18 x 15	AR	4.00
5870.	Citron et Orange	16 x 20	PENN	1.00
				1.98 (Pr.)
5871.	Classical Head	24 x 20	PENN	1.00
5872.	The Cock	20 x 15	AP	8.00
		9 x 7	NYGS	.50
5873.	Compote Dish and Pitcher by the Window	24 x 30	PENN	1.00
				1.98 (Pr.)
		21 x 28-1/2	NYGS	16.00
5874.	La Compotier	15 x 20-oval	AR	7.50
5875.	Contemplation	10 x 8	ESH	1.00
5876.	The Couple	10 x 7	AR	2.00
5877.	Curtain for the Ballet "Parade"	8 x 10	ESH	1.00
		6 x 7	NYGS	.50
5878.	Dancers	7 x 6	CFA	1.00
5879.	Les Demoiselles D'Avignon	8 x 10	MMA	.35
5880.	Dining Room	8 x 10	ESH	1.00
5881.	The Family	10 x 8	ESH	1.00
5882.	Family Dispossessed	14 x 10	CFA	5.00
5883.	Family of Saltimbanques	24 x 26	AA	15.00
		7 x 7	NYGS	.50
5884.	Femme a la Mantilla Blanche	20 x 24	DAC	6.00
5885.	Femme Bleue	24 x 17-1/2	NYGS	7.50
		19 x 16	CFA	7.50
5886.	Femme Que Pleure	23-1/2 x 19	NYGS	12.00
5887.	Fillette a la Boule	23 x 16	CAC	15.00
5888.	Fillette au Chien	27 x 18	NYGS	12.00
5889.	Fish Net	8 x 6	CFA	1.00
5890.	Fisherman's Farewell	7 x 6	CFA	1.00
5891.	Flower Seller	14 x 21	NYGS	12.00
5892.	Flowers	10 x 8	ESH	1.00
5893.	Flowers, 1903	25 x 19	NYGS	15.00
5894.	Forces of Life and the Spirit Triumphing over Evil (Unesco Mural)	8 x 10	ESH	1.00
5895.	Girl in a Chair	10 x 7	AR	2.00
5896.	Girl on a Beach Ball	10 x 8	ESH	1.00
5897.	Girl on a Divan	8 x 10	AR	2.00
5898.	Girl on the Wall	28 x 22	CFA	15.00
5899.	Girl with a Jug	26 x 21	NYGS	18.00
5900.	Girl with Mandolin	23-1/2 x 17	NYGS	12.00
5901.	Glass Bottle and Newspaper	6 x 8	CFA	1.00

5902.	Gourmet	28 x 20-1/2	NYGS	12.00
		20 x 14-1/2	NYGS	7.50
		8 x 6	NYGS	.50
5903.	Green Still Life	19 x 26	MMA	12.00
5904.	Grille	9 x 6	CFA	1.00
5905.	Guernica	16-1/2 x 35-1/2	NYGS	12.00
		8-1/2 x 19	MMA	4.00
5906.	Guitar	17 x 22	AP	10.00
5907.	Guitar and Bottle	16 x 15	CFA	7.50
5908.	Guitar and Grapes	25 x 18-1/2	AA	12.00
5909.	Harlequin	7 x 4	CFA	1.00
5910.	Harlequin, 1917	28-1/2 x 22	NYGS	15.00
5911.	Harlequin	22-1/2 x 17	ESH	10.00
5912.	Harlequin, 1923	10 x 8	ESH	1.00
5913.	Harlequin and Boy	23 x 18-1/2	NYGS	15.00
5914.	Harlequin and Companion	23-1/2 x 18-1/2	PENN	1.00
5915.	Harlequin and Mirror	24 x 19	PENN	1.00
5916.	Harlequin on Horseback	24 x 16-1/2	NYGS	15.00
		14 x 10	NYGS	3.00
5917.	Harlequin's Family	7 x 5	CFA	1.00
5918.	Harlequin with Mask	17-1/2 x 22-1/2	ESH	10.00
5919.	Head of a Woman	20 x 14	NYGS	12.00
		7 x 7	NYGS	.50
5920.	The Ironer	9 x 5	NYGS	.50
5921.	L'Italienne	22 x 15	ESH	10.00
5922.	Juan-les Pins	24 x 30	DAC	8.00
		11 x 14	DAC	2.80
		8 x 10	ESH	1.00
5923.	Jeune Homme et Cheval	19-1/2 x 12-1/2	NYGS	18.00
5924.	Juggler with Still Life	28-1/2 x 20	NYGS	15.00
5925.	Landscape	20 x 28	NYGS	16.00
5926.	Landscape with Dead Tree	17-1/2 x 22-1/2	ESH	10.00
5927.	Lemon and Oranges	14 x 17	CFA	5.00
5928.	Liseuse Grise	24 x 14	PENN	1.00
5929.	Little Girl with Basket	9 x 4	NYGS	.50
5930.	Little Shepherd	21 x 15-1/2	NYGS	7.50
		15-1/2 x 11-1/2	NYGS	3.00
5931.	Lovers	27 x 20	NYGS	12.00
		24 x 18	PENN	1.00
				1.98 (Pr.)
		23 x 18	HNA	5.95
		20 x 15	AP	7.50
		14 x 11	NYGS	3.00
5932.	Ma Jolie	23-1/2 x 21	AR	12.00
5933.	Madame Jacqueline R.	8 x 6	CFA	1.00
5934.	Man with Guitar	8 x 6	CFA	1.00
5935.	Mandolin and Guitar	19-1/2 x 28	AA	15.00
5936.	Maternité, 1903	18 x 16	NYGS	10.00
5937.	Maternity	26 x 20	AR	15.00
		19 x 15	AR	7.50

5938.	Maternity	19 x 15	PENN	1.00
				1.98 (Pr.)
5939.	Modern Madonna	24 x 24	CAC	18.00
5940.	The Mother	24 x 16-1/2	NYGS	12.00
5941.	Mother and Child, 1922	28 x 22-1/2	NYGS	15.00
		20 x 16	PENN	1.00
				1.98 (Pr.)
5942.	Mother and Child, 1921	25 x 28	NYGS	15.00
5943.	Mother and Child (Blue)	27-1/2 x 21-1/2	IA	15.00
		24 x 18-1/2	PENN	1.00
5944.	The Mothers	14-1/2 x 18	ESH	10.00
		8 x 10	ESH	1.00
5945.	Moulin de la Galette	21-1/2 x 28	NYGS	15.00
5946.	The Muse, 1935	8 x 10	AR	2.00
5947.	Nature Morte	24 x 30	DAC	8.00
		11 x 14	DAC	2.80
5948.	Nature Morte au Cerises	15 x 23-1/2	PENN	1.00
5949.	Nature Morte aux Poissons	19-1/2 x 24	NYGS	18.00
5950.	Nude, Half-Length	24 x 19	NYGS	10.00
		14 x 11	NYGS	2.00
5951.	Nude with a Towel	28 x 21-1/2	NYGS	15.00
5952.	Old Guitarist	30 x 20	NYGS	18.00
5953.	Palette and Bust	14 x 18	CFA	7.50
5954.	Pierrot, 1918	24 x 19	PENN	1.00
				1.98 (Pr.)
		10 x 8	ESH	1.00
5955.	Pierrot and Harlequin	10 x 7-1/2	MMA	3.00
5956.	Pierrot with Flowers	21 x 15-1/2	NYGS	7.50
		15-1/2 x 11-1/2	NYGS	3.00
5957.	Pierrot with Mask	21 x 15-1/2	NYGS	7.50
		15-1/2 x 11-1/2	NYGS	3.00
5958.	Pigeons	22-1/2 x 17	ESH	10.00
5959.	Portfolio (6)		PENN	2.98 set
	La Casserole Emaillee	11 x 14		
	La Liseuse Grise	14 x 8-1/2		
	The Lovers	14 x 10-1/2		
	Portrait de Femme	14 x 11		
	Still Life, Tete Antique	10-1/2 x 14		
	The Tragedy	14 x 9		
5960.	Portrait, 1938	10 x 8	ESH	1.00
5961.	Portrait de Femme	22-1/2 x 18	PENN	1.00
5962.	Portrait of Gertrude Stein	8 x 7	NYGS	.50
5963.	Portrait of Jaimes Sabartes	10 x 8	ESH	1.00
5964.	Portrait of Madame "Z"	22-1/2 x 18	ESH	10.00
5965.	Portrait of a Young Woman, Version XIII	22-1/2 x 18	ESH	10.00
		10 x 8	ESH	1.00

5966.	Poster	28-1/2 x 19-1/2	PENN	1. 00
5967.	Rooster	14 x 11	AP	5. 00
5968.	Saltimbanque Seated with a Boy	8 x 10	ESH	1. 00
5969.	Self-Portrait as Harlequin at Lapin Agile	19 x 19	ESH	10. 00
5970.	Seated Bather	28 x 23	NYGS	15. 00
5971.	Sculptor and Models	16-1/2 x 24	PENN	1. 00
5972.	Seated Nude	22 x 16	ESH	10. 00
5973.	Seated Woman	7 x 5	CFA	1. 00
5974.	Sleeping Peasants	8 x 10	MMA	. 35
5975.	Southern Landscape	15 x 22-1/2	ESH	10. 00
5976.	Les Soupeurs	16-1/2 x 24	PENN	1. 00
				1. 98 (Pr.)
5977.	Still Life	8 x 5	CFA	1. 00
5978.	Still Life	16 x 20	IA	7. 50
5979.	Still Life in a Land-scape	8 x 10	ESH	1. 00
5980.	Still Life, 1901	21 x 28-1/2	NYGS	15. 00
5981.	Still Life, 1918	18 x 24	NYGS	10. 00
5982.	Still Life, Antique Bust	17-1/2 x 24	AR	12. 00
		8 x 10	AR	2. 00
5983.	Still Life, Antique Head	18 x 24	PENN	1. 00
				1. 98 (Pr.)
		18 x 23	HNA	5. 95
		15 x 20	NYGS	7. 50
5984.	Still Life with Black Head	5 x 7	NYGS	. 50
5985.	Still Life with Casserole	18 x 23	HNA	5. 95
5986.	Still Life with Fish	24 x 18	DAC	6. 00
		10 x 8	ESH	1. 00
5987.	Still Life with Guitar	18 x 22-1/2	AA	12. 00
		18 x 22	ESH	10. 00
		14 x 18	CFA	7. 50
5988.	Still Life with Mandolin	11 x 14	DAC	2. 80
5989.	Still Life with Mandolin, 1923	20-1/2 x 28	NYGS	15. 00
5990.	Still Life with Mandolin, 1924	17 x 23	NYGS	10. 00
5991.	Still Life with Red Shawl	8 x 7	NYGS	. 50
5992.	Still Life with Wallpaper	13 x 17	NYGS	10. 00
5993.	Still Life with Yellow Jug	5 x 7	NYGS	. 50
5994.	The Studio	21 x 31	CFA	15. 00
		18 x 22-1/2	ESH	10. 00
		8 x 10	MMA	. 35
5995.	La Table Mise	8 x 10	ESH	1. 00
5996.	Tete de Jeune Fille	24 x 17-1/2	NYGS	7. 50

5997.	Tete de Jeune Homme	24 x 17-1/2	NYGS	7.50
5998.	Three Musicians	21 x 22-1/2	MMA	6.00
		17 x 19	PENN	1.00
		6 x 6	CFA	1.00
5999.	La Toilette	28 x 18	NYGS	15.00
		9 x 6	CFA	1.00
6000.	The Tragedy	25 x 16	PENN	1.00
				1.98 (Pr.)
		24 x 15-1/2	NYGS	12.00
		23 x 18	HNA	5.95
6001.	Tumblers	10 x 8	ESH	1.00
6002.	Two Children	18-1/2 x 22-1/2	AP	10.00
6003.	Two Harlequins	26 x 19	NYGS	12.00
		14 x 10	NYGS	3.00
		9 x 7	NYGS	.50
		8 x 5-1/2	NYGS	.50
6004.	Two Sisters	8 x 5	CFA	1.00
6005.	Ulysses and the Sirens	8 x 5	CFA	1.00
6006.	The Violin	24 x 18	CFA	15.00
6007.	White Clown	20 x 13	PENN	1.00
				1.98 (Pr.)
6008.	The Window	8 x 6	CFA	1.00
6009.	Woman, A Portrait	21 x 15-1/2	PENN	1.00
6010.	Woman Asleep	7 x 5	NYGS	.50
6011.	Woman Before a Mirror	27-1/2 x 22	NYGS	18.00
6012.	Woman Carrying Bread	10 x 8	ESH	1.00
6013.	Woman in Blue Stockings	9 x 7	NYGS	.50
6014.	Woman in White	22 x 18	AP	3.00
		17 x 14	CFA	7.50
6015.	Woman of Majorca	10 x 8	ESH	1.00
6016.	Woman Sitting	28 x 21	CFA	15.00
		17 x 14	CFA	7.50
6017.	Woman on a Wall	7 x 6	CFA	1.00
6018.	Woman with a Cape	23-1/2 x 16	PENN	1.00
6019.	Woman with a Fan	6 x 5	CFA	1.00
6020.	Woman with a Fish Hat	27-1/2 x 22	NYGS	12.00
6021.	Woman with a Flowered Hat	19-1/2 x 16	AR	7.50
6022.	Woman with a Hat	19 x 16	CFA	7.50
6023.	Young Girl with Arm Upraised	19 x 16	CFA	7.50

PICKEN. GEORGE ALEXANDER   American   1898-

6024.	Hawthorne, New York	7 x 20	NYGS	5.00

PICKERGILL, H.

6025.	Lady in Blue	28 x 22	CFA	10.00

PICKETT, JOSEPH   American   1848-1918

6026.	Coryell's Ferry	23 x 30	CFA	12.00
6027.	Manchester Valley	22-1/2 x 30	MMA	5.50
		22 x 29-1/2	NYGS	12.00
		8 x 10	MMA	.35
		5 x 7	NYGS	.50

PICOT

6028. Eros and Psyche	10 x 12		CFA	2.50
PIEPER, JOSEF	German		1907-	
6029. Children with Bird	19 x 24		CFA	15.00
6030. Half-Nude	25-1/2 x 19		ESH	10.00
6031. Reminiscence	15 x 28		CFA	15.00
PIERO DELLA FRANCESCA (FRA SAN SEPOLCRO)			Italian	
1416-1492				
6032. Annunciation	15 x 9		IA	3.00
6033. Battista Sforza,				
Duchess of Urbino	15 x 11		IA	3.00
6034. Chosroes Defeated				
by Heraclius	7 x 15		IA	3.00
6035. Details of No. 6034 (2)	15 x 11		IA	3.00 ea.
6036. Death and Burial of				
Adam	11 x 15		IA	3.00
6037. Adam--Detail of No.				
6036	11 x 15		IA	3.00
6038. Two Figures--Detail				
of No. 6036	15 x 11		IA	3.00
6039. Dream of Constantine				
(Detail)	15 x 11		IA	3.00
6040. Empress Helen and				
the Invention of the				
Cross	15 x 11		IA	3.00
6041. Federico di Montefeltro,				
Duke of Urbino	15 x 11		IA	3.00
6042. Flagellation	10 x 14		IA	3.00
6043. Madonna of Senigallia	12 x 10		IA	3.00
6044. Resurrection	12 x 10		IA	3.00
6045. Queen of Sheba Adoring				
the Cross	15 x 11		IA	3.00
6046. Queen of Sheba--				
Detail of No. 6045	15 x 11		IA	3.00
6047. Queen of Sheba and				
Maids	18 x 23		HNA	5.95
6048. Recognition of the				
Cross	11 x 15		IA	3.00
6049. Solomon's Reception				
of the Queen of				
Sheba	11 x 15		IA	3.00
6050. Victory of Constantine				
over Maxentius	11 x 14		IA	3.00
PIERO DI COSIMO	Italian		1462-1521	
6051. Portrait of a Florentine				
Lady (The Magdalene)	14 x 11		IA	3.00
6052. Simonetta Vespucci				
(Cleopatra?)	14 x 10		IA	3.00
PIERRE, GUSTAVE	French		1875-	
6053. Antique Bas-Relief				
(Panel of 5)	7 x 25		CFA	15.00

PIKE, JOHN	American	1911-	
6054. Ahead of the Wind	18 x 26	DAC	6.00
	11 x 14	DAC	2.00
6055. Bearsville Store	18 x 26	DAC	6.00
	11 x 14	DAC	2.00
6056. Campers	18 x 26	DAC	6.00
	11 x 14	DAC	2.00
6057. Fritzi and Fred	18 x 26	DAC	6.00
	11 x 14	DAC	2.00
6058. I'll Show the Way	18 x 26	DAC	6.00
	11 x 14	DAC	2.00
6059. Lake Lure	21 x 27	NYGS	10.00
6060. Perfect Morning	21 x 27	NYGS	10.00
6061. Water in the Flatlands	18 x 26	DAC	6.00
	11 x 14	DAC	2.00
PINTURICCHIO (BERNARDINO DI BETTO) Italian 1454-1513			
6062. Assumption of the Virgin	15 x 11	IA	3.00
6063. The "Cavaliere di Rodi", Alberto Arringhieri	10 x 12	IA	3.00
6064. Madonna and Child	13 x 11	IA	3.00
6065. Madonna and Child and Saints	14 x 9	IA	3.00
6066. Madonna and Saints	14 x 10	IA	3.00
6067. Meeting of Frederic III with Eleanor of Portugal	15 x 9	IA	3.00
6068. Nativity	15 x 10	IA	3.00
6069. Virgin--Detail of No. 6068	15 x 11	IA	3.00
	11 x 8-1/2	IA	1.75
6070. Portrait of a Boy	18 x 12-1/2	NYGS	16.00
PIOMBO, SEBASTIANO DEL	Italian	1485-1547	
6071. Christopher Columbus	10 x 8	NYGS	.50
6072. Giovane Romana	7 x 5	NYGS	.50
6073. Portrait of a Young Roman Lady	23 x 18	HNA	5.95
PIOT, A.			
6074. Poppy Girl	29 x 22	AA	10.00
PIPER, JOHN	English	1903-	
6075. Cottages	16 x 20	NYGS	10.00
6076. St. Mary Le Port	18 x 15	AP	6.00
PIPPAL, HANS ROBERT	Austrian	1915-	
6077. Girl with a Flower	24 x 18	IA	12.00
6078. Young Girl	24 x 18	IA	12.00
PIRONIN, HORTENSE	French		
6079. Coin du Port a Treboul	18-1/2 x 25	RL	6.00
6080. Pier Head	22-1/2 x 18	RL	6.00
6081. Sunny Brittany	18-1/2 x 25	RL	6.00
PISANO, GIOVANNI	Italian	c. 1245-1314	
6082. Madonna and Child (Ivory)	15 x 11	IA	3.00

PISANELLO, ANTONIO	Italian	1377-1455	
6083. Princess of Este	13 x 10	IA	3.00
6084. Vision of St. Eustace	21 x 25-1/2	NYGS	12.00
PISIS, FILIPO DE	Italian	1896-	
6085. Chiesa della Salute	30 x 23	NYGS	15.00
6086. Flowers	24-1/2 x 19	NYGS	12.00
6087. La Strada	23 x 35	CFA	15.00
PISSARRO, CAMILLE	French	1830-1903	
6088. Avenue de L'Opera			
in 1900	24 x 30	ESH	15.00
6089. Blossoming Plum Tree	19 x 24	CFA	15.00
6090. Boulevard Montmartre	20 x 25	AR	12.00
	18 x 23	HNA	5.95
	15-1/2 x 18-1/2	AP	5.00
6091. Boulevard Montmartre			
at Night	20 x 25-1/2	NYGS	12.00
6092. Bridge at Bruges	18 x 21-1/2	NYGS	12.00
	18 x 21	CFA	12.00
6093. Chestnut Trees	15 x 19-1/2	AP	7.50
6094. Church at Knoche	8 x 10	ESH	1.00
6095. Church and Castle at			
Eragny	8 x 10	ESH	1.00
6096. Conversation	13 x 10	IA	3.00
6097. Entrance to a Village	18 x 22-1/2	ESH	10.00
	8 x 10	ESH	1.00
6098. Flowery Palm Trees	10 x 12	IA	3.00
6099. French Winter Scene	24 x 30	DAC	8.00
6100. Garden of Tuileries	23 x 33	CFA	18.00
6101. Gypsy Wagon	13 x 16	NYGS	12.00
6102. L'Hermitage	10 x 8	ESH	1.00
6103. Landscape	16 x 19	AP	5.00
6104. Meadow at Mont			
Foucauld	8 x 10	ESH	1.00
6105. Morning at the Louvre	6 x 8	CFA	1.00
6106. L'Oise near Pontoise	16-1/2 x 19-1/2	NYGS	10.00
6107. Orchard	8 x 10	ESH	1.00
6108. Le Pavillon de Flore	8 x 10	ESH	1.00
6109. Place du Theatre			
Francais	7 x 9	CFA	1.00
6110. Le Pont de Pierre,			
Rouen	16-1/2 x 23	PENN	1.00
6111. Le Pont Neuf	8 x 7	NYGS	.50
6112. Pontoise	24 x 30	PENN	1.00
6113. Les Quais a Rouen	20 x 23-1/2	PENN	1.00
6114. Red Roofs	18 x 22	ESH	10.00
	8 x 10	ESH	1.00
	7 x 9	NYGS	.50
	7 x 8	CFA	1.00
6115. River Bank	21-1/2 x 36	AA	15.00
6116. Road	6 x 8	CFA	1.00
6117. Road Along the Railway	6 x 9	NYGS	.50
6118. Road to Ennery	18 x 22-1/2	ESH	10.00

6119. Road to Louveciennes	18 x 23	HNA	5.95
	8 x 10	ESH	1.00
6120. Seine at Marly	17 x 23	NYGS	15.00
6121. Seine from the Pont Neuf	18 x 22	ESH	10.00
6122. Snow Effects--Norwood	7 x 10	NYGS	.50
6123. Street in Rouen	22-1/2 x 18	ESH	10.00
	10 x 8	ESH	1.00
6124. Street in Upper Norwood	7 x 8	NYGS	.50
6125. Towpath	24-1/2 x 30	ESH	15.00
	8 x 10	ESH	1.00
PITTMAN, OSMUND	English	1874-	
6126. Orte on the Tiber	17 x 24	RL	5.00
PITTONI, GIOVAN BATTISTA	Italian	1687-1767	
6127. Nativity	15 x 11	IA	3.00
PLATT, DOROTHY			
6128. Angel Wing Begonia	13 x 19	CFA	5.00
6129. Begonia Venusta	19 x 13	CFA	5.00
6130. Buseri Phaseoulus	19 x 13	CFA	5.00
6131. Clematis	19 x 13	CFA	5.00
6132. Geranium	13 x 19	CFA	5.00
6133. Hibiscus	19 x 13	CFA	5.00
PLOCKHORST, BERNHARD	German	1825-1907	
6134. Christ Blessing the Children	28 x 20	IA	6.00
	20 x 14-1/2	IA	4.00
	10-1/2 x 7-1/2	NYGS	.50
	10 x 7	IA	10.00 (Grav.)
6135. Christ's Entry into Jerusalem	6 x 10	NYGS	.50
6136. The Good Shepherd	28 x 21	IA	6.00
	20 x 14	IA	4.00
	12 x 9	IA	3.50
	10 x 7	NYGS	.50
6137. Guardian Angel	10 x 6	IA	10.00
6138. Holy Family	10 x 7	NYGS	.50
PLUIM, R.			
6139. Paris Views (6)	11 x 14	DAC	1.20 ea.

Montmartre, Sacre Coeur
Notre Dame
Place de la Concorde
Place de L'Opera
Quai des Grands Augustins
Rue Mouffetard

PODESTI, FRANCESCO	Italian	1800-1895	
6140. Verdi and the Countess Zaccarial	7-1/2 x 22-1/2	NYGS	7.50
POEPPEL, MAX	German		
6141. Moonlight	19 x 25	CFA	15.00

POITEAU
  6142. Fruit Prints, Antique (5) 13 x 10   NYGS 3.00 ea.
                    (6) 10 x 7   NYGS 2.00 ea.
POLLAIUOLO, ANTONIO (BENCI, ANTONIO) Italian 1433-1498
  6143. Coronation of the
           Virgin, and Saints   14 x 10   IA   3.00
  6144. Hercules and Antaeus 7 x 4   IA   1.50
  6145. Hercules and Nessus   7 x 10   NYGS   .50
  6146. Hercules and the Hydra 7 x 5   IA   1.50
  6147. Portrait of a Lady   15 x 11   IA   3.00
POLLAIUOLO, PIERO (BENCI, PIERO) Italian   1443-1496
  6148. Galleazzo Maria Sforza 15 x 10   IA   3.00
POLLARD, J.
  6149. Blenheim Leaving Star
           Hotel   11 x 16   CFA   12.00
  6150. Elephant Castle, Brighton 12 x 15   CFA   12.00
  6151. Hyde Park Corner   11 x 16   CFA   12.00
  6152. North Country Mails   11 x 16   CFA   12.00
  6153. Royal Mail   11 x 16   CFA   10.00
  6154. West Country Mails   11 x 16   CFA   12.00
POLLOCK, JACKSON   American   1912-1956
  6155. Composition   24 x 19   PENN   1.00
  6156. Number 27   13-1/2 x 29-1/2 NYGS 15.00
  6157. Water Beast   13-1/2 x 39-1/2 NYGS 18.00
POLLONI, SILVIO   Italian   1888-
  6158. Tropical Fish (6)   9 x 7   NYGS 5.00 set
                                    or 1.00 ea.
POMPEIAN FRESCOES
  6159. Bacchante   14 x 11   IA   3.00
  6160. Chariot Race of Cupids 11 x 15   IA   3.00
  6161. Cupids as Dyers   10-1/2 x 15   IA   3.00
  6162. Cupids as Florists   10 x 15   IA   3.00
  6163. Cupids as Locksmiths 11 x 14-1/2 IA   3.00
  6164. Cupids as Perfumers   11 x 15   IA   3.00
  6165. Little Girls as Florists 10-1/2 x 15   IA   3.00
PONTORMO (CARRUCCI, JACOPO) Italian   1494-1557
  6166. Cosimo De'Medici,
           Pater Patriae   15 x 11   IA   3.00
  6167. Giuliano De'Medici   15 x 11   IA   3.00
POOR, HENRY VARNUM   American   1888-
  6168. Bessie   5 x 7   NYGS   .50
  6169. Chess Game   8 x 7   NYGS   .50
  6170. Fruit   5 x 7   NYGS   .50
  6171. Head of Lynn   9 x 7   NYGS   .50
  6172. Lynn in Blue   5 x 7   NYGS   .50
  6173. Man in Brown Jerkin 9 x 7   NYGS   .50
  6174. March Snow   8 x 7   NYGS   .50
  6175. March Sun   6 x 7   NYGS   .50
  6176. Mural   9 x 5   NYGS   .50
  6177. Red-Haired Girl   9 x 7   NYGS   .50
  6178. Three Sisters   9 x 6   NYGS   .50
  6179. Writer   8 x 7   NYGS   .50

6180. Young Man in Seersucker Coat	9 x 7	NYGS	.50
PORDENONE, GIOVANNI	Italian	1483-1539	
6181. Study of a Nude	11 x 7	AR	3.00
PORTER, SOPHIE	American		
6182. Coffee Pot	15 x 15	NYGS	7.50
6183. From Garden and Orchard	28 x 14	NYGS	10.00
6184. Fruits and Flowers	28 x 14	NYGS	10.00
6185. Tea Pot	15 x 15	NYGS	7.50
PORTINARI, CANDIDO	Brazilian	1903-	
6186. Coffee Bearers	24-1/2 x 30	NYGS	18.00
	6 x 7-1/2	NYGS	.50
POSTELS, ROBERT DE			
6187. Happy Hours	16 x 34	NYGS	10.00
	10-1/2 x 22	NYGS	5.00
POT, HENDRIK GERRITSZ	Dutch	1600-1657	
6188. Miser	11 x 10	IA	3.00
POTHAST, BERNARD J. C.	Dutch	1882-	
6189. Her First Lesson	21 x 25-1/2	NYGS	10.00
POTRONAT, L.			
6190. Landscapes (6)	12 x 16	DAC	2.00 ea.
	8 x 10	DAC	.80 ea.
At the Wharf			
Going Ashore			
Marine Plaza			
Old Road			
Seaview Hill			
Winding Shore			
6191. Saint Raphael	22 x 28	IA	12.00
POTTER, PAUL	Dutch	1625-1665	
6192. Calving Cow	10-1/2 x 9	AR	3.00
POUCETTE			
6193. Boats at Deauville	19-1/2 x 15	PENN	1.00
6194. Harlequin and Mandolin	20 x 10	PENN	1.00
6195. Harlequin with Guitar	20 x 10	PENN	1.00
6196. Imaginary Landscape	19-1/2 x 15	PENN	1.00
POURBUS, FRANS (THE YOUNGER) Flemish		1568-1622	
6197. Portrait of a Man	15 x 11	IA	3.00
6198. A Youth	15 x 11	IA	3.00
POUSSIN, NICOLAS	French	1594-1665	
6199. Annunciation	8 x 9	AR	3.00
6200. Assumption of the Virgin	26 x 19	NYGS	12.00
6201. Funeral of Phocion	7 x 10	NYGS	.50
6202. Holy Family on the Steps	19-1/2 x 28	IA	15.00
6203. Ponte, Molle, Rome	9 x 15	CFA	4.00
POUWELLS, PIETER			
6204. Flower Scenes (2)	22 x 12	DAC	2.80 ea.
	12 x 6	DAC	.80 ea.
	10 x 6	DAC	.28 ea.

PREDIS, AMBROGIO DE	Italian	1455-1520	
6205. Portrait of a Youth	15 x 12	IA	3.00
PREHISTORIC ART			
6206. Drawing from the			
Lascaux Caves	9-1/2 x 17	ESH	5.00
6207. Falling Bison	17-1/2 x 25	AP	7.50
6208. Grazing Reindeer	17-1/2 x 25	AP	7.50
6209. Jumping Cow	18 x 23	HNA	5.95
6210. Lascaux Caves:			
Chinese Horse	17-1/2 x 22-1/2	ESH	10.00
Great Hall of			
the Bulls	14-1/2 x 30	ESH	15.00
Hall of the Bulls,			
Left Side	8 x 10	ESH	1.00
Detail, Left Side	8 x 10	ESH	1.00
Hall of the Bulls,			
Right Side	8 x 10	ESH	1.00
Red Horse, Bull and			
Brown Horses	8 x 10	ESH	1.00
Right Side of the			
Divertical Axial	8 x 10	ESH	1.00
Second Bull and			
Red Horse	8 x 10	ESH	1.00
Second Chinois			
Horse on the			
Right Side	8 x 10	ESH	1.00
Troupeau Dit "Des			
Caerfs Nageant"	8 x 10	ESH	1.00
PRENDERGAST, MAURICE	American	1859-1924	
6211. Acadia	8 x 10	MMA	.35
6212. Boat Loading	14-1/2 x 24	PENN	1.00
6213. Central Park	14 x 21-1/2	NYGS	12.00
PRENTICE, L. W.			
6214. Basket of Apples	20 x 16	CFA	7.50
6215. Pail of Apples	20 x 16	CFA	7.50
PRESSMANE, JOSEPH	Polish-French	1904-	
6216. Enghien in the Snow	17-1/2 x 21	ESH	10.00
PRETI, CLITOFONTE	Italian	19th Century	
6217. Maternity	15 x 10	IA	3.00
PRICE			
6218. Lyric Art (4)	9 x 28	DAC	4.00 ea.
PRIESTMAN, BERTRAM	English	1868-	
6219. Abbey on the Hill	19 x 23	RL	6.00
PRIMATICCIO, FRANCESCO	Italian	1504-1570	
6220. Ceres on a Couch	7-1/2 x 11	AR	3.00
PRINZ, KARL LUDWIG	Austrian	1875-	
6221. Lilac Time	19-1/2 x 29	NYGS	7.50
PROOM, AL			
6222. Accent in White	15 x 30	AA	12.00
6223. Basket	15 x 30	AA	12.00
PROTIC, MIODRAG	Serbian	Contemporary	
6224. Still Life with Pitcher	21 x 35	NYGS	12.00

PRUD'HON, PIERRE PAUL	French	1758-1823	
6225. Head of Vengeance	19 x 15	NYGS	6.00
PURRMANN, HANS	German	1880-	
6226. Castagnola	26 x 29	CFA	15.00
6227. Fountain in Triente	28 x 23	ESH	12.00
6228. Landscape Ischia	23 x 28	CFA	15.00
6229. Road with Palm Tree	18 x 23	HNA	5.95
6230. Street Scene	22 x 27-1/2	NYGS	15.00
PUSHMAN, HOVSEP	American	Contemporary	
6231. When Autumn is Here	23 x 16	NYGS	10.00
PUVIS DE CHAVANNES, PIERRE	French	1824-1898	
6232. Hope	11 x 12	IA	3.00
PUY, JEAN	French	1876-	
6233. Port at Douellan	8 x 10	ESH	1.00
6234. Red Sails	14-1/2 x 22-1/2	ESH	10.00

Q

QUIZET, LEON ALPHONSE	French	1885-1955	
6235. Moulin de la Galette	20 x 24	NYGS	12.00

R

RACOFF			
6236. Red Rose	11 x 14	DAC	2.00
	6 x 8	DAC	1.00
6237. Tea Rose	11 x 14	DAC	2.00
	6 x 8	DAC	1.00
RAEBURN, (SIR) HENRY	Scotch	1756-1823	
6238. Boy and Rabbit	26 x 20	CAC	7.50
	20 x 16	CAC	5.00
	12 x 9	CAC	2.00
6239. Col. Charles Christie	28 x 23	CAC	10.00
6240. Drummond Children	11 x 7	NYGS	.50
6241. English Officer	28 x 22	CAC	10.00
6242. Miss Eleanor Urquhart	19 x 16	CAC	7.50
RAFFAELLINO DEL GARBO	Italian	1466/70-1524	
6243. Studies of Hands for Madonna	12-1/2 x 9-1/2	AR	4.00
RAFFAELLO SANZIO (RAPHAEL)	Italian	1483-1520	
6244. Alba Madonna	24" circle	NYGS	16.00
	16 x 16	PENN	1.00
	8-1/2" circle	NYGS	.50
	8" circle	NYGS	.50
6245. Andrea Navagero and Agostino Beazzino	10 x 15	IA	3.00
6246. Angiolo Doni	15 x 11	IA	3.00
6247. Ansidei Madonna	20 x 13	CAC	10.00
6248. Bindo Altoviti	23 x 17-1/2	AA	7.50
6249. Classic Figures (4)	18 x 8	CFA	4.00 ea.
6250. Coronation of the Virgin	15 x 9	IA	3.00
6251. La Disputa	18 x 24	IA	7.50
	8 x 11	IA	1.75

6252. La Donna Gravida	14 x 11	IA	3.00
6253. La Donna Velata	10 x 8	NYGS	.50
6254. Entombment	11 x 12	IA	3.00
6255. Fire in the Borgo	7 x 10	NYGS	.50
6256. Four Designs	9 x 14	AR	3.00
6257. Francesco Maria della Rovere	15 x 11	IA	3.00
	9 x 7	NYGS	.50
6258. Heraclitus	9 x 7	NYGS	.50
6259. Holy Family	13 x 8	CFA	2.50
6260. Maddalena Doni	15 x 11	IA	3.00
6261. Madonna "La Belle Jardiniere"	15 x 10	IA	3.00
6262. Madonna del Cardelino	16 x 12	IA	3.00
	10 x 8	IA	1.50
	9 x 7	IA	1.75
6263. Madonna of Foligno	15 x 10	IA	3.00
6264. Angel--Detail of No. 6263	15 x 11	IA	3.00
6265. Madonna del Granduca	30 x 20	ESH	15.00
	24 x 13-1/2	NYGS	7.50
	21 x 14	AP	5.00
	16 x 11	IA	3.00
	10 x 8	ESH	1.00
	10 x 5-1/2	NYGS	.50
6266. Madonna della Sedia (Madonna of the Chair)	29" circle	IA	12.00
	20" circle	IA	10.00
	12" circle	IA	3.50
	11" circle	IA	3.00
	8-1/2" circle	IA	1.75
6267. Madonna della Tenda	28 x 20	CAC	15.00
	22 x 17	CAC	12.00
6268. Madonna of Maison d'Orleans	14 x 8	IA	3.00
6269. Madonna of San Sisto (Sistine)	35 x 26	CAC	15.00
	27 x 24	CFA	12.00
	27 x 24	CAC	25.00
	24 x 18	IA	7.50
	21 x 15-1/2	NYGS	5.00
	15 x 11	IA	3.00
	10 x 7	NYGS	.50
6270. Madonna with the Pomegranate	16 x 11-1/2	AR	5.00
6271. Marriage of the Virgin	15 x 10	IA	3.00
6272. The Virgin--Detail of No. 6271	10 x 8	IA	1.50
6273. La Muta	14 x 11	IA	3.00
6274. Niccolini-Cowper Madonna	24 x 16-1/2	NYGS	7.50
6275. Pope Julius II	13 x 11	IA	3.00

6276.	Pope Julius II Praying	7 x 9	NYGS	.50
6277.	Portrait of Leo X and Two Cardinals	15 x 11	IA	3.00
6278.	Portrait of Maddalena Strozzi-Doni	15 x 11	IA	3.00
6279.	Portrait of Perugino (Supposed)	15 x 10	IA	3.00
6280.	Resurrection of Christ	13 x 11	IA	3.00
6281.	St. Jerome	15 x 11	IA	3.00
6282.	St. John in the Desert	12 x 11	IA	3.00
6283.	A Scribe	9 x 7	NYGS	.50
6284.	Self-Portrait	14 x 11	IA	3.00
6285.	Studies of Movements	14 x 9	AR	3.00
6286.	School of Athens	18 x 24	IA	7.50
		8 x 11	IA	1.75
6287.	Small Cowper Madonna	22-1/2 x 16	PENN	1.00
				1.98 (Pr.)
		21 x 16	NYGS	7.50
6288.	Three Studies of the Virgin	11 x 8	AR	3.00
6289.	Tommaso Inghirami	15 x 11	IA	3.00
6290.	Transfiguration	15 x 10	IA	3.00
6291.	Young Woman--Detail of No. 6290.	15 x 10	IA	3.00
6292.	Two Muses	9 x 7	NYGS	.50
6293.	Two Muses	10 x 7	NYGS	.50
6294.	Veiled Lady (Fornarina?)	15 x 11	IA	3.00
6295.	The Virgin	10 x 8	IA	1.50
		9 x 7	IA	1.75
6296.	Virgin with the Blue Diadem (Virgin of the Veil)	15 x 11	IA	3.00
6297.	Young Man	19 x 14	CAC	7.50
RAIBOLINO, FRANCESCO		See FRANCIA, IL		
RAIN, CHARLES		American	1911-	
6298.	Dark Stranger	24 x 30	CFA	15.00
RAJKO		Yugoslavian	Contemporary	
6299.	Hawaii, 1963	24 x 20	NYGS	7.50
6300.	Tahiti, 1963	24 x 20	NYGS	7.50
RAKER, JAMES		American	Contemporary	
6301.	Afternoon	10 x 8	AR	2.00
6302.	Becalmed	10 x 8	AR	2.00
6303.	Boy with Horse	10 x 8	AR	2.00
6304.	Redbird and Cat	10 x 8	AR	2.00
RAOUX, JEAN		French	1677-1734	
6305.	Young Girl Reading a Letter	19 x 15	CFA	10.00
RAPHAEL		See RAFFAELLO SANZIO		
RAWSON, CARL				
6306.	Autumn Farewell	19-1/2 x 25	IA	6.00
6307.	Landscapes (6)	12 x 15	IA	10.00 set
	Autumn Reflections			
	Fruitage of Autumn			

                 Offshore Wind
                 Superior Days
                 Where the Fisherfolk Live
6308. Winter   25 x 32   IA   12.00
RAY, ROBERT
6309. Sunflowers   26-1/2 x 38   IA   12.00
RAY, RUTH
6310. Noble Steeds (4)   18 x 24   DAC   6.00 ea.
                             9 x 12   DAC   1.20 ea.
                 Copper Queen
                 Golden Ruler
                 Handsome Witch
                 Storm King
REDON, ODILON   French   1840-1916
6311. Blue Vase on Dark
         Background   10 x 8   ESH   1.00
6312. Cyklops   8 x 10   MMA   .35
6313. Field Flowers   16-1/2 x 21   PENN   1.00
                             11 x 14   DAC   2.80
6314. Flowers   18 x 23   HNA   5.95
6315. Flowers in a Blue Vase 23 x 17-1/2   AR   12.00
6316. Flowers in a Jar   22 x 16   ESH   10.00
                             20-1/2 x 12-1/2 PENN   1.00
6317. Girl with Flowers   18 x 23   PENN   1.00
                                                        1.98 (Pr.)
6318. Large Green Vase   23 x 18   HNA   5.95
                             22 x 17   PENN   1.00
                                                        1.98 (Pr.)
6319. Ophilie   26 x 18   PENN   1.00
                                                        1.98 (Pr.)
6320. Phaeton   19 x 23-1/2   NYGS   10.00
6321. Red Boat   18 x 24   CFA   12.00
6322. Still Life   21 x 16   AA   7.50
6323. Turquoise Vase with
         Flowers   23 x 18   HNA   5.95
6324. Vase of Flowers   26 x 21   HNA   5.95
                             22-1/2 x 18   ESH   10.00
                             20-1/2 x 12-1/2 PENN   1.00
6325. Vase of Flowers   26 x 19   MMA   6.50
6326. Vase with Flowers   8 x 6   NYGS   .50
6327. Wildflowers   24 x 18   NYGS   10.00
REDOUTE, PIERRE JOSEPH   French   1759-1840
6328. Cactus   19 x 14   CFA   5.00
6329. Choix de Fleurs   19 x 14   CFA   7.50
6330. Mixed Bouquet   19 x 14   CFA   5.00
6331. Red and Pink Roses   19 x 14   CFA   5.00
6332. Rose du Bengale   8 x 5   CFA   3.00
6333. Rose de Bordeau   8 x 5   CFA   3.00
6334. Rose d'Enfante   11 x 19   CAC   3.00
6335. Rose de France   8 x 5   CFA   3.00
6336. Rose d'Hudson   8 x 5   CFA   3.00
6337. Roses de Cumberland   15 x 10   CAC   5.00

6338. Roses des Indes	8 x 5	CFA	3. 00
6339. Roses de Paris	8 x 5	CFA	3. 00
6340. Rosier a Cent Feuilles	15 x 10	CAC	5. 00
6341. Rosier des Parfumeurs	15 x 10	CAC	5. 00
6342. Rosier Grandeur Royale	15 x 10	CAC	5. 00
6343. Yellow and Pink Roses	19 x 14	CFA	5. 00

REED

6344. Canterbury Pilgrims	16 x 60	CAC	10. 00

REGAN

6345. Liberty Island	24 x 40	DAC	8. 00
6346. The Seasons (4)	24 x 8	DAC	2. 00 ea.
6347. Sunset on the Snow	24 x 40	DAC	8. 00

REGGIANINI

6348. Mother's Birthday	19 x 27	AA	9. 00

REGIER

6349. Southern Street Scenes (6)	10 x 8	DAC	. 60 ea.

        Corner Shop
        Sail Patches
        Sea View Dock
        Sunnyside Way
        Sunny South

REGNAULT, HENRI	French	1843-1871	
6350. Automdon	16 x 17	CAC	3. 50
REHN, FRANK K. M.	American	1848-1914	
6351. In the Glittering Moonlight	24 x 36	NYGS	15. 00
REIMER, T. E			
6352. The Bay, Capri	20 x 27	RL	7. 50
REMBRANDT HARMENSZ VAN RIJN	Dutch	1606-1669	
6353. Admiral's Wife	36-1/2 x 29-1/2	NYGS	20. 00
6354. Adoration des Bergers	8 x 9	NYGS	4. 00
6355. Anatomy Lesson	17-1/2 x 23-1/2	NYGS	18. 00
6356. Apostle Paul	26 x 20	IA	12. 00
6357. Aristotle Contemplating a Bust of Homer	28 x 27	CFA	12. 50
6358. Artist's Mother	24 x 18-1/2	NYGS	10. 00
6359. Artist's Son, Titus	30-1/2 x 23	NYGS	18. 00
	19-1/2 x 17	NYGS	10. 00
	14 x 10-1/2	NYGS	4. 00
6360. Bathsheba	10 x 10	CFA	2. 50
6361. Bethsabea Bathing	11 x 11	IA	3. 00
6362. Bridal Couple	20 x 30	DAC	6. 00
6363. Christ and Disciples at Emmaus	8 x 10	ESH	1. 00
6364. Danae	25-1/2 x 28	NYGS	15. 00
6365. Descent from the Cross	28 x 21-1/2	IA	12. 00
6366. Elephants	10 x 14	CFA	3. 00
6367. Girl with a Broom	26 x 22	NYGS	12. 00
	23 x 18	HNA	5. 95
	19-1/2 x 17	IA	4. 00
6368. Golden Helmet	26 x 20	IA	18. 00

		25 x 19	IA	18.00
		23 x 17	IA	4.00
		21 x 15-1/2	AP	5.00
		10 x 8	ESH	1.00
6369.	Good Samaritan	11 x 13	IA	3.00
6370.	Hendrikje Stoffels	29 x 20	NYGS	22.00
		23 x 18	HNA	5.95
6371.	Jacob's Dream	27 x 33	IA	18.00
		20 x 23-1/2	DAC	6.00
6372.	Judah Asking Jacob	7 x 9-1/2	AR	3.00
6373.	Man at a Door	8 x 5	AR	3.00
6374.	Man with a Golden	26 x 19-1/2	NYGS	18.00
	Helmet	24 x 18	DAC	6.00
		23 x 18	HNA	5.95
		7 x 5	NYGS	.50
6375.	The Mill	25 x 30	NYGS	16.00
6376.	Night Watch	37 x 44	IA	24.00
		23 x 28	NYGS	10.00
		20 x 23-1/2	DAC	6.00
6377.	Old Man with a Red Hat	7 x 5	NYGS	.50
6378.	Philosopher	24 x 18-1/2	NYGS	12.00
6379.	Polish Rider	25 x 29	IA	15.00
		14 x 12	NYGS	4.00
6380.	Portrait of a Lady	10 x 7	NYGS	.50
6381.	Portrait of a Lady with			
	an Ostrich-Feather			
	Fan	23 x 18	HNA	5.95
6382.	Portrait of an Old Man	14 x 11	IA	3.00
6383.	Portrait of Rembrandt			
	and Saskia	24 x 20	DAC	6.00
6384.	Rembrandt's Mother	13 x 11	ESH	5.00
6385.	Rest on the Flight			
	into Egypt	8 x 12-1/2	AR	3.00
6386.	St. Joseph's Dream	23 x 18	NYGS	10.00
6387.	Saskia	19-1/2 x 16	IA	12.00
		19 x 16	CFA	6.00
6388.	Saskia at Toilet Table	9-1/2 x 7-1/2	AR	3.00
6389.	Self-Portrait	18-1/2 x 15	NYGS	15.00
		11 x 8	NYGS	.50
6390.	Self-Portrait	13 x 11	IA	3.00
6391.	Self-Portrait as an officer	13 x 11	IA	3.00
6392.	Self-Portrait	13 x 11	IA	3.00
6393.	Self-Portrait	26-1/2 x 22	NYGS	18.00
		10 x 8	NYGS	.50
		8 x 6	NYGS	.50
6394.	Stormy Landscape	7 x 10	AR	3.00
6395.	Student	30 x 33-1/2	NYGS	18.00
		25-1/2 x 29	AA	10.00
		16 x 19	CFA	6.00
6396.	Study of a Young Man	8 x 5-1/2	AR	3.00
6397.	Syndics of the			
	Drapers Guild	7 x 10	NYGS	.50

6398.	Supper at Emmaus	26-1/2 x 25-1/2	NYGS	25.00
		26 x 25	IA	18.00
		11 x 11	IA	3.00
		8 x 8	NYGS	.50
6399.	Three Elephants	10 x 14	AR	3.00
6400.	Toilette of Saskia	9 x 7	CFA	3.00
6401.	Young Girl at an Open Half-Door	26 x 22	NYGS	12.00
		14 x 12	NYGS	4.00
		9 x 7	NYGS	.50
		8 x 6-1/2	NYGS	.50
6402.	Young Girl at a Window	18-1/2 x 16	IA	7.50
6403.	Young Girl at Open Half-Window	30 x 24	CFA	15.00

REMINGTON, FREDERIC   American   1861-1909

6404.	Aiding a Comrad	8 x 12	NYGS	1.50
6405.	Argument with the Town Marshall	16 x 24	AA	5.00
6406.	Attack on the Supply Wagons	16 x 24	AA	5.00
6407.	Buckskins (8)	12 x 16	DAC	1.60 ea.
	Arizona Cowboy			
	Army Packer			
	A Breed			
	Cavalry Officer			
	Cheyenne Buck			
	Old Raymon			
	Sioux Chief			
	Trapper			
6408.	Bronco Busters (2)	17 x 12	PENN	1.00 set
	Running Bucker			
	Sunfisher			
6408a	Change of Ownership	8 x 12	NYGS	1.50
6409.	Coming and Going of the Pony Express	13-1/2 x 20	AA	5.00
6410.	Dismounted: The Fourth Troopers Moving	20 x 29	AA	12.00
6411.	Emigrants	17-1/2 x 26	NYGS	10.00
		8 x 12	NYGS	1.50
6412.	Fight for the Water Hole	8 x 12	NYGS	1.50
6413.	Flight	8 x 12	NYGS	1.50
6414.	New Year on the Cimarron	8 x 12	NYGS	1.50
6415.	Old Time Plains Fight	17 x 24	PENN	1.00
6416.	Scout: Friends or Enemies?	19-1/2 x 29	AA	12.00
6417.	Victory Dance	20-1/2 x 29	AA	12.00

REMON, J. P.

6418.	Paysage	22 x 17	NYGS	16.00

RENAULT, FERNAND   French
  6419. Larkspur and
        Marguerites   21-1/2 x 17-1/2   RL   7.50
  6420. Marne in Summer   19 x 24   RL   7.50
RENI, GUIDO   Italian   1575-1642
  6421. Adoration of the Shep-
        herds by Night   22 x 14   RL   7.50
  6422. Archangel Michel   15 x 11   IA   3.00
  6423. Aurora   6 x 13   IA   3.00
  6424. Bacchus   14 x 11   IA   3.00
  6425. Baptism of Jesus   15 x 11   IA   3.00
  6426. Beatrice Cenci   15 x 11   IA   3.00
  6427. Cardinal Bernardino
        Spada   15 x 9   IA   3.00
  6428. Christ on the Cross 15 x 11   IA   3.00
  6429. Cleopatra   15 x 11   IA   3.00
  6430. Ecce Homo   14 x 10   IA   3.00
  6431. Massacre of the
        Innocents   15 x 9   IA   3.00
  6432. St. John the Baptist 13 x 11   IA   3.00
  6433. St. Joseph   13 x 11   IA   3.00
RENOIR, PIERRE AUGUSTE   French   1841-1919
  6434. After the Luncheon 31-1/2 x 25-1/2   NYGS   18.00
  6435. Amazon   26 x 22   NYGS   12.00
  6436. Artist Sisley and his
        Wife   21 x 15   NYGS   15.00
  6437. Au Cirque Fernando
        (Two Little Circus
        Girls)   10 x 8   ESH   1.00
  6438. At the Concert   23 x 18   HNA   5.95
  6439. At the Grenouilliere 12 x 16   AA   3.00
  6440. Bal a Bougival   32 x 17   NYGS   18.00
  6441. Balancoire (The Swing) 31 x 24-1/2   NYGS   15.00
                         24 x 18   PENN   1.00
                                                1.98 (Pr.)
                         7 x 5   CFA   1.00
  6442. The Bath   18-1/2 x 15-1/2   NYGS   16.00
  6443. Bather with Griffon 15 x 9   IA   3.00
  6444. Bathers   7 x 10   NYGS   .50
  6445. Bathers at Guernsey 12-1/2 x 16   NYGS   10.00
  6446. Bathing Woman on a
        Rock   19-1/2 x 15-1/2   AP   5.00
  6447. Bergere   15 x 11   NYGS   6.00
  6448. Boating   24 x 30   DAC   8.00
                         11 x 14   DAC   2.80
  6449. Boating Party at Chatou 18 x 23   HNA   5.95
  6450. Boating Party   16 x 22-1/2   ESH   10.00
                         8 x 10   ESH   1.00
  6451. Bord de la Seine a
        Champrosay   21 x 25   NYGS   12.00
  6452. Breakfast   31 x 26   CFA   18.00
  6453. Bunch of Roses   8 x 10   ESH   1.00

6454. By the Seashore	22 x 17-1/2	NYGS	7.50
	8 x 6	NYGS	.50
6455. Caillebotte Children	6 x 8	CFA	1.00
6456. Chalands sur la Seine	18 x 24-1/2	PENN	1.00
6457. Child in White	24 x 19-1/2	NYGS	7.50
6458. Detail of No. 6457	16 x 12-1/2	NYGS	4.00
6459. Children at the Seashore	25 x 18	PENN	1.00
	23 x 18	HNA	5.95
6460. Claude Desinant	12 x 9-1/2	NYGS	4.00
6461. Cliffs at Guernsey	18-1/2 x 22	ESH	10.00
6462. Confidences	23 x 18	HNA	5.95
6463. Cup of Chocolate	12 x 10	NYGS	.50
6464. Dance at Bougival	26 x 21	HNA	5.95
6465. Dancer	30-1/2 x 20-1/2	NYGS	15.00
6466. Excursionist	13 x 10	IA	3.00
6467. Farm of Collettes	8 x 10	ESH	1.00
6468. Farmhouse, les Colettes	8 x 10	ESH	1.00
6469. Field Flowers	30 x 22-1/2	NYGS	22.00
6470. Fille au Chapeau	13 x 9	NYGS	5.00
6471. Fillette a la Gerbe	10 x 8	ESH	1.00
6472. Flowers and Cat	21 x 17	PENN	1.00
6473. Fruits of the Midi	15 x 20	CFA	7.50
6474. Gabrielle and Coco	9 x 8	NYGS	.50
6475. Gabrielle at her Toilette	9 x 7	NYGS	.50
6476. Gabrielle and Rose	24 x 19-1/2	PENN	1.00
	12 x 10	CFA	2.50
6477. Garden at les Collettes	8 x 10	ESH	1.00
6478. Garden Walk	8 x 10	ESH	1.00
6479. Girl Adjusting Earrings	23 x 19	PENN	1.00
			1.98 (Pr.)
6480. Girl in Pink	6 x 8	CFA	1.00
6481. Girl in Violet	16 x 11	CFA	5.00
6482. Girl Lying at Water's Edge	6 x 8	CFA	1.00
6483. Girl Reading	22 x 18	NYGS	12.00
	21 x 17	PENN	1.00
	10 x 8	ESH	1.00
	9 x 7	NYGS	.50
6484. Girl with a Cat	26-1/2 x 20	AA	12.00
	24 x 19	NYGS	7.50
6485. Girl with a Falcon	13 x 8	NYGS	.50
6486. Girl with Flowing Hair	25-1/2 x 21	NYGS	22.00
6487. Girl with a Hat	21 x 16	CFA	7.50
	20-1/2 x 16	AR	7.50
6488. Girl with a Watering Can	29-1/2 x 22	NYGS	15.00
	24 x 17-1/2	PENN	1.00
			1.98 (Pr.)
	23 x 18	HNA	5.95
	22 x 16	NYGS	10.00

		14 x 11	NYGS	3.00
		9 x 6	CFA	1.00
6489.	Girls in Open Air	19 x 16	NYGS	16.00
6490.	Girls Picking Flowers	16-1/2 x 21	NYGS	10.00
6491.	Les Grands Boulevards	16-1/2 x 20-1/2	IA	6.00
		8 x 9	NYGS	.50
6492.	Guitar Player	9 x 7	NYGS	.50
6493.	Her First Night	15 x 12	AR	3.00
6494.	In the Meadow	28 x 22	AA	15.00
		24 x 19	PENN	1.00
				1.98 (Pr.)
6495.	In the Nursery	24 x 30	NYGS	16.00
6496.	Jean Renoir Drawing	17-1/2 x 21	NYGS	15.00
6497.	Jean Renoir Sewing	21-1/2 x 18	AA	7.50
6498.	Jeanne Samary	8 x 7	NYGS	.50
6499.	Jeune Baigneuse	15-1/2 x 12	NYGS	2.00
6500.	Jeune Femme en Bleu	15-1/2 x 10	NYGS	12.00
6501.	Jeune Femme Assise dans l'Herbe	19 x 21-1/2	NYGS	20.00
6502.	Jeune Fille	15-1/2 x 12	NYGS	2.00
6503.	Jeunes Filles Assises	25-1/2 x 21	NYGS	18.00
6504.	Lady at the Piano	24 x 20	DAC	6.00
		22 x 17-1/2	NYGS	7.50
		14 x 11	NYGS	3.00
6505.	Lady Sewing	20 x 16-1/2	AJ	7.50
		20 x 16	CFA	7.50
		9 x 7-1/2	IA	.50
6506.	Lady with a Muff	15 x 10-1/2	NYGS	3.00
6507.	Lady with a Parasol	18-1/2 x 22	NYGS	15.00
		18 x 22	NYGS	12.00
6508.	Landscape	10 x 13-1/2	AR	5.00
6509.	Landscape near Menton	18 x 23	HNA	5.95
6510.	Large Vase of Flowers	30 x 24	IA	4.00
		24 x 18	IA	3.00
		22-1/2 x 17	IA	4.00
6511.	La Liseuse	17 x 14-1/2	NYGS	7.50
		10 x 8	ESH	1.00
6512.	Liseuse Blanche	24 x 20	PENN	1.00
6513.	Little Gleaner	13 x 11	IA	3.00
6514.	Little Margot Berard	16 x 12-1/2	MMA	4.00
6515.	Little Nude in Blue	20 x 16	NYGS	7.50
6516.	La Loge	28 x 22-1/2	NYGS	15.00
		23-1/2 x 16	PENN	1.00
				1.98 (Pr.)
6517.	Lucie Berard	15-1/2 x 12	NYGS	2.00
6518.	Luncheon of the Boating Party (Three Figures)	20 x 24	NYGS	7.50
6519.	Luncheon of the Boating Party (Fourteen Figures)	26-1/2 x 36	AA	18.00
6520.	Girl with a Dog-- Detail of No. 6519	22-1/2 x 16	ESH	10.00

6521.	Madame Charpentier and Her Children	24 x 30	NYGS	12.00
6522.	Madame Henriot	23 x 18	HNA	5.95
		10 x 8	MMA	.35
6523.	Madame Renoir	23 x 18	HNA	5.95
6524.	Madame Tilla Durieux	8 x 10	MMA	.35
6525.	Mademoiselle Irene	24 x 20	DAC	6.00
		19-1/2 x 16	IA	12.00
		18 x 14-1/2	IA	5.00
6526.	Mademoiselle Lacaux	22 x 17-1/2	NYGS	7.50
6527.	Meadow	8 x 10	MMA	.35
6528.	Mixed Flowers in a Vase	23 x 18	HNA	5.95
6529.	Moss Roses	10 x 8	ESH	1.00
6530.	Mother and Child	10 x 6	CFA	1.00
6531.	Mother and Children	24 x 15	NYGS	10.00
6532.	Moulin de la Galette	23-1/2 x 31-1/2	NYGS	15.00
		16-1/2 x 22-1/2	ESH	10.00
		20 x 24	PENN	1.00
				1.98 (Pr.)
6533.	Profile of Woman-- Detail of No. 6532	14-1/2 x 10-1/2	AJ	2.50
		10 x 8	ESH	1.00
6534.	Still Life, Glassware-- Detail of No. 6532	10 x 8	ESH	1.00
6535.	Musical Mendes Sisters	24 x 20	DAC	6.00
6536.	Near the Lake	20 x 24	NYGS	7.50
6537.	Noirmoutier	17 x 21	CAC	7.50
6538.	Nu	11 x 10-1/2	NYGS	6.00
6539.	Nu au Soleil (Nude in the Sun)	26 x 21	AJ	12.00
		8 x 6	CFA	1.00
6540.	Nude Studies	12-1/2 x 16	ESH	10.00
6541.	Les Nymphes	15 x 20	PENN	1.00
6542.	Oarsmen at Chatou	28-1/2 x 35	NYGS	18.00
6543.	On the Terrace	30 x 24	IA	4.00
		27 x 22	NYGS	12.00
		23 x 18	HNA	5.95
		22 x 18	IA	3.00
		20 x 16	AP	7.50
		10 x 8	IA	.50
		9 x 7	IA	.50
6544.	Paris Boulevard in Spring	19-1/2 x 24	NYGS	20.00
6545.	Petites Anemones	18 x 14-1/2	NYGS	20.00
6546.	Petitie Fille au Chapeau	21 x 16	PENN	1.00
6547.	Picnic	19-1/2 x 24	PENN	1.00
6548.	Pink Roses	10 x 8	ESH	1.00
6549.	Place Clichy	25-1/2 x 21-1/2	NYGS	15.00
		10 x 8	ESH	1.00
6550.	Pont de Chemin de Fer	20 x 24	PENN	1.00
6551.	Portrait de Jeune Fille	15-1/2 x 12	NYGS	12.00

6552.	Portrait of a Model	10 x 8	ESH	1.00
6553.	Portrait of a Young Girl	25-1/2 x 21	IA	12.00
		25 x 21	IA	15.00
		23 x 18	PENN	1.00
		20-1/2 x 16	IA	4.00
		13 x 10-1/2	IA	3.00
6554.	Portrait of Gabrielle	23 x 16	PENN	1.00
				1.98 (Pr.)
6555.	Printemps a Chatou	22 x 27	NYGS	15.00
6556.	Reader	16 x 12	AA	3.00
6557.	Reading Girl	22 x 18	CFA	12.00
6558.	Reading Girl in White	18 x 20	ESH	10.00
6559.	Rose and Blue	23 x 15	AA	10.00
		14 x 9	NYGS	3.00
		9 x 5	CFA	1.00
6560.	Roses	25 x 21	CFA	15.00
		20-1/2 x 17	NYGS	10.00
		10 x 8	ESH	1.00
6561.	Roses in an Ochre Vase	10 x 8	ESH	1.00
6562.	Roses Mousseuses	21 x 16	PENN	1.00
6563.	Rower's Lunch	20 x 24	DAC	6.00
6564.	Seated Bather	8 x 10	MMA	.35
6565.	Seated Nude	8 x 6	CFA	1.00
6566.	Seine at Argenteuil	18 x 21-1/2	NYGS	15.00
		8 x 10	ESH	1.00
6567.	Seine at Chatou	18 x 23	HNA	5.95
6568.	Self-Portrait	11 x 8	NYGS	.50
		10 x 8	MMA	.35
6569.	Serenade	13-1/2 x 10	NYGS	5.00
6570.	Sitting Nude	9 x 7	CFA	1.00
6571.	Skiff	24 x 30	DAC	8.00
		18 x 24	NYGS	12.00
6572.	Sloping Pathway in a Field	6 x 8	CFA	1.00
6573.	Small Painter	14 x 11	AR	4.00
6574.	Smiling Woman	14 x 11	IA	3.00
6575.	Spring Flowers	23 x 18	HNA	5.95
6576.	Still Life with Peaches	21 x 25-1/2	MMA	5.50
6577.	Strand of Gernesey	12 x 16	AJ	10.00
6578.	Swing	31 x 24-1/2	NYGS	15.00
		24 x 18	PENN	1.00
				1.98 (Pr.)
		22 x 17	ESH	10.00
		16 x 12	AA	3.00
		7 x 5	CFA	1.00
6579.	Therese Berard	9 x 7	NYGS	.50
6580.	Tree near the Farm	19 x 22	ESH	10.00
		8 x 10	ESH	1.00
6581.	Two Children in White	24 x 14-1/2	PENN	1.00
6582.	Two Girls at the Piano	26 x 21	HNA	5.95
6583.	Two Girls in Blue	23 x 18	HNA	5.95

6584.	Two Girls in a Meadow	8 x 6	CFA	1.00
6585.	Two Sisters	28 x 22	NYGS	15.00
		24 x 19-1/2	PENN	1.00
				1.98 (Pr.)
		14 x 11	NYGS	3.00
6585.	Vase of Roses	10 x 8	ESH	1.00
6586.	Venice--Gondola	21 x 25	NYGS	15.00
6587.	Venice--St. Marks Square	24-1/2 x 31	NYGS	18.00
6588.	View of the Post Office	8 x 10	ESH	1.00
6589.	Washerwomen	20 x 16	PENN	1.00
6590.	White Roses	8 x 10	ESH	1.00
6591.	Woman Asleep	8 x 6	CFA	1.00
6592.	Woman in a Veil	16 x 11	AR	7.50
		15 x 11	AP	5.00
		10 x 8	ESH	1.00
6593.	Woman Tying Up Her Shoe	18 x 20-1/2	NYGS	15.00
6594.	Woman with a Cat	24 x 19-1/2	PENN	1.00
				1.98 (Pr.)
		14 x 11	NYGS	3.00
6595.	Woman with Lilacs	22-1/2 x 18	NYGS	12.00
6596.	Women in a Field	23 x 28	ESH	15.00
		8 x 10	ESH	1.00
6597.	Women with Hats	8 x 10	ESH	1.00
6598.	Young Girl	25 x 21	CFA	15.00
		10 x 8	ESH	1.00
6599.	Young Girl at Piano	8 x 6	CFA	1.00
6600.	Young Girl Combing Her Hair	8 x 6	CFA	1.00
6601.	Young Girl with Daisies	22 x 18-1/2	ESH	10.00
6602.	Young Girl with a Sheaf of Flowers	10 x 8	ESH	1.00
6603.	Young Shepherd	20 x 24-1/2	NYGS	7.50
RENOUF, EMILE		French	1845-1894	
6604.	The Helping Hand	22 x 32	IA	10.00
		11 x 14	IA	3.00
REUTHER, WOLF		German	1917-	
6605.	Cock	25 x 20	IA	12.00
6606.	Duet	24 x 20	IA	15.00
6607.	El Toro	25 x 20	IA	15.00
6608.	Rooster	25 x 19	CFA	15.00
REYNOLDS, (SIR) JOSHUA		English	1723-1792	
6609.	Age of Innocence	20 x 16	CAC	6.00
		16 x 13	NYGS	5.00
		12 x 9	CAC	2.00
		10 x 8	ESH	1.00
6610.	Captain Bligh	28-1/2 x 23	AA	10.00
6611.	Dr. Samuel Johnson	10 x 8	NYGS	.50
6612.	Georgiana Elliott	29-1/2 x 24-1/2	NYGS	12.00
6613.	Heads of Angels	20 x 16	CAC	5.00
		10 x 8	ESH	1.00

6614.	Infant Samuel at Prayer	24 x 20	IA	7.50
		23 x 18-1/2	IA	7.50
		14 x 10	IA	2.00
		11 x 8	IA	1.75
		10 x 8	NYGS	.50
6615.	Lady Betty Hamilton	31 x 22	NYGS	12.00
		23-1/2 x 16-1/2	NYGS	10.00
		18 x 12-1/2	NYGS	5.00
		14 x 10	NYGS	3.00
6616.	Lady Caroline Howard	20 x 16	CAC	7.50
6617.	Lady Elizabeth Delme			
	and Her Children	31 x 19	CAC	12.00
6618.	Lady in Yellow	19-1/2 x 16	NYGS	10.00
6619.	Master Hare	12-1/2 x 10	IA	3.00
		12 x 10	IA	3.00
		10 x 8	IA	1.75
6620.	Miss Bowles	17 x 13	CAC	5.00
6621.	Miss Mary Hickey	19 x 16	CAC	7.50
6622.	Nellie O'Brien	16 x 13	CAC	5.00
		10 x 8	NYGS	.50
6623.	Portrait of a Lady	28 x 22	CAC	6.00
6624.	Simplicity	17 x 14	CAC	5.00
		17 x 13	CAC	5.00
		12 x 9	CAC	2.00
6625.	Young Shepherd	18 x 15	CAC	10.00

RIASNI, B.

6626.	Bouquets (6)	16 x 12	DAC	1.40 ea.
		10 x 8	DAC	.60 ea.

RIBERA, JOSE DE (LO SPAGNOLETTO)   Spanish   1588-1652

6627.	Madonna and Child	24 x 20	IA	7.50
6628.	St. Mary of Egypt	14 x 11	IA	3.00

RICHARDS, F. T.

6629.	Golf through the Ages			
	(6)	10 x 6	CFA	30.00 set

RICHARDSON, VOLNEY ALLAN   American   1880-

6630.	Bowl of Mums	25 x 30	AA	10.00
6631.	Crabapple and Dogwood	25 x 30	AA	10.00

RICHTER, GUSTAV KARL LUDWIG   German   1823-1884

6632.	Artist's Sister	27-1/2 x 20	NYGS	7.50
		11 x 9	NYGS	1.50

RICHTER, HERBERT DAVIS   English   1874-1955

6633.	Enduring Charms	21 x 25	RL	7.50
6634.	Exquisite	21-1/2 x 18	RL	10.00
6635.	Georgian Mirror	25 x 19	RL	7.50
6636.	Magical Sunlight	18 x 21-1/2	NYGS	7.50
6637.	Old English Charm	19 x 23	NYGS	7.50
6638.	Tudor Cottage	18 x 23	NYGS	7.50

RIEFEL, CARLOS VON

6639.	Fruits (8)	16 x 20	IA	4.50 ea.
	Apples			
	Apricots			
	Cherries			

	Grapes		
	Peaches		
	Pears		
	Plums		
	Strawberries		

RIETTI, ARTURO	Italian	1863-1942	
6640. Toscanini	21-1/2 x 18	AA	10.00
RIFU			
6641. Yujo	26 x 10-1/2	PENN	1.00
RIGHETTI, RENATO	Italian (Res. France)	1916-	
6642. Cap Martin	13-1/2 x 29	RL	7.50
6643. Old Town, Mentone	17 x 21-1/2	RL	6.00
RINALDI, M.			
6644. Atlantic Sunrise	20 x 24	IA	7.50
6645. Breaking Surf	27-1/2 x 30	IA	12.00
6646. Rocky Point	20 x 24	IA	7.50
RIOPELLE, JEAN-PAUL	Canadian	Contemporary	
6647. Du Noir Que se Leve	24 x 19	NYGS	15.00
RITTER, JULIAN			
6648. Clowns (6)	18 x 14	IA	4.00 ea.
	10 x 8	IA	2.00 ea.

	Adlai		
	Gent		
	Helter		
	Skelter		
	Maestro		
	Micky		

RIVERA, DIEGO	Mexican	1886-1958	
6649. Delfina Flores	26 x 20	NYGS	12.00
6650. Flower Seller	13-1/2 x 18	NYGS	6.00
	6 x 8	NYGS	.50
6651. Flower Vendor	28 x 28	NYGS	12.00
	17-1/2 x 17-1/2	NYGS	5.00
6652. Indian Girl	16 x 12	NYGS	4.00
6653. Man and Machinery			
(Mural)	10 x 8	NYGS	.50
6654. Mother's Helper	13-1/2 x 18	NYGS	6.00
	6 x 8	NYGS	1.00
6655. Oaxaca	6 x 8	NYGS	1.00
6656. Rug Weaver	10-1/2 x 15-1/2	NYGS	4.00
	6 x 8	NYGS	1.00
ROBBIA, ANDREA DELLA	Italian	1435-1525	
6657. Head of a Child	13 x 11	IA	3.00
ROBBIA, LUCA DELLA	Italian	1400-1482	
6658. Madonna of the Apple	15 x 11	IA	3.00
ROBERT, CHARLES (TASSY)	French	1882-	
6659. Maternity	27 x 19	CFA	10.00
ROBERT, HUBERT	French	1733-1808	
6660. Fountains	28 x 24	NYGS	15.00
6661. Landscape	15 x 8	IA	3.00
6662. Old Bridge	27 x 35-1/2	NYGS	18.00
6663. Old Temple	28 x 24	NYGS	15.00

6664. Park Landscape	14-1/2 x 7-1/2	IA	3. 00
6665. Paysage	10 x 10-1/2	NYGS	4. 00
6666. Roman Garden	28 x 20	NYGS	10. 00
	14 x 10	NYGS	4. 00
6667. Ruins of a Porch	14-1/2 x 7-1/2	IA	3. 00
6668. Terrace	28 x 20	NYGS	10. 00
	14 x 10	NYGS	4. 00
6669. View of Antique			
Thermos	12 x 17-1/2	AR	4. 00
ROBERTI, DOMENICO	Italian	1642-1707	
6670. Spring	32 x 10	AL	15. 00
6671. Summer	32 x 10	AL	15. 00
6672. Tempio Borghese	32 x 12	AL	15. 00
6673. Tempio Calonna	32 x 12	AL	15. 00
6674. Tempio Corsini	32 x 11	AL	15. 00
6675. Tempio Doria	32 x 11	AL	15. 00
ROBERTI, ERCOLE	Italian	c. 1456-1496	
6676. Ginevra Bentivoglio	20-1/2 x 14-1/2	NYGS	10. 00
6677. Giovanni Bentivoglio	20-1/2 x 14-1/2	NYGS	10. 00
ROBIN, GEORGES	French	1903-	
6678. Chateau Landon (Apres			
Midi de Printemps)	19-1/2 x 24	RL	7. 50
6679. Christmas Morning	23-1/2 x 32	RL	10. 00
6680. Golden Sands,			
Finisterre	18-1/2 x 25	RL	7. 50
6681. Low Tide, Fouesnant	18 x 25	RL	7. 50
6682. Normandy Bridge	22 x 18	RL	6. 00
6683. River Scene, Quimper	18 x 25	RL	7. 50
6684. Sunday Afternoon	22 x 18	RL	6. 00
ROBINSON, WILLIAM HEATH	English	1872-1944	
6685. Nature's Plenty	25 x 30	CFA	15. 00
ROBUSTI, JACOPO	See TINTORETTO		
ROCHE, MARGUERITE			
6686. Provincial Picnic	25 x 32	NYGS	12. 00
ROCKWELL, NORMAN	American 1894-		
6687. Four Seasons (4)	11 x 8	NYGS	4. 00 sheet
RODEWALD, CLAUDE			
6688. Bois de Boulogne	18 x 23-1/2	AA	12. 00
6689. Champs Elysees	12 x 9	AA	3. 00
6690. Cour de Rohan	14 x 20	AA	10. 00
6691. Fiacre	18-1/2 x 24	AA	12. 00
6692. Monaco	18 x 24	AA	10. 00
6693. Montmartre	20 x 24	AA	12. 00
6694. Moulin Rouge	16 x 20	AA	10. 00
6695. Nice	18 x 24	AA	10. 00
6696. Paris Scenes (8)	6 x 8	AA	1.50 ea.
6697. Petit Cafe	14 x 20	AA	10. 00
6698. Place du Tertre	16 x 20	AA	10. 00
6699. Place Pigalle	12 x 9	AA	3. 00
6700. Rue Boulanger	12 x 9	AA	3. 00
6701. Rue Royale	20 x 24	AA	12. 00
6702. Sacre Coeur	12 x 9	AA	3. 00

6703. Les Tuileries	18 x 23-1/2	AA	12.00
ROGERS, JOHN			
6704. At Anchor	12 x 16	DAC	1.20
	9 x 12	DAC	.80
	6 x 8	DAC	.40
6705. Church Road	12 x 16	DAC	1.20
	9 x 12	DAC	.80
	6 x 8	DAC	.40
6706. Sails Set	12 x 16	DAC	1.20
	9 x 12	DAC	.80
	6 x 8	DAC	.40
6707. Stonehenge Farm	12 x 16	DAC	1.20
	9 x 12	DAC	.80
	6 x 8	DAC	.40
6708. Village Road	12 x 16	DAC	1.20
	9 x 12	DAC	.80
	6 x 8	DAC	.40
6709. Village Stream	12 x 16	DAC	1.20
	9 x 12	DAC	.80
	6 x 8	DAC	.40
6710. Water Mill	12 x 16	DAC	1.20
	9 x 12	DAC	.80
	6 x 8	DAC	.40
ROHLFS			
6711. Artichoke Blossoms	22 x 15-1/2	NYGS	18.00
6712. Canna Indica	30 x 22	NYGS	22.00
6713. Green Seascape	30 x 22	NYGS	24.00
6714. Lilies on a Red Back-			
ground	19 x 26	NYGS	18.00
6715. Still Life	20 x 28	NYGS	24.00
ROHNER, G.			
6716. St. Romain	20 x 30	RL	12.50
ROHRICHT, WOLF	German	1886-1953	
6717. Frozen River	19 x 25	ESH	7.50
6718. Osteria	24 x 20	ESH	12.00
6719. Summer in Italy	21 x 25-1/2	ESH	10.00
ROJAS, R. RIERA	Spanish	Contemporary	
6720. La Cuadrilla	23 x 24	NYGS	10.00
6721. El Matador	23 x 24	NYGS	10.00
6722. Picador Y			
Banderilleros	23 x 24	NYGS	10.00
6723. Picadores	23 x 24	NYGS	10.00
ROKA, C.			
6724. Gypsy Girl	24 x 19-1/2	IA	12.00
			15.00
			(On Canvas)
ROLING, ALPHONS	Dutch	1904-	
6725. Bouquet with Anemones	20 x 17	PENN	1.00
6726. Bouquet with Tulips	20 x 17	PENN	1.00
ROLOFF, A.			
6727. Horses in a Storm	24 x 30	IA	12.00

ROMAKO, ANTON
 6728. Gardener   19 x 15   ESH 6.00
ROMAN PAINTING
 6729. Bacchante   22 x 18   ESH 10.00
 6730. Women Playing with
    a Goat   20-1/2 x 18 ESH 10.00
ROMANO, GIULIO (GIANNUZZI, GIULIO) Italian 1492-1546
 6731. Apollo and the Muses 11 x 25   IA   7.50
           7 x 15   IA   3.00
ROMANO, UMBERTO   American 1905-
 6732. Lancer   20 c 25-1/2 NYGS 15.00
ROMBOUTS, THEODOR Flemish   1597-1637
 6733. Gamblers   11 x 15   IA   3.00
ROMNEY, GEORGE   English   1734-1802
 6734. Elizabeth Sutherland 9 x 8   CFA 6.00
 6735. Lady Hamilton   19 x 17   CAC 7.50
 6736. Lady Hamilton as a
    Bacchante   25 x 20   CAC 10.00
           16 x 13   CAC 5.00
 6737. Little Bo Peep   20 x 15   NYGS 7.50
 6738. Madame de Genlis 19 x 14   CAC 10.00
 6739. Miss Willoughby 23 x 18   HNA 5.95
           20 x 15-1/2 NYGS 7.50
           11-1/2 x 9 NYGS .50
 6740. Mrs. Davenport   19-1/2 x 16 NYGS 7.50
           12 x 10   NYGS .50
ROSA, SALVATORE   Italian   1615-1673
 6741. Bridge of Tivoli   11 x 15   IA   3.00
 6742. Landscape: Peace
    Setting Fire to the
    Weapons   10 x 15   IA   3.00
 6743. Seascape   11 x 15   IA   3.00
ROSE, IVER   American 1899-
 6744. Hi Ya Folks   22 x 16   NYGS 10.00
 6745. Show's On   22 x 16   NYGS 10.00
ROSENTHAL, TOBY EDWARD American 1848-1917
 6746. Cardinal's Portrait 19 x 24   IA   7.50
           9-1/2 x 12 IA   1.50
 6747. His Madonna   24-1/2 x 19 NYGS 7.50
           14 x 11   NYGS 3.00
 6748. Seine Madonna   24-1/2 x 19 NYGS 7.50
           14 x 11   NYGS 3.00
ROSENSTOCK, W.
 6749. Glory of Summer 28 x 22   AA   7.50
 6750. Summer Symphony 28 x 22   AA   7.50
ROSS, C. CHANDLER   American 1888-1952
 6751. Autumn Pleasures 28 x 34   NYGS 7.50
 6752. Eastern Tranquility 20 x 24   NYGS 7.50
 6753. Eternal East   26 x 22   NYGS 10.00
 6754. Oriental Rider   26 x 22   NYGS 10.00
 6755. Oriental Simplicity 20 x 24   NYGS 7.50
 6756. Thoroughbreds   28 x 34   NYGS 7.50

ROSSELLI, COSIMO	Italian	1439-1507	
6757. Madonna and Child with Two Angels	16 x 10	IA	3.00
ROSSI, CARLO			
6758. Breakers at Sunset	20 x 39	IA	12.00
ROSSITER, ANTHONY	English	1926-	
6759. Spring in Grasmere	17 1/2 x 28	RL	10.00
ROSSO, FIORENTINO	Italian	1494-1541	
6760. Moses Defending the Daughters of Jethro	15 x 11	IA	3.00
ROTARI, PIETRO	Italian	1707-1762	
6761. Girl with Flowers in her Hair	20 x 15 1/2	NYGS	7.50
ROTH			
6762. Canal in Yonne	18 x 23	PENN	1.00
6763. Les Fillettes (4)	8 x 10	DAC	1.20 ea.
ROTIG, S. F.			
6764. L'Alerte	17 1/2 x 24	IA	15.00
6765. Ducks Landing	17 1/2 x 24	IA	15.00
6766. Setters et Canards	16 x 23 1/2	IA	10.00
ROUART, HENRI	French	1833-1912	
6767. Bouquet	22 x 16 1/2	NYGS	16.00
ROUAULT, GEORGES	French	1871-1958	
6768. Afterglow, Galilee	19 x 25	NYGS	16.00
6769. L'Ange Gardien	15 x 12	NYGS	16.00
6770. Bouquet No. 1	14 x 9 1/2	NYGS	5.00
6771. Bouquet No. 2	14 x 9 1/2	NYGS	5.00
6772. El Chinois	24 x 17	PENN	1.00
6773. Christ and the Fishermen	20 1/2 x 29	NYGS	16.00
6774. Christ and the High Priest	19 x 13	IA	7.50
6775. Christ Mocked	29 1/2 x 23	AP	7.50
	26 x 20	CFA	7.50
6776. Christian Intimacy	15-1/2 x 22	IA	10.00
6777. Le Cirque (4)	12 x 8	AR	5.00 ea.
6778. Clown	25 x 18	PENN	1.00
			1.98(Pr.)
6779. Clown	23 x 16-1/2	NYGS	10.00
6780. Dream	8 x 10	MMA	.35
6781. Ecce Homo	30 x 21	IA	15.00
6782. Fleurs Decoratives	16 x 10	NYGS	15.00
6783. Flight into Egypt	22 x 17	ESH	10.00
6784. Flowers	14 x 11	DAC	2.80
6785. Flowers in a Vase	22 x 18	PENN	1.00
6786. Harlequin and Dog	23-1/2 x 15	AR	12.00
6787. Heads of Two Clowns	24 x 18	PENN	1.00
			1.98(Pr.)
6788. L'Hiver	15 x 11	NYGS	16.00
6789. Jeanne D'Arc	16 x 13	CAC	6.00
6790. Madame "X"	20 x 14	AR	7.50
6791. Motherhood	18-1/2 x 14-1/2	IA	5.00

6792. Old King	25 x 17	PENN	1.00
	23 x 16	ESH	10.00
	11 x 7	NYGS	.50
6793. Parade	23-1/2 x 15	AR	12.00
6794. Passion	10 x 8	ESH	1.00
6795. Pierrot	30 x 19-1/2	AA	15.00
	24 x 19	CFA	7.50
	12-1/2 x 8-1/2	NYGS	4.00
	9 x 6	NYGS	.50
6796. Pierrots	21 x 16-1/2	NYGS	16.00
6797. Sacre-Coeur	9 x 5-1/2	NYGS	8.00
6798. La Sainte Face	23 x 17	NYGS	20.00
	20 x 14	IA	7.50
6799. Sainte-Marthe	18 x 14-1/2	NYGS	18.00
6800. Seated Clown (Wise Pierrot)	26 x 21	HNA	5.95
6801. Small Magician	24 x 19	PENN	1.00
			1.98(Pr.)
6802. Sorrowing Christ	10 x 8	ESH	1.00
6803. Stella Vespertina	16 x 10	NYGS	16.00
6804. La Sybelle	21 x 15	AR	10.00
6805. Three Judges	26 x 20-1/2	MMA	7.50
	8 x 10	MMA	.35
6806. Veronique	19 x 14	NYGS	18.00
6807. Wounded Clown	30-1/2 x 18	ESH	15.00

ROUAULT, I.

6808. Sainte Therese de l'Enfante Jesue	16 x 10-1/2	NYGS	12.00

ROUSSEAU, HENRI JULIEN (LE DOUANIER) French 1844-1910

6809. Banks of the Oise	17-1/2 x 21-1/2	NYGS	10.00
6810. Basket of Flowers	8 x 10	MMA	.35
6811. Bois de Vincennes	20 x 24	CFA	15.00
6812. Bouquet of Field Flowers	10 x 8	ESH	1.00
6813. Carnival Night	23 x 18	HNA	5.95
6814. Cart	16-1/2 x 22	ESH	10.00
6815. Cascade	15-1/2 x 20	NYGS	7.50
	15 x 20	CFA	7.50
6816. Dream	8 x 10	MMA	.35
6817. Edge of the Woods	7 x 11	NYGS	.50
6818. Equatorial Jungle	26 x 23-1/2	NYGS	12.00
6819. Flowers	14-1/2 x 12	AR	3.00
6820. In the Forest	21-1/2 x 18-1/2	NYGS	12.00
6821. In the Park	14 x 18	CFA	7.50
6822. Jungle, Setting Sun	18 x 26	PENN	1.00
			1.98(Pr.)
6823. Jungle Sunset	18 x 23	HNA	5.95
6824. Landscape with Fisherman	8 x 10	ESH	1.00
6825. Lion in the Jungle	15 x 18	CAC	10.00
6826. Moulin Rouge	18-1/2 x 24	NYGS	12.00
6827. Sleeping Gypsy	20 x 31	MMA	6.50

		8 x 10	MMA	.35
		4 x 9	NYGS	.50
6828.	Snake Charmer	19 x 21	ESH	10.00
		10 x 11	CFA	2.50
6829.	Springtime in the Valley of the Bievre	20 x 17	AA	7.50
6830.	Still Life with Flowers	8 x 10	ESH	1.00
6831.	Summer	8 x 10	ESH	1.00
6832.	Tiger Hunt	16-1/2 x 20	NYGS	10.00
6833.	Toll Gate	16 x 12-1/2	NYGS	10.00
6834.	Vase of Flowers	14-1/2 x 12	AP	3.00
6835.	Virgin Forest at Sunset	19-1/2 x 27-1/2	NYGS	15.00
6836.	Walk in the Bois de Vincennes	17-1/2 x 21	ESH	10.00
6837.	Waterfall	24 x 31	NYGS	18.00
		8 x 10	MMA	.35
ROUSSEAU, THEODORE		French	1812-1867	
6838.	The Oaks	9 x 14	IA	3.00
ROYBOT, (ROYBET), FERDINAND French			1840-1920	
6839.	Cavalier	30 x 24	CFA	7.50
ROWLANDSON		English		
6840.	Wnd of the Mall	13 x 18-1/2	NYGS	7.50
ROYO				
6841.	Flamenco Dancer No. 1	25 x 20	CFA	15.00
RUBENS, PETER PAUL		Flemish	1577-1640	
6842.	Artist's Son, Nicholas	12 x 9	CFA	3.50
6843.	Artist's Son, Nicholas, Age 2	10 x 8	CFA	3.50
6844.	Chapeau de Paille	18 x 12-1/2	NYGS	5.00
6845.	Christ Child, St. John and Angels	21 x 34	NYGS	12.00
6846.	Dressing of Venus	23 x 18	HNA	5.95
6847.	Duke of Buckingham	15 x 10-1/2	AR	5.00
6848.	Enfant au Bourelet	9 x 7	NYGS	4.00
6849.	Flemish Kermis	6 x 10	NYGS	.50
6850.	Four Philosophers	13 x 11	IA	3.00
6851.	Helen Fourment and her Children	12 x 9	CFA	2.50
		9 x 7	NYGS	.50
6852.	Holy Family	14 x 11	IA	3.00
6853.	Isabelle Brant, First Wife	14 x 11	IA	3.00
6854.	Judgment of Paris	7 x 10	NYGS	.50
6855.	Lady of the Court	14 x 11	AR	5.00
6856.	Landscape with Rainbow	29 x 38	NYGS	28.00
6857.	Maid of Honor	14 x 11	CFA	5.00
6858.	Peasant Girl	15 x 10	AR	4.00

6859.	Portrait of a Child	14 x 10	NYGS	18.00
6860.	Praying Hands	18 x 15	NYGS	7.50
6861.	2 Details of No. 6860	10 x 15	NYGS	3.00 ea.
6862.	Rubens and his First Wife	10 x 8	NYGS	.50
6863.	St. Catherine	15 x 9	AR	4.00
6864.	St. Sebastian Suc- coured by Angels	14 x 10	IA	3.00
6865.	Self-Portrait	15 x 11	IA	3.00
6866.	Venus and Adonis	10 x 15	IA	3.00
		8 x 10	NYGS	.50
6867.	Virgin and Child	11 x 8	NYGS	.50
6868.	Virgin and Child with Forget-Me-Nots	21 x 15-1/2	IA	8.00
6869.	Wolf and Fox Hunt	7 x 11	NYGS	.50
6870.	Young Warrior	14 x 11	AR	6.00
RUBIN, REUVEN		Roumanian	1893-	
6871.	Arabian Horses	22 x 36	NYGS	18.00
6872.	Cheval Arabe	30 x 20-1/2	NYGS	16.00
6873.	Dromedaires	30 x 21	NYGS	16.00
6874.	Mother and Child	25-1/2 x 19	NYGS	15.00
6875.	Springtime in Galilee	19-1/2 x 26	RL	10.00
6876.	Women of Galilee	25-1/2 x 19	NYGS	15.00
RUBINO				
6877.	Ceres	31 x 10	NYGS	12.00
6878.	Returning Victor	12 x 36	NYGS	15.00
6879.	Roman Parade	12 x 36	NYGS	15.00
6880.	Terpsichore	31 x 10	NYGS	12.00
RUBLEV				
6881.	Holy Trinity	27 x 22	NYGS	20.00
RUNGE, JURGEN				
6882.	Bay near Monaco	22 x 28	ESH	12.00
6883.	Boats on the Shore	18 x 24	ESH	10.00
6884.	Calm Lake	24 x 31	CFA	12.00
6885.	Landscape in Northern Germany	18 x 24	ESH	10.00
6886.	Mandello near Comer Sea	23-1/2 x 20	IA	12.00
6887.	Limone at Garda Lake	23 x 19	CFA	12.00
6888.	Limone near Garda See	23-1/2 x 20	IA	12.00
RUSSELL, CHARLES M.		American	1865-1926	
6889.	Ambushed	14 x 11	CFA	1.00
6890.	At Close-Quarters	10 x 11	CFA	1.00
6891.	Bad One	16 x 24	AA	8.00
6892.	Bell Mare	30 x 20	AA	12.00
6893.	Bolter	14 x 10	CFA	1.00
6894.	Bronc to Breakfast	8 x 15	CFA	1.00
6895.	Buffalo on the Move	11 x 16	CFA	1.00
6896.	Call of the Law	9 x 13	CFA	1.00

6897.	Camp Cook's Troubles	13-1/2 x 20	AA	5.00
6898.	Capturing the Grizzly	8 x 15	CFA	1.00
6899.	Carson's Men	9 x 14	CFA	1.00
6900.	Cinch Ring	8 x 15	CFA	1.00
6901.	Cowboy's Life	14 x 11	CFA	1.00
6902.	Cowboy Sport	9 x 13	CFA	1.00
6903.	Deadline of the Range	9 x 14	CFA	1.00
6904.	Desperate Stand	9 x 13	CFA	1.00
6905.	Discovery of Last Chance Gulch	18 x 30	AA	12.00
6906.	Disputed Trail	14 x 11	CFA	1.00
6907.	Doubtful Visitor	13-1/2 x 20	AA	5.00
6908.	Heads or Tails	8 x 14	CFA	1.00
6909.	Hold-Up	8 x 13	CFA	1.00
6910.	Indians	18 x 24	PENN	1.00
6911.	Jerk Line	24 x 36	IA	15.00
		9 x 14	CFA	1.00
6912.	Jerked Down	12-1/2 x 20	AA	5.00
		8 x 15	CFA	1.00
6913.	Last Chance or Bust	9 x 12	CFA	1.00
6914.	Laugh Kills Lonesome	18 x 30	AA	12.00
6915.	Lewis and Clark Meeting the Flatheads	14 x 30	IA	10.00
6916.	Loops and Swift Horses are Surer than Lead	9 x 13	CFA	1.00
6917.	Mad Cow	8 x 12	CFA	1.00
6918.	Meat's not Meat till it's in the Pan	9 x 13	CFA	1.00
6919.	Pipe of Peace	9 x 14	CFA	1.00
6920.	Pony Raid	11 x 16	CFA	1.00
6921.	Porfolio (6)		PENN	2.98 set
	Indians and Scouts Talking	9 x 14		
	Intruders	9-1/2 x 14		
	Letter to George W. Farr	10-1/2 x 14		
	Squaw Travois	9-1/2 x 14		
	Surprise Attack	10 x 14		
	When Cows were Wild	9 x 14		
6922.	Prospectors	8 x 12	CFA	1.00
6923.	Rainy Morning in a Cow Camp	8 x 11	CFA	1.00
6924.	Rider of the Rough String	9 x 13	CFA	1.00
6925.	Roping a Grizzly	8 x 11	CFA	1.00

6926.	Roping a Wolf	8 x 11	CFA	1.00
6927.	Roundup	14 x 30	AA	10.00
6928.	Sagebrush Sport	8 x 14	CFA	1.00
6929.	Salute of the Robe Trade	22-1/2 x 36	AA	15.00
6930.	Scattering the Riders	8 x 11	CFA	1.00
6931.	Serious Predicament	8 x 15	CFA	1.00
6932.	Slick Ear	9 x 13	CFA	1.00
6933.	Smoke of a Forty-Five	9 x 12	CFA	1.00
6934.	Strenuous Life	9 x 14	CFA	1.00
6935.	Tenderfoot	8 x 11	CFA	1.00
6936.	There's Danger Ahead when Sioux and Blackfeet Meet	8 x 15	CFA	1.00
6937.	Tight Dally and Loose Latgo	9 x 13	CFA	1.00
6938.	Toll Collectors	16-1/2 x 24-1/2	PENN	1.00
6939.	Two of a Kind Win	9 x 13	CFA	1.00
6940.	Wagon Boss	22-1/2 x 36	AA	15.00
		10 x 16	CFA	1.00
6941.	Warning Shadows	9 x 13	CFA	1.00
6942.	When Cows were Wild	20 x 28	PENN	1.00
6943.	When Horseflesh Comes High	8 x 15	CFA	1.00
6944.	When Horses Turn Back	9 x 13	CFA	1.00
6945.	When Mules Wear Diamonds	9 x 13	CFA	1.00
6946.	When Nose of Horse Beats Eyes of Man	9 x 13	CFA	1.00
6947.	When Tracks Spell Meat	9 x 13	CFA	1.00
6948.	Where Guns were Their Passports	24 x 36	IA	15.00
6949.	Who Killed the Bear, or "The Price of his Robe"	9 x 13	CFA	1.00
6950.	Whose Meat?	9 x 13	CFA	1.00
6951.	Wild Horse Hunters	9 x 14	CFA	1.00
RUSSELL, JOHN		English	1745-1806	
6952.	Girl with Cherries	14 x 11	IA	3.00
		13-1/2 x 10	IA	3.00
		9-1/2 x 7	IA	1.75
RUYSCH, RACHEL		Dutch	1664-1750	
6953.	Basket of Flowers	11 x 15	IA	3.00
6954.	Flowers and Fruit	14 x 11	IA	3.00
6955.	Fruit	11 x 15	IA	3.00
6956.	Fruit, Flowers and Insects	14 x 11	IA	3.00

6957. In Full Bloom	20 x 16	NYGS	7.50
RUYSDAEL, JACOB VAN	Dutch	1625-1682	
6958. Flemish Landscape	25 x 35	CFA	20.00
6959. Forest Scene	18 x 23	HNA	5.95
6960. Heart of the Forest	28-1/2 x 37	NYGS	24.00
6961. Holland Landscape	25 x 35	IA	20.00
6962. Landscape	11 x 14	IA	3.00
6963. Landscape, After the Rain	11 x 14	IA	3.00
6964. Lane through the Village	7 x 8	NYGS	.50
6965. Mill	8 x 10	NYGS	.50
6966. Rough Sea	18 x 23	HNA	5.95
6967. Wheatfields	5 x 7	NYGS	.50
6968. Windmill at Wijk	18 x 23	HNA	5.95
RYDER, ALBERT PINKHAM	American	1847-1917	
6969. Forest of Arden	10 x 8	NYGS	.50
6970. Moonlit Cove	13-1/2 x 16-1/2	NYGS	7.50
6971. Toilers of the Sea	10 x 12	NYGS	12.00
	6-1/2 x 7-1/2	NYGS	.50
SAALBURG, ALLEN	American	1899-	
6972. Wild Horses	12-1/2 x 18	NYGS	3.00
SAALBURG, LESLIE	American	Contemporary	
6973. Autos (2) Country Town	15 x 30	AA	15.00 ea.
6974. Autos, Antique (6)	10 x 14	CFA	30.00 set or 6.00 ea.

Ford, Model K, 1907
Mercedes, 1909
Packard, 1912
Pierce Arrow, 1905
Seagrave, 1911 (Fire
        Engine)
Simplex, 1910

6975. Autos, Antique (10)	10 x 14	CFA	50.00 set or 6.00 ea.

Columbia, 1905
Knox, 1904
Locomobile, 1907
Maxwell, 1911
Mercer, 1911
Packard, 1916
Renault, 1908
Stanley, 1911
Welch, 1907
White, 1910

SAAR, F.	German		
6976. Lady in Orchid	11 x 9	CAC	1.50
6977. Lilac Time	11x 9	CAC	1.50
SAAVEDRA, SANTOS			
6978. Citando	15-1/2 x 23	IA	4.00

6979.	Pase Ayudado Por			
	Alto	15-1/2 x 23	IA	4.00
SADLER, WALTER DENDY		English	1854-1923	
6980.	Awakening	13 x 18	CAC	7.50
6981.	Breach of Promise	14 x 19	CFA	12.00
6982.	Christening	22 x 15	CAC	7.50
6983.	Darby and Joan	14 x 19	CFA	12.00
				(H.C.)
6984.	End of Skein	14 x 19	CFA	12.00
				(H.C.)
6985.	First of September	14 x 20	CAC	7.50
6986.	For All my Fancy			
	Dwells on Nancy	18 x 13	CAC	7.50
6987.	For Fifty Years	14 x 19	CFA	12.00
				(H.C.)
6988.	Health to the Bride	18 x 24	CAC	7.50
6989.	Hearts are Trumps	14 x 20	CAC	7.50
6990.	Hunting Morn	15 x 20	CAC	7.50
6991.	Little Mortgage	14 x 19	IA	12.00
6992.	Marriage by			
	Registrar	18 x 24	CAC	7.50
6993.	Morning Gossip	15 x 20	CAC	7.50
6994.	Nearly Done	14 x 19	CFA	12.00
				(H.C.)
6995.	New Will	14 x 19	IA	12.00
6996.	The Old and the			
	Young	13 x 18	CAC	7.50
6997.	Patience	11 x 15	CAC	6.00
6998.	Plaintiff and Defen-			
	dant	14 x 19	CFA	12.00
6999.	Rivals	12 x 17	CAC	7.50
7000.	Scandal and Tea	12 x 17	CAC	7.50
7001.	Squire's Song	15 x 19	CAC	7.50
7002.	Uninvited Guests	13 x 19	CAC	7.50
7003.	Whig and Tory	14 x 11	CAC	6.00
SAITO, KYOSHI		Japanese	Contemporary	
7004.	Cat	21-1/2 x 12-1/2	AP	7.50
SALIETTI, ALBERTO		Italian	1892-	
7005.	Collector's Still life	21-1/2 x 27-1/2	NYGS	12.00
7006.	Still Life: Apples	20 x 15	NYGS	5.00
7007.	Stiff Life: The Red			
	Table	23 x 27-1/2	NYGS	10.00
7008.	Still Life with Fruit			
	(6)	7-1/2 x 6	NYGS	1.00 ea.
	Apples			
	Cherries			
	Grapes			
	Oranges			
	Plums			
	Strawberries			
SALINAS, PORFIRIO		American	1910-	
7009.	Blue Bonet Time	25-1/2 x 31-1/2	NYGS	10.00

		17 x 21	NYGS	5.00
		9 x 11	NYGS	1.00
7010.	Blue Bonnet Trail	25-1/2 x 31-1/2	NYGS	10.00
		17 x 21	NYGS	5.00
		9 x 11	NYGS	1.00
SALIS, PIETRO VON		Swiss	1877-	
7011.	Landscape in the			
	Alps	21 x 30	CAC	12.00
SALISBURY, FRANK O.		English	1874-	
7012.	Franklin D. Roosevelt	26 x 21	NYGS	7.50
		17 x 13-1/2	NYGS	3.00
		10-1/2 x 8-1/2	NYGS	1.50
SALLMAN, WARNER E.				
7013.	The Boy Christ	20 x 16	IA	1.50
		14 x 11	IA	1.00
		10 x 8	IA	.50
7014.	The Christ	20 x 16	DAC	2.00
		14 x 11	DAC	1.20
		12 x 9	DAC	.80
		10 x 8	DAC	.50
		8 x 6	DAC	.40
7015.	Christ at Dawn	20 x 16	IA	1.50
		14 x 11	IA	1.00
7016.	Christ at Heart's			
	Door	40 x 30	IA	10.00
		20 x 16	IA	1.50
		14 x 11	IA	1.00
		10 x 8	IA	.50
7017.	Christ in Gethsemane	20 x 16	IA	1.50
		14 x 11	IA	1.00
		10 x 8	IA	.50
7018.	Christ our Pilot	20 x 16	IA	1.50
		14 x 11	IA	1.00
		10 x 8	IA	.50
7019.	Crown of Thorns	14 x 11	IA	1.00
7020.	Follow Thou Me	20 x 16	IA	1.50
		14 x 11	IA	1.00
7021.	Head of Christ	40 x 30	IA	10.00
		28 x 22	IA	5.00
		20 x 16	IA	1.50
		14 x 11	IA	1.00
		10 x 8	IA	.50
7022.	His Presence	40 x 26	IA	10.00
		23-1/2 x 15	IA	1.50
		15 x 10	IA	1.00
		10 x 6-1/2	IA	.50
7023.	Jesus, the Children's	20 x 16	IA	1.50
	Friend	14 x 11	IA	1.00
		10 x 8	IA	.50
7024.	Jesus, Light of the	40 x 30	IA	10.00
	World	20 x 16	IA	1.50
		14 x 11	IA	1.00

		10 x 8	IA	.50
7025.	The Lord is my	40 x 30	IA	10.00
	Shepherd	20 x 16	IA	1.50
		14 x 11	IA	1.00
		10 x 8	IA	.50
7026.	The Mother of	20 x 16	IA	1.50
	Christ	14 x 11	IA	1.00
7027.	We Would See Jesus	20 x 16	IA	1.50
		14 x 11	IA	1.00

SALVI, GIOVAN BATTISTA See SASSOFERRATO

SALVO, COSMO DE   American   1894-
7028.	Bali Beauties	24 x 20	NYGS	7.50
		14 x 11	NYGS	3.00
		7-1/2 x 6	NYGS	1.00
7029.	Tropical Bounty	24 x 20	NYGS	7.50
		14 x 11	NYGS	3.00
		7-1/2 x 6	NYGS	1.00

SALZBURG MASTER   German   c.1516
7030.   Portrait of a Boy   14-1/2 x 10-1/2   AR   6.00

SAMMAN
7031.   Guardian of the
        Coast   23 x 29   CAC   12.00

SAMPLE, PAUL   American   1896-
7032.   America--Its Soil
        (Map)   22 x 32-1/2   NYGS   5.00
7033.   Hunters   17-1/2 x 21   NYGS   7.50
7034.   Maple Sugaring in   17 x 22   NYGS   7.50
        Vermont   6 x 7   NYGS   .50

SANDROCK
7035.   Blast Furnace   14 x 30   CAC   12.00

SANGUINETTI, EDWARD PHINEAS Italian   c. 1880
7036.   Great Metropolitan
        Stakes   14 x 22   NYGS   5.00

SANO DI PIETRO   Italian   1406-1481
7037.   Coronation of the
        Virgin   16 x 11   IA   3.00
7038.   Marriage of Count
        Sanseverino   15 x 10   IA   3.00
7039.   Virgin Annunciate   8" circle   IA   1.50

SANTI, GIOVANNI   Italian   1435-1494
7040.   St. Jerome   12 x 11   IA   3.00

SARGENT, JOHN SINGER   American   1856-1925
7041.   Asher Wertheimer   10 x 6   NYGS   .50
7042.   Boats at Anchor   13 x 18   AJ   6.00
7043.   Burning Incense   23 x 18   HNA   5.95
7044.   El Jaleo   23-1/2 x 36   NYGS   18.00
7045.   Oyster Gatherers of
        Cancale   22 x 33-1/2   NYGS   15.00
7046.   Robert de Civrieux   11 x 6   NYGS   .50
7047.   White Ships   12 x 18   NYGS   7.50
7048.   William M. Chase   11 x 7   NYGS   .50

SARTO, ANDREA DEL (ANDREA D'AGNOLO) Italian 1486-1531
7049.   Birth of the Virgin 16 x 11   IA   3.00

7050.	Head of a Child	14-1/2 x 10-1/2	NYGS	5.00
7051.	Last Supper (S.	10 x 28	IA	10.00
	Salvi)	9 x 15	IA	3.00
7052.	St. Philip the Apostle--			
	Detail of No. 7051	15 x 11	IA	3.00
7053.	Head of St. Philip--			
	Detail of No. 7051	15 x 11	IA	3.00
7054.	Jesus and St. John--			
	Detail of No. 7051	15 x 11	IA	3.00
7055.	Madonna and Child			
	with St. John	15 x 10	IA	3.00
7056.	Madonna del Sacco	15 x 10	IA	3.00
7057.	Madonna of the			
	Harpies	13 x 11	IA	3.00
7058.	Detail of No. 7057	15 x 11	IA	3.00
7059.	The Redeemer	15 x 9	IA	3.00
7060.	St. John the Baptist	15 x 10	IA	3.00
7061.	Two Angels	15 x 8	IA	3.00

SARULLO, PASQUALE, O. P. M. Italian   1828-1893

7062.	Immaculate Virgin	15 x 11	IA	3.00
7063.	Madonna and Child	15 x 11	IA	3.00

SASSETTA, STEFANO DI GIOVANNI Italian   1392-1450

7064.	Journey of the Magi	8 x 11	NYGS	.50
		7 x 10	NYGS	.50
		6 x 9	NYGS	.50
7065.	Legend of St. Francis	5 x 7	NYGS	.50

SASSOFERRATO (SALVI, GIOVAN BATTISTA) Italian 1609-1685

7066.	Blue Madonna	20 x 16	CAC	7.50
7067.	Madonna of the			
	Rosary	14 x 10	IA	3.00
7068.	Virgin of Sorrow	13 x 10	IA	3.00
		10 x 8	IA	1.50

SAVAGE, EDWARD   American   1761-1817

7069.	The Washington			
	Family	21 x 28	NYGS	12.00

SAVARY, ROBERT   French   1920-

7070.	Orchestra	18 x 22	ESH	10.00

SAVIGNE

7071.	Still Life Composi-			
	tions (4)	12 x 24	DAC	2.80 ea.

SAVITT

7072.	Horses, Thorough-			
	bred (8)	12 x 16	DAC	1.40 ea.
	Flying Hoofs			
	Horse's Head, Facing Right			
	Horse's Head, Facing Left			
	Mare and Reclining Colt			
	Mare and Standing Colt			
	Over the Hurdle			
	Thoroughbred, Facing Left			
	Thoroughbred, Facing Right			

SAVOLDO, GIOVANNI GIROLAMO Italian 1480-1548

7073.	Gaston de Foix	11 x 15	IA	3.00

7074.	Raphael and Tobias	7 x 9	NYGS	.50
7075.	Tobias and the Archangel	11 x 14	IA	3.00

SAYRE, F.G.

| 7076. | Carpet of Allah | 22 x 28 | CFA | 7.50 |

SCALCO

| 7077. | Still Life with Clock | 24 x 30 | DAC | 8.00 |

SCHAFER, EMIL   Swiss   1878-1959

7078.	In the Mountains near Rome	29 x 22	CAC	12.00
7079.	Moor and Bridge	13 x 18	CFA	5.00
7080.	Moorland	13 x 18	CFA	5.00

SCHALDACH, WILLIAM J.

| 7081. | Black Bass | 14 x 17 | AA | 5.00 |
| 7082. | Brook Trout | 14 x 17 | AA | 5.00 |

SCHALK

| 7083. | Toros Rojos | 18 x 24 | CFA | 15.00 |

SCHALKEN, GOFFREDO   Dutch   1643-1706

| 7084. | Woman with a Candlestick | 14 x 11 | IA | 3.00 |

SCHATTE

| 7085. | Autumn Day | 28 x 22 | CAC | 12.00 |

SCHEDONI, BARTOLOMEO   Italian   1570-1615

| 7086. | Putto-Detail from "Christian Charity" | 15 x 7 | IA | 3.00 |

SCHEFFER

| 7087. | Fragrance of Spring | 24 x 30 | DAC | 6.00 |

SCHENK, ERIC

7088.	American Beauty Rose	22 x28	CFA	10.00
7089.	Luscious Tea Rose	22 x 28	CFA	10.00
7090.	Peach Hibiscus	22 x 28	CFA	10.00
7091.	Sky Hibiscus	22 x 28	CFA	10.00

SCHINDLER   Austrian   1780-1830

| 7092. | Park Landscape | 15 x 22 | AJ | 7.50 |

SCHLEIBNER, KASPER   German   1863-

7093.	Christ in the Wheatfields	26-1/2 x 38	IA	12.00
7094.	Coena Domini	27-1/2 x 39-1/2	IA	12.00
		20 x 28	IA	6.00
7095.	Immaculate Heart of Mary	13-1/2 x 9-1/2	IA	1.50
7096.	Last Supper	27-1/2 x 39-1/2	IA	12.00
		19-1/2 x 28	IA	6.00
		9 x 13	IA	1.00
7097.	Sacred Heart of Jesus	13-1/2 x 9-1/2	IA	1.50

SCHLEMMER

| 7098. | Airplanes, Famous (8) | 8 x 10 | DAC | .80 ea. |
| | | 6 x 8 | DAC | .40 ea. |

7099. Locomotives, Famous (6)	8 x 10	DAC	.80 ea.
	6 x 8	DAC	.40 ea
SCHLERETH, HANS	German	1897-	
7100. Sun Flowers	27-1/2 x 24	ESH	12.00
SCHMALZ, HERBEET			
7101. Return from Calvary	16 x 24	IA	7.50
	8 x 12	IA	1.50
SCHMIDT			
7102. Sailing	16 x 12	CFA	3.00
SCHMIDT, PETER JO			
7103. In the Alps	23 x 28	ESH	10.00
SCHMIDT-ROTTLUFF, KARL	German	1884-	
7104. Around a Hyacinth	23 x 26	NYGS	22.00
7105. Magnolias	22 x 30	ESH	10.00
SCHNARS-ALQUIST, CARL WILHELM		1885-	
7106. In the Tropics (Eight Bells)	24 x 37	IA	15.00
	24 x 36	CAC	15.00
SCHOBER, PETER JAKOB	German	1897-	
7107. Evening	23-1/2 x 31-1/2	ESH	10.00(Pr.)
SCHOLEI			
7108. Bavarian Boy	9 x 12	ESH	1.50(Pr.)
7109. Bavarian Girl	9 x 12	ESH	1.50(Pr.)
7110. Fishing Boats	16 x 20	ESH	5.00(Pr.)
7111. Heatherland	23-1/2 x 31-1/2	ESH	10.00(Pr.)
7112. Late Summer Day	19-1/2 x 27-1/2	ESH	8.00(Pr.)
7113. Summer Day	16 x 20	ESH	5.00(Pr.)
SCHONGAUER, MARTIN	German	c.1430-1491	
7114. Holy Family	10 x 7	NYGS	6.50
SCHREIBER, GEORGES	American	1904-	
7115. Center Ring	11 x 6	NYGS	10.00
7116. Haying	12 x 16	NYGS	5.00
7117. In Tennessee	12 x 16	NYGS	5.00
7118. Mississippi Moon	17 x 20-1/2	NYGS	7.50
SCHREYVOGEL, CHARLES	American	1861-1912	
7119. Rough Riders	14-1/2 x 19-1/2	NYGS	4.00
SCHRIMPF, GEORG	German	1889-	
7120. By the Lake	20 x 35	CFA	15.00
7121. Osterseen	22 x 31	CFA	12.00
SCHUCH, CHARLES	German	1846-1903	
7122. Still Life	24-1/2 x 30	NYGS	20.00
7123. Still Life of Apples	22 x 30	CFA	15.00
SCHULZE, E.			
7124. Fextal (Engadin)	25-1/2 x 34	IA	12.00
SCHURR, CLAUDE	French	1921-	
7125. Fishing Boats	23 x 28	RL	12.50
7126. Harbour Pattern	19 x 26	RL	12.50
SCHUTZ, KARL	Austrian	1745-1800	
7127. Vienna from the Belvedere	15 x 23	AR	10.00
SCHWACHA, GEORGE	American	1908-	
7128. Central Park	30 x 14	CFA	15.00
7129. Fifth Avenue	30 x 14	CFA	15.00
7130. Times Square	14 x 30	CFA	15.00

SCHWARTZ, DAVIS F.
7131.	California Lake	12 x 16	IA	2.00
7132.	Carmel Mission in Moonlight	20 x 16	IA	3.00
7133.	Coast near Monterey	8 x 10	IA	1.00
7134.	Cypress Point	16 x 20	IA	3.00
7135.	Early Autumn	16 x 20	IA	3.00
7136.	Eucalyptus Trees	8 x 10	IA	1.00
7137.	Fisherman's Cabin	16 x 20	IA	3.00
7138.	Fisherman's Wharf, San Francisco	12 x 16	IA	2.00
7139.	Lake Region	16 x 20	IA	3.00
7140.	Mark Twain's Cabin	16 x 20	IA	3.00
7141.	Mission near San Xavier Del Bac, Tucson	12 x 16	IA	2.00
7142.	Monterey Wharf	12 x 16	IA	2.00
7143.	Mount Diablo, California Ranch	16 x 20	IA	3.00
7144.	Old Customs House, Monterey	16 x 20	IA	3.00
7145.	On the Road to China Camp	15 x 20	IA	3.00
7146.	Poplar Trees	10 x 8	IA	1.00
7147.	Russian River, California	8 x 10	IA	1.00
7148.	San Carlos Church in Moonlight	20 x 16	IA	3.00
7149.	San Francisco Harbor	8 x 10	IA	1.00
7150.	San Francisco Wharf	8 x 10	IA	1.00
7151.	San Juan Capistrano Mission	16 x 20	IA	3.00
7152.	Santa Barbara Mission	12 x 16	IA	2.00
7153.	Sleepy Hollow Road	16 x 20	IA	3.00
7154.	Southern California Coast	12 x 16	IA	2.00
7155.	Tranquility	16 x 20	IA	3.00

SCHWENINGER
7156.	Duet	21 x 16	AA	7.50
7157.	Language of Flowers	21 x 16	AA	7.50

SCHWIND, MORITZ VON   Austrian   1804-1871
7158.	Anna, Daughter of the Artist	9 x 7	NYGS	8.00
7159.	Bread Slicer	24 x 18	NYGS	10.00
7160.	Emperor Maximilian in Prayer	18-1/2 x 13-1/2	AJ	6.00
7161.	Ruebezahl	25 x 15	NYGS	18.00

SCIARPELLONI, LORENZO see LORENZO DI CREDI
SCOTT, PETER
7162.	Water Fowl (6)	14 x 17	DAC	3.00 set

SEBASTIANO DEL PIOMBO See PIOMBO, SEBASTIANO DEL

SEGHERS, HERKULES	Dutch	1589-1638	
7163. Landscape	9 x 15	IA	3.00
SEGONZAC, ANDRE DUNOYER DE	French	1885-	
7164. Bay of St. Tropez	29-1/2 x 24	NYGS	16.00
7165. Garden Bouquet	20 x 26	PENN	1.00
7166. Hills Beyond the Bay	22-1/2 x 30-1/2	NYGS	15.00
7167. Landscape	17 x 23-1/2	NYGS	10.00
7168. Landscape with River	17 x 23	NYGS	15.00
7169. Village Square	17 x 22-1/2	NYGS	15.00
7170. Village Street	22-1/2 x 16-1/2	ESH	10.00
SEKKYO			
7171. Bull	20 x 13-1/2	PENN	1.00
7172. Eagle	20 x 13-1/2	PENN	1.00
SERPA, IVAN FERREIRA	Brazilian	1923-	
7173. Construction No. 75	15-1/2 x 15-1/2	NYGS	10.00
SERTON			
7174. Fruits, Still Life	8 x 10	DAC	.80
(4)	6 x 8	DAC	.40
SERUSIER			
7175. Landscape (The Talisman)	8 x 10	MMA	.35
SESSIONS, JAMES M.	American	1882-1962	
7176. After the Catch	17-1/2 x 24	IA	10.00
7177. Backwater	17-1/2 x 24	IA	10.00
7178. Blue Harbor	17-1/2 x 24	IA	10.00
7179. Driving Home for Gloucester	17-1/2 x 24	IA	10.00
7180. Fisherman's Wharf	22 x 28	NYGS	12.00
7181. Fishermen	20 x 26	NYGS	12.00
7182. Geese Coming in	17-1/2 x 24	IA	10.00
7183. Gloucester	17-1/2 x 24	IA	10.00
7184. Good Breeze	20 x 26	NYGS	12.00
7185. Grouse Shooting	20 x 26	NYGS	12.00
7186. Herring Boats	17-1/2 x 24	IA	10.00
7187. Misty Morning	20 x 26	NYGS	12.00
7188. Outward Bound	20 x 26	NYGS	12.00
7189. Pawtucket Inlet	17-1/2 x 24	IA	10.00
7190. Pioneers	17-1/2 x 24	IA	10.00
7191. Ready to Sail	22 x 28	NYGS	12.00
7192. Road to the Cove	17-1/2 x 24	IA	10.00
7193. Strike of a Steel-head	17-1/2 x 24	IA	10.00
7194. Trout Stream	20 x 26	NYGS	12.00
7195. Vermont Farm	17-1/2 x 24	IA	10.00
SEURAT, GEORGES PIERRE	French	1859-1891	
7196. Afternoon at the "Grande Jatte"	8 x 10	ESH	1.00
7197. Circus	25 x 20	PENN	1.00
7198. Fishing Fleet	25-1/2 x 22	MMA	16.00
7199. Fishing Fleet at Port-En-Bessin	21 x 25-1/2	NYGS	16.00

7200.	Harbour at Honfleur	20 x 24	PENN	1.00
				1.98(Pr.)
7201.	Landscape	8 x 10	ESH	1.00
7202.	Seine at Courbevoie	22-1/2 x 18	ESH	10.00
7203.	Side Show	20 x 30	NYGS	18.00
		6 x 9	NYGS	.50
7204.	Study for the "Grande			
	Jatte"	8 x 10	ESH	1.00
7205.	Sunday Afternoon on	24 x 36	IA	18.00
	the Island of La	24 x 35-1/2	AJ	18.00
	Grande Jatte	18 x 27	PENN	1.00
				1.98(Pr.)
		7 x 11	NYGS	.50
		5 x 7	NYGS	.50
7206.	Sunday at Port En			
	Bessin	17 x 21	AP	5.00
7207.	Sunday on the Grande	24 x 36	CFA	18.00
	Jatte	8 x 10	ESH	1.00
SEVERINI, GINO		Italian	1883-	
7208.	Dynamic Hieroglyphic	8 x 10	MMA	.35
7209.	Mandolin and Fruit	17 x 21	NYGS	10.00
7210.	Still Life with Pipe	13 x 18	NYGS	15.00
SHAHN, BEN		American	Contemporary	
7211.	Handball	8 x 10	MMA	.35
7212.	Laissez Faire	12 x 18	AR	5.00
7213.	Ohio Magic	18 x 23	HNA	5.95
7214.	Poster	27 x 20-1/2	PENN	1.00
7215.	Poster	26-1/2 x 18	PENN	1.00
7216.	Silent Night	22 x 28	AR	5.00
SHANNON, JAMES J.		American	1862-1923	
7217.	Fairy Tales	8 x 10	NYGS	.50
SHAUNS, F.				
7218.	Bouquet of Lilacs	16 x 20	IA	3.50
SHAW, BARBARA		English	Contemporary	
7219.	Floral Fantasy	20 x 16	CFA	5.00
7220.	Flower Piece, 1949	20 x 16	RL	10.00
7221.	Flower Piece, 1951	20 x 16	RL	10.00
7222.	Medley of Flowers	20 x 16	CFA	5.00
SHAYER, WILLIAM J.		English	1788-1879	
7223.	Half-Way House	24 x 36	AA	12.00
7224.	Lord William	20 x 25	AA	20.00
7225.	Woodland Rest	28 x 36	NYGS	12.00
		20 x 26	NYGS	7.50
SHEELER, CHARLES		American	1883-	
7226.	American Interior	18-1/2 x 17	NYGS	5.00
7227.	American Landscape	7 x 9	NYGS	.50
7228.	Bucks County Barn	18-1/2 x 24	NYGS	12.00
7229.	Pertaining to Yachts	20 x 24	NYGS	12.00
	and Yachting	18 x 23	HNA	5.95
SHEETS, MILLARD F.		American	1907-	
7230.	First-Born	6 x 7	NYGS	.50
7231.	Ho Ho Kane (South	22 x 30	IA	12.00
	Seas)			

7232.	Road to the Sea	21-1/2 x 29-1/2	NYGS	12.00
7233.	Toilers at Sunset	14 x 20	NYGS	7.50
SHEPHERD, DAVID		English	1931-	
7234.	Britania over Kilimanjaro	21 x 28	RL	7.50
7235.	Shepherd Street	18-1/2 x 22	RL	7.50
SHEPLER, DWIGHT CLARK		American	1905-	
7236.	Night Action off Savo	16 x 24	NYGS	3.00
7237.	On the Glacier	14 x 20	NYGS	6.00
7238.	Powder Snow	14 x 20	NYGS	6.00
7239.	Task Force of Two Navies	16 x 24	NYGS	3.00
7240.	Tulagi Secured	16 x 24	NYGS	3.00
7241.	Unloading Operations	12 x 18	NYGS	3.00
SHERRIN, DANIEL				
7242.	Harp of Trees	22 x 32	CFA	10.00
7243.	Peaceful Evening	22 x 32	CFA	10.00
SHERWIN, FRANK		English	1896-	
7244.	Blue Studio, St. Ives	12 x 16	RL	1.50
7245.	Concarneau	14 x 18	CFA	5.00
7246.	Coniston	14 x 18	CFA	5.00
7247.	Dundrum Bay, Co. Down	12 x 16	RL	1.50
7248.	Derwentwater	14 x 18	CFA	5.00
7249.	Llanberris	14 x 18	CFA	5.00
7250.	Loch Katrine	14 x 18	CFA	5.00
7251.	Loch Lomond	14 x 18	CFA	5.00
7252.	Mountains of Mourn	12 x 16	RL	1.50
7253.	Off Cowes, Isle of Wight	12 x 16	RL	1.50
7254.	Return to Harbour	12 x 16	RL	1.50
7255.	Sailing Dinghies on the Clyde	12 x 16	RL	1.50
7256.	Sailing in the Solent	12 x 16	RL	1.50
7257.	Sunflowers	12 x 16	RL	1.50
7258.	Sunny Terrace, Lake Como	12 x 16	RL	1.50
SHINN, EVERETT		American	1876-	
7259.	Revue	18 x 24	PENN	1.00
SHORTT, ANGUS H.				
7260.	Canada Geese	17 x 24-1/2	IA	5.00
SHULKIN, ANATOL		American	1899-	
7261.	Fairy Tale	24 x 19	NYGS	10.00
SHUMAKER, PHILIP				
7262.	Autumn Reflections	24 x 36	DAC	8.00
		18 x 26	DAC	6.00
		12 x 18	DAC	2.00
7263.	Boats in Harbor	16-1/2 x 24	PENN	1.00
7264.	Monhegan Gold	24 x 48	DAC	10.00
		24 x 36	DAC	8.00
		18 x 26	DAC	6.00
		12 x 18	DAC	2.00

7265.	Mountain Retreat	24 x 36	DAC	8.00
		18 x 26	DAC	6.00
		12 x 18	DAC	2.00
7266.	Peaceful Valley	24 x 36	DAC	8.00
		18 x 26	DAC	6.00
		12 x 18	DAC	2.00
7267.	Sea in Splendor	24 x 38	DAC	10.00

SIGNAC, PAUL French 1863-1935

7268.	Harbor	18 x 24	NYGS	10.00
7269.	Harbor of St. Tropez	22 x 18	CFA	12.00
7270.	Paris	27 x 34	CFA	18.00
7271.	Port of Paimpol	11-1/2 x 30	ESH	15.00
7272.	Quay at Clichy	17 x 24	PENN	1.00
7273.	Venice--St. Maria della Salute	26 x 32-1/2	NYGS	18.00
7274.	Yellow Sails	24 x 30	ESH	15.00

SIGNORELLI, LUCA Italian 1450-1523

7275.	Anti-Christ	11 x 14	IA	3.00
7276.	Detail of No. 7275	15 x 11	IA	3.00
7277.	Calling of the Elects	11 x 14	IA	3.00
7278.	The Damned	11 x 14	IA	3.00
7279.	Detail of No. 7278	11 x 15	IA	3.00
7280.	Empidocles of Agri- gentum	15 x 11	IA	3.00
7281.	Last Judgement	11 x 15	IA	3.00
7282.	Madonna and Child	12" circle	IA	3.00
7283.	Portrait of Dante	15 x 12	IA	3.00
7284.	Virgil	15 x 12	IA	3.00

SIGNORINI, TELEMACO Italian 1835-1901

7285.	Street in Settignano	10 x 15	IA	3.00

SILVERMAN

7286.	Boats in Harbor	16-1/2 x 24	PENN	1.00
7287.	Fanni's Circus	18-1/2 x 24	PENN	1.00
7288.	Festival in the Square	18-1/2 x 24	PENN	1.00
7289.	Fisherman's Port	18-1/2 x 24	PENN	1.00

SIMEONE, ADOLFO Italian 1885-

7290.	Christ with the Children	22 x 32	IA	8.00
7291.	Madonna of the Rosary	19-1/2 x 28	IA	8.00

SIMON-SCHAFER, HANS-ALBERT

7292.	In the Mountains near Rome	23 x 29-1/2	ESH	12.00

SIMONE DA PESARO Italian 1612-1648

7293.	Holy Family	15 x 11	IA	3.00

SIMPSON

7294.	President Kennedy	24 x 20	CAC	7.50

SINKO, LOUIS-ARMAND 1934-

7295.	Bouquet	19-1/2 x 24	NYGS	12.00

SIRONI, MARIO Italian 1893-

7296.	Return of the Mythe	20 x 24	NYGS	12.00

SISLEY, ALFRED	French	1839-1899	
7297. L'Abrevoir	12 x 16	AR	3.00
7298. Afternoon at Moret-			
Sur-Loing	8 x 10	ESH	1.00
7299. At Daybreak	11 x 13	IA	3.00
7300. Autumn Leaves	10 x 8	ESH	1.00
7301. Avenue	8 x 10	ESH	1.00
7302. Banks of the Loing	20 x 25	CFA	15.00
	8 x 10	ESH	1.00
7303. Banks of the Oise	16 x 19-1/2	NYGS	10.00
7304. Barges at St.			
Mammes	20 x 26	CFA	15.00
7305. Boat during Inunda-			
tion	7 x 8	CFA	1.00
7306. Bridge in Moret	18 x 23	HNA	5.95
7307. Canal de L'Ourcq	24 x 30	PENN	1.00
7308. Canal St. Martin	19 x 25	AJ	12.00
7309. Covered Bridge	24 x 30	PENN	1.00
7310. La Croix-Blanche,			
St. Mammes	18 x 23	HNA	5.95
7311. Early Snow in Louve-			
ciennes	18 x 23	HNA	5.95
7312. Floods at Marly in			
1875	18-1/2 x 22-1/2	ESH	10.00
7313. L'Inondation a Port	15 x 20	PENN	1.00
Marly	7 x 9	NYGS	.50
7314. Island of La Grande			
Jatte	17 x 22-1/2	ESH	10.00
7315. Landscape	17 x 22-1/2	AR	12.00
7316. Landscape with			
House	7 x 9	NYGS	.50
7317. Loing Canal	18 x 22	ESH	10.00
7318. Loing at Moret	8 x 10	ESH	1.00
7319. Loing at Moret,			
Sept. Afternoon	8 x 10	ESH	1.00
7320. Molesey Weir	7 x 9	NYGS	.50
7321. Moret-Sur-Loing,	18 x 22-1/2	ESH	10.00
Morning Sunshine	8 x 10	ESH	1.00
7322. Port Marly	15 x 24	AJ	10.00
	11 x 18	CFA	5.00
7323. Regatta at Hampton			
Court	8 x 10	ESH	1.00
7324. River Seine	17 x 22-1/2	ESH	10.00
7325. Seine at Marly	8 x 10	ESH	1.00
	7 x 9	NYGS	.50
7326. Seine at St. Cloud	18-1/2 x 22-1/2	ESH	10.00
7327. September Afternoon			
at Moret	8 x 10	ESH	1.00
7328. Small Square at	19 x 28	PENN	1.00
Argenteuil	15-1/2 x 22-1/2	ESH	10.00
7329. Snow at Louveciennes	8 x 6	CFA	1.00
7330. Springtime at Moret	8 x 10	ESH	1.00

7331.	Street at Louveciennes	22-1/2 x 18	ESH	10.00
7332.	Street at Marly	8 x 10	ESH	1.00
7333.	Street in Moret	24 x 30	CFA	15.00
7334.	Tugboat	15-1/2 x 21	PENN	1.00
				1.98(Pr)
7335.	View of St. Martin	19 x 25	CFA	12.00
7336.	Village de Sablons	18 x 21-1/2	ESH	10.00
7337.	Village of Voisins	8 x 10	ESH	1.00

SITZMANN, E. R.

7338.	Happy Hollow	22 x 28	CFA	7.50

SKINNER, VIOLET — English — Contemporary

7339.	Into the Happy Lands	18 x 32	RL	7.50
7340.	Mares' Tails in the Sky	20 x 30	RL	7.50
7341.	Wild White Horses	17 x 32	RL	7.50

SLOAN, JOHN — American — 1871-1951

7342.	McSorley's Bar	8 x 10	NYGS	.50
7343.	Wake of the Ferry Boat II	18 x 22	NYGS	12.00

SLOANE, ERIC

7344.	Autumn in New England	24 x 36	CFA	15.00
7345.	Canvas Backs	18 x 24	AA	7.50
7346.	End of Summer	24 x 36	CFA	15.00
7347.	New England in December	24 x 36	CFA	15.00

SLUYTERMAN, GEORG

7348.	Lueneburger Moorlands	23 x 30	ESH	10.00

SMEELE

7349.	Zuider-Zee Towns (6)	7 x 7-1/2	DAC	.40 ea

SMITH, ALICE

7350.	American Homes of Yesteryear (4)	18 x 11	DAC	2.00 ea.
		8 x 5-1/2	DAC	.60 ea.
	Mid-Victorian			
	New Orleans			
	Ornate Victorian			
	Town House			
7351.	Early West (4)	11 x 14	DAC	1.00 ea.
7352.	Nostalgia (4)	11 x 14	DAC	2.80 ea.
	Anticipation			
	Ballet Life			
	Pantry Charm			
	Souvenirs			

SMITH, FRANK V.

7353.	Sunlit Seas	25 x 30	IA	10.00

SMITH, JESSIE WILLCOX — American

7354.	Morning Mist	24 x 30	CFA	10.00
7355.	We Give Thee Thanks	16 x 15-1/2	NYGS	3.00

SMITH, LAWRENCE BEALL — American — 1909-

7356.	Frolic	17 x 22	NYGS	7.50

SMITH, MINNA WALKER		American	1883-	
7357.	Purity	24 x 20	IA	10.00
SMITH, WALLACE H.		American	1901-	
7358.	Hell Gate Bridge, New York	11 x 19	NYGS	5.00
SNAPPER				
7359.	Bridge in Paris	24 x 48	DAC	10.00
7360.	Chicago Views (4)	12 x 30	DAC	4.00 ea.
		8 x 17	DAC	1.20 ea.
7361.	Continental Views (8)	12 x 30	DAC	4.00 ea.
		8 x 17	DAC	1.20 ea.
7362.	Italy (4)	12 x 18	DAC	4.00 ea.
		8 x 12	DAC	1.00 ea.
7363.	New York Scenes (6)	12 x 30	DAC	4.00 ea.
		8 x 17	DAC	1.20 ea.
SODOMA, IL (BAZZI, GIOVANNI ANTONIO) Italian 1477-1549				
7364.	Madonna and Child with Infant St. John	22 x 18	AA	7.50
7365.	Scourging of Christ	15 x 11	IA	3.00
7366.	St. Sebastian	15 x 11	IA	3.00
7367.	Head--Detail of No. 7366	18 x 14	IA	3.00
7368.	Trance of St. Catherine	15 x 11	IA	3.00
SOHL, WILL		German	1906-	
7369.	The Cove	25 x 19	ESH	7.50
SOLARIO, ANDREA		Italian	1460-1527	
7370.	Charles D'Amboise	9 x 6	NYGS	.50
7371.	Madonna with the Green Cushion	10 x 8	ESH	1.00
7372.	Virgin Nursing the Child	14 x 11	IA	3.00
SOLIMENA, FRANCESCO		Italian	1657-1747	
7373.	Supper at Emmaus	7 x 10	NYGS	.50
SOORD, ALFRED		English	1869-1915	
7374.	Lost Sheep	20 x 13	IA	4.00
		10 x 8	IA	.50
		10 x 6	NYGS	.50
SORBI, RAFFAELE		Italian	1844-1931	
7375.	Promenade of Leopold I	10 x 15	IA	3.00
SOROLLA Y BASTIDA, JUAQUIN Spanish			1863-1923	
7376.	Two Sisters, Valencia	12 x 8	NYGS	.50
SOUTER, J.B.		Scotch	Contemporary	
7377.	English Rose	17 x 14	RL	2.50
7378.	Glory of the Garden	16 x 12	RL	3.50
7379.	Summer's Pride	16 x 12	RL	3.50
SOUTINE, CHAIM		French	1894-1943	
7380.	Alley of Trees	8 x 10	MMA	.35

7381.	Big Tree	24 x 19	PENN	1.00
7382.	Chartres Cathedral	30 x 16-1/2	ESH	15.00
		10 x 8	MMA	.35
7383.	Choir Boy	22-1/2 x 18	ESH	10.00
7384.	Cook Boy	8 x 6	NYGS	.50
7385.	Girl in Pink	19 x 12	CFA	7.50
7386.	Woman in a Blue			
	Robe	10 x 8	ESH	1.00
7387.	Portrait of a Boy	24 x 16-1/2	NYGS	10.00
		22 x 15	PENN	1.00

SOYER, MOSES   Russian-American 1899-

7388.	Blue Dancer	20 x 9	PENN	1.00
7389.	Dancers at Rest	24 x 20	PENN	1.00
				1.98(Pr.)
7390.	Dancers Reposed	20 x 24	PENN	1.00
				1.98(Pr.)
7391.	Red Dancer	20 x 9	PENN	1.00
7392.	Seven Dancers	23 x 18	HNA	5.95
		21 x 20	PENN	1.00
				1.98(Pr.)

SOYER, RAPHAEL   American   1899-

7393.	Farewell to Lincoln			
	Square	18 x 23	HNA	5.95
7394.	Flower Vendor	16-1/2 x 20	NYGS	5.00
7395.	Modern Tempo	20 x 15-1/2	NYGS	7.50

SPAGNA, GIOVANNI DI PIETRO Italian   1500-1530

7396.	Study of a Nude			
	Male Model	10 x 6	AR	3.50

SPAGNOLETTO, LO See RIBERA, JOSE DE
SPAGNOLO, LO See CRESPI, GIOVANNI (OR GIUSEPPI)
   MARIA
SPEICHER, EUGENE   American   1883-

7397.	Jean Bellows	9 x 8	NYGS	.50
7398.	Nude Back	16 x 20	NYGS	5.00

SPENCER

7399.	Stallions, Celebrated			
	(6)	24 x 14	AA	7.50

SPENCER, ROBERT   American   1879-1931

7400.	Color Grandeur	24 x 40	DAC	8.00
7401.	Falling Leaves	24 x 40	DAC	8.00
7402.	Herder's View	8 x 12	DAC	1.00
7403.	Homesteader	12 x 20	DAC	2.00
7404.	Late Summer	24 x 40	DAC	8.00
7405.	Roadside Dwellings	24 x 40	DAC	8.00
7406.	Scenic Lane	24 x 40	DAC	8.00
7407.	Summer Sequel	24 x 40	DAC	8.00
7408.	Winter Wonderland	24 x 40	DAC	8.00
7409.	Young Skippers	24 x 40	DAC	8.00

SPINELLI, GAETANO   Italian   1887-1945

7410.	Adoration	16 x 20	IA	7.50
7411.	Expectation	25 x 17	IA	7.50
7412.	Detail of No. 7411	21 x 20	IA	7.50

7413.	Maternal Joys	13 x 11	IA	3.00
7414.	Prelude	20 x 20	IA	7.50
SPIRO, GEORGE		Polish	1909-	
7415.	Don Quixote	22 x 18	RL	10.00
SPITZ				
7416.	Wine Taster	9 x 12	ESH	2.00(Pr.)
SPITZWEG, KARL		German	1808-1885	
7417.	Bookworm	14-1/2 x 8	AJ	2.50
7418.	Cactus' Friend	10-1/2 x 5-1/2	AJ	1.75
7419.	Pensionists	10-1/2 x 6	AJ	2.00
7420.	Poor Poet	20 x 24	DAC	6.00
SPRICK, RICHARD		German	1901-	
7421.	In Mallorca	12 x 16	ESH	4.00
SPROTTE, SIEGWARD		German	1913-	
7422.	Noon in Blue	24 x 32	CFA	15.00
7423.	Northern Light	22 x 31	CFA	15.00
SPY				
7424.	Divorce	12-1/2 x 7-1/2	IA	2.50
		9 x 6	IA	1.50
7425.	Judges the Claimant	12 x 8	IA	2.50
		9 x 6	IA	1.50
7426.	Lord Chief Justice	12 x 7-1/2	IA	2.50
		9 x 6-1/2	IA	1.50
7427.	Umpire	12 x 7-1/2	IA	2.50
		9 x 5-1/2	IA	1.50
SPYKER, JAN				
7428.	Holland Today (4)	16 x 12	DAC	1.40
SPYROPOULOS, JANNIS		Greek	Contemporary	
7429.	Oracle	36 x 23-1/2	NYGS	15.00
STABLI, ADOLF				
7430.	Stroll to the Lake	18 x 29	CFA	12.00
STAHL, BEN		American	1910-	
7431.	Nativity	17 x 29	DAC	4.00
		15 x 27	PENN	1.00
STANG				
7432.	Last Supper (After	21-1/2 x 41	IA	10.00
	Da Vinci)	16 x 30	IA	5.00
		7 x 9	IA	2.00
		6-1/2 x 12	IA	1.00
STARNINA, GHERARDO		Italian	1354-1403	
7433.	The Thebaid	11 x 15	IA	3.00
STEEL, KENNETH		English	1906-	
7434.	Palma, Majorca	17 x 21-1/2	RL	6.00
7435.	Pollenza, Majorca	17 x 21-1/2	RL	6.00
7436.	Puerto Alcudia	17 x 21-1/2	RL	6.00
STEEN, JAN		Dutch	1626-1679	
7437.	Baptismal Party	6 x 7	NYGS	.50
7438.	Dancing Couple	22 x 30	AA	15.00
7439.	Eve of St. Nicholas	9 x 8	NYGS	.50
7440.	Family Repast	13 x 11	IA	3.00
7441.	In the Bower	8 x 10	AR	3.00
STEFULA, GYORGY		German	1913-	
7442.	Province Gate	18 x 21	CFA	10.00

7443. Provincial Basket	19 x 23	CFA	10.00

STEIJNS-BROMBERG, NETTIE

7444. Dr. Albert Einstein	20 x 16	NYGS	5.00

STEINHAUSEN, WILHELM

7445. Return from Our	23-1/2 x 22	IA	7.50
Lord's Supper	8 x 7-1/2	IA	.75

STEINKE, BETTINA

7446. Bringing Flowers Singing	16 x 12	IA	5.00
7447. Jumping Deer	16 x 12	IA	5.00
7448. Santa Clara Indian Girl	17-1/2 x 15-1/2	IA	6.00
7449. Taos Indian Boy	16 x 12	IA	5.00
7450. Taos Indian Girl	16 x 12	IA	5.00

STEINLAUF

7451. Composition II	28 x 12	CFA	20.00
7452. Doves	28 x 12	CFA	20.00
7453. Expression I	28 x 12	CFA	20.00
7454. Fishing Boats I	12 x 28	CFA	20.00
7455. Fishing Boats II	12 x 28	CFA	20.00
7456. Flower Vendor	28 x 12	CFA	20.00
7457. Girl with Dove	19 x 15	CFA	20.00
7458. Juanita	28 x 12	CFA	20.00
7459. Lolita	28 x 12	CFA	20.00
7460. Rosita	28 x 12	CFA	20.00
7461. Sisters	28 x 12	CFA	20.00
7462. Watermelon Boy	28 x 12	CFA	20.00

STEINMANN, AUGUST   American   Contemporary

7463. Pacific Surf	18 x 24	IA	7.50

STELLA, JOSEPH   American   1880-1946

7464. Voice of the Night- ingale	20 x 18-1/2	NYGS	7.50

STEVENS, SANFORD

7465. El Cambo	16 x 20	CFA	5.00
	7 x 9	CFA	1.50
7466. Flower Market	16 x 20	CFA	5.00
	7 x 9	CFA	1.50
7467. Market Day	20 x 16	CFA	5.00
	9 x 7	CFA	1.50
7468. Mexican Street Scene	20 x 16	CFA	5.00
	9 x 7	CFA	1.50
7469. Siesta Time	16 x 20	CFA	5.00
	7 x 9	CFA	1.50
7470. Tropical Village	16 x 20	CFA	5.00
	7 x 9	CFA	1.50

STEVENSON, BRUCE   American   Contemporary

7471. Treasure Island	18 x 24-1/2	RL	7.50

STEVENSON, ESTHER

7472. April Showers	29 x 15	CFA	7.50
7473. I Pledge Allegiance	20 x 16	CFA	5.00
7474. Little Girl	20 x 16	CFA	5.00
7475. On the Beach	29 x 15	CFA	7.50

STEWART
7476.	Persian Pottery	20 x 16	PENN	1.00
				1.98 (Pr
7477.	Zinnias	16 x 20	PENN	1.00
				1.98(Pr.)

STEWART, ARTHUR
7478.	Big Sky	24 x 40	NYGS	15.00

STEWART, CHARLES   Scotch
7479.	Tapa Cloth	16-1/2 x 45	IA	12.00

STEWART, ETHELYN CROSBY   American   1900-
7480.	Magnolias	19 x 15-1/2	RL	7.50
7481.	Pine Screen	20-1/2 x 26	RL	10.00
7482.	Zinnias (Sung Vase)	19 x 15-1/2	RL	7.50

STOCKER, HANS   Swiss   1896-
7483.	Creation	18 x 23	HNA	5.95

STOKES, F.H.
7484.	Crusader	16 x 20	AA	7.50
7485.	Hoop, Jr.	16 x 20	AA	7.50
7486.	Stymie	24 x 20	AA	7.50
7487.	War Knight	24 x 20	AA	7.50

STONE, W.B.
7488.	Hay Wagon	24 x 47-1/2	AA	15.00

STRANG, RAY   American   1893-
7489.	Curiosity	14 x 11	NYGS	3.00
		7-1/2 x 6	NYGS	1.00
7490.	Deer at the Water Hole	7-1/2 x 10	NYGS	1.00
7491.	Double Trouble	24 x 28	NYGS	7.50
		11 x 14	NYGS	3.00
		7-1/2 x 10	NYGS	1.00
7492.	Lazybones	14 x 11	NYGS	3.00
		7-1/2 x 6	NYGS	1.00
7493.	Lost and Found	7-1/2 x 10	NYGS	1.00
7494.	Playmates	14 x 11	NYGS	3.00
		7-1/2 x 6	NYGS	1.00
7495.	Poppies and Mommies	7-1/2 x 10	NYGS	1.00
7496.	Silver Creek	7-1/2 x 10	NYGS	1.00
7497.	Slow Poke	24 x 28	NYGS	7.50
		11 x 14	NYGS	3.00
		7-1/2 x 10	NYGS	1.00
7498.	Summer Storm	7-1/2 x 10	NYGS	1.00
7499.	Taffy	14 x 11	NYGS	3.00
		7-1/2 x 6	NYGS	1.00
7500.	Wild Horses	7-1/2 x 10	NYGS	1.00

STRATER, HENRY   American   1896-
7501.	Colts at Soda Springs	11-1/2 x 19	NYGS	5.00
7502.	Winter in the Verde Valley	15 x 20	NYGS	5.00

STREVENS
7503.	L'Epoque Heureuse	8 x 12	DAC	1.00

7504.	Flora-Dora Girls	14 x 11	DAC	1.20 ea.
	(Heads((4)	10 x 8	DAC	.80 ea.
		8 x 6	DAC	.60 ea.
7505.	Flora-Dora Girls	14 x 11	DAC	1.20 ea.
	(Figures) (4)	10 x 8	DAC	.80 ea.
		8 x 6	DAC	.60 ea.

STRIGEL, BERNHARD   German   1460-1528

7506.	Portrait of Charles			
	V	15 x 8	IA	3.00

STRY, IRENE   American   Contemporary

| 7507. | First Love | 24 x 30 | DAC | 6.00 |

STUART, GILBERT   American   1755-1828

7508.	George Washington	16 x 12	NYGS	15.00
				(H.C. Grav.)
		16 x 12	NYGS	7.50
				(Sep. Grav.)
7509.	Detail of No.7508	9-1/2" oval	NYGS	5.00
				(H.C. Grav.)
7510.	George Washington	18 x 15	NYGS	5.00
		9 x 7-1/2	NYGS	1.00
7511.	George Washington	29 x 24	NYGS	12.00
		10 x 8	NYGS	.50
		8 x 7-1/2	NYGS	.50
7512.	George Washington	28 x 22	CFA	7.50
7513.	Martha Washington	16 x 12	NYGS	15.00
				(H.C. Grav.)
		16 x 12	NYGS	7.50
				(Sep. Grav.)
7514.	Mr.Richard Yates	22 x 18	NYGS	12.00
7515.	Skater	18 x 23	HNA	5.95

STUEMPFIG, WALTER   American   1914-

| 7516. | West Wildwood | 15 x 20 | IA | 7.50 |

STUTZ, A.

7517.	Chrysanthemums	23 x 28	IA	7.50
7518.	Delphinium	22 x 28	IA	7.50
7519.	Phlox	22 x 28	IA	7.50

STYKA, ADAM   Polish   1890-

7520.	Westerns(6)	14 x 18	DAC	2.00 ea.
		10 x 12	DAC	1.00 ea.

      Broncobuster
      Palomino
      Pursuit
      Ride 'Em Cowboy
      Round Up
      Two Friends

SUARDI, BARTOLOMMEO (IL BRAMANTINO) Italian 1468-1535

7521.	Agony of Man	10-1/2 x 6	AR	3.00
7522.	Holy Family	15 x 11	IA	3.00

SULLY, THOMAS   American   1783-1872

7523.	Anne W. Waln	20 x 16	AA	6.00
7524.	Boy with Torn Hat	18 x 14	IA	12.00
7525.	Lady with a Harp:			
	Eliza Ridgely	18 x 23	HNA	5.95

7526.	Major John Biddle	27-1/2 x 23	NYGS	12.00
		11 x 9	NYGS	1.50
7527.	Major Thomas Biddle	20 x 16	NYGS	10.00
7528.	Miss Pearce	28 x 23	AA	10.00
7529.	Mrs. James Mont- gomery	20 x 17	NYGS	10.00

SUSSMAYR, J.

7530.	Lake Starnberger and Rose Island	23-1/2 x 31-1/2	NYGS	12.00
7531.	Serenity	25 x 31	CFA	12.00

SUSTERMANNS, JUSTUS   Flemish   1597-1681

7532.	Prince Waldemar Christian of Dane- mark	15 x 10	IA	3.00

SWABIAN SCHOOL   German   15th Century

7533.	Two Lovers	24 x 14	NYGS	10.00

SVET

7534.	Lilacs	18 x 23	HNA	5.95

SWINNERTON, JAMES   American   1875-

7535.	Agathla Needle	26 x 20	IA	12.00
7536.	Arizona Desert	30 x 40	IA	20.00
7537.	Aspen Grove	28 x 34	IA	15.00
7538.	Blooming Desert	16 x 21	NYGS	5.00
7539.	Blossoming Palo Verde Tree	16 x 12	IA	3.50
7540.	Blossoming Smoke Tree	28 x 34	IA	15.00
7541.	Deep Canyon	24 x 36	IA	15.00
7542.	Desert Cacti	21 x 47	DAC	8.00
		14 x 22	DAC	2.80
		11 x 24	DAC	2.80
7543.	Desert End	28 x 34	IA	18.00
7544.	Desert Horizon	24 x 40	DAC	8.00
		14 x 22	DAC	2.80
7545.	Desert Smoke Tree	16 x 12	IA	3.50
7546.	Desert Smoke Tree in Bloom	12 x 16	IA	3.50
7547.	Desert Study No. 1 (Smoke Tree)	16 x 20	IA	5.00
7548.	Desert Study No. 2 (Palo Verde)	16 x 20	IA	5.00
7549.	Desert Study No. 3 (Saguaro and Palo Verde	16 x 20	IA	5.00
7550.	Desert Study No. 4 (Saguaro and Iron- wood)	16 x 20	IA	5.00
7551.	Desert Valley	30 x 12	IA	10.00
7552.	Field Sketch of Desert Ironwood Tree	12 x 16	IA	3.50
7553.	Field Sketch of Juniper Tree	12 x 16	IA	3.50

7554.	Grand Viewpoint, Grand Canyon, Arizona	28 x 34	IA	18.00
7555.	Ironwood Tree	24 x 18	IA	10.00
7556.	Palo Verde Tree in Bloom	28 x 34	IA	15.00
7557.	Palm Canyon	30 x 12	IA	10.00
7558.	Salton Sea	24 x 40	DAC	8.00
		14 x 22	DAC	2.80
7559.	Salton Sea	24 x 18	IA	10.00
7560.	Smoke Tree in Corner of Desert	12 x 16	IA	3.50
7561.	Sunset in the Sand Country	30 x 40	IA	20.00

- T -

TADEMA See ALMA-TADEMA				
TAKIS, NICHOLAS		American	1903-	
7562.	Airship	8 x 6	CFA	1.50
7563.	Blue Baloon	8 x 6	CFA	1.50
7564.	Broadway	9 x 15	CFA	2.00
7565.	Croquet	8 x 6	CFA	1.50
7566.	Red Baloon	8 x 6	CFA	1.50
7567.	Still Life (4)	8 x 6	CFA	1.50 ea.
TAMAYO, RUFINO		Mexican	1899-	
7568.	Animals	8 x 10	MMA	.35
7569.	Mandolins and Pineapples	19-1/2 x 27-1/2	NYGS	15.00
7570.	Troubadour	10 x 8	AP	.50
		8 x 6	NYGS	.50
TAMM, F.W.				
7571.	Still Life with Flowers	30 x 24	CFA	12.00
TANGUY, YVES		French	1900-	
7572.	Five Strangers	34 x 28	CFA	15.00
7573.	Mama, Papa is Wounded	8 x 10	MMA	.35
7574.	Rapidity of Sleep	20 x 16	CFA	7.50
TAPIES, ANTONIO		Spanish	1923-	
7575.	Pintura, 1958	22 x 26-1/2	NYGS	15.00
TARRANT, MARGARET		English	Contemporary	
7576.	All Things Wise and Wonderful	18 x 22	IA	7.50
		15 x 18-1/2	IA	4.50
		9-1/2 x 12	IA	2.00
7577.	At Bethlehem	12 x 14	IA	4.50
7578.	Behold, I Send you Forth	18-1/2 x 23	IA	7.50
		13 x 16	IA	4.50
		9-1/2 x 12	IA	2.00
7579.	He Prayeth Best Who Loveth Best	23 x 18	IA	7.50
		16 x 13	IA	4.50
		12 x 9	IA	2.00

7580.	Lesser Brethren	16-1/2 x 12-1/2	IA	4.50
		12 x 9	IA	2.00
7581.	Lilies of the Field	11 x 18	IA	4.50
		8 x 13	IA	2.00
7582.	Loving Shepherd	19 x 23	IA	7.50
		13-1/2 x 16-1/2	IA	4.50
		9-1/2 x 12	IA	2.00
7583.	O Come Let Us Sing Unto the Lord	18 x 28	IA	5.00
7584.	Suffer Little Children	14 x 25	IA	7.50
		11 x 18	IA	4.50
		8 x 13	IA	2.00

TAUBER

7585.	Chrysanthemums	12 x 20	ESH	4.00(Pr.)
7586.	Cornfield	19-1/2 x 27-1/2	ESH	8.00(Pr.)
7587.	Haus Am See	9-1/2 x 19-1/2	ESH	4.00(Pr.)
7588.	Jolly Farmer	7 x 9	ESH	1.50(Pr.)
7589.	Lonely Farm	9-1/2 x 19-1/2	ESH	4.00(Pr.)
7590.	Old Forester	7 x 9	ESH	1.50(Pr.)
7591.	Sun Flowers	12 x 20	ESH	4.00(Pr.)
7592.	Sunny Day	23-1/2 x 31-1/2	ESH	10.00(Pr.)
7593.	Trade Master	7 x 9	ESH	1.50(Pr.)

TAUBES, FREDERIC   Austrian   1900-

7594.	Girl with a Finch	17-1/2 x 12	NYGS	10.00(Pr.)
7595.	Rehearsal	8 x 10	AP	.50

TAYLOR, L. CAMPBELL   English   1874-

7596.	Before the Mirror	21-1/2 x 15	NYGS	3.00
7597.	Blue Room	21 - 18-1/2	RL	10.00
7598.	Golden Shrine	23 x 19	NYGS	3.00
7599.	Her First Ball Dress	24 x 20	NYGS	12.00
7600.	Interior	22 x 19	NYGS	3.00
7601.	Lady with a Harp	21 x 19	RL	10.00
7602.	Lady in White Dress	23 x 20	NYGS	3.00
7603.	The Letter	23 x 19-1/2	NYGS	3.00
7604.	Mafalda	23-1/2 x 19-1/2	NYGS	6.00
		16 x 13-1/2	NYGS	2.50
7605.	Models from the Ballet	19 x 12	RL	10.00
7606.	Patchwork Quilt	21 x 17-1/2	NYGS	12.00
7607.	Quiet Hour	22-1/2 x 13-1/2	NYGS	3.00
7608.	Regency Days	21-1/2 x 18	RL	10.00
7609.	Sampler	21 x 18	RL	10.00
7610.	Serenity	22 x 18	RL	10.00
7611.	Top of the Hill	22 x 20	RL	10.00

TCHEKHONINE, SERGE   Danish   1898-

7612.	Dignity	20 x 14-1/2	NYGS	12.00
7613.	Elegance	20 x 14-1/2	NYGS	12.00

TCHELITCHEW, PAVEL   American   1898-1957

7614.	Balustrade	13-1/2 x 11	AR	6.00
7615.	Head of Winter	8 x 10	MMA	.35

7616.	Hide and Seek	11 x 12	MMA	1.50
TEAGUE, DONALD		American	1897-	
7617.	Western Life (4)	12 x 30	DAC	4.00ea.
		6 x 15	DAC	1.20ea.
TENIERS, DAVID (THE YOUNGER) Flemish			1582-1649	
7618.	Country Festival	8 x 10	AP	.50
7619.	Drinkers and Gam- blers	9 x 10	AR	3.00
7620.	Eaves-Dropped Tete- a-Tete	9,x 15	IA	3.00
7621.	Hockey Players	15-1/2 x 22-1/2	ESH	10.00
7622.	Kermesse	11 x 14	IA	3.00
TERBORCH, GERARD		Dutch	1617-1681	
7623.	Concert	23 x 18	HNA	5.95
7624.	Dutch Woman Drink- ing	12 x 11	IA	3.00
7625.	Gallant Soldier	14 x 11	IA	3.00
7626.	Letter	8 x 10	AP	.50
7627.	Lute Player	91-1/2 x 14	NYGS	10.00
7628.	Suitor's Visit	18 x 17	NYGS	10.00
TER BRUGGHEN, HENDRIK See BRUGGHEN, HENDRIK TER				
THAYER, ABBOTT HANDERSON American			1849-1921	
7629.	Virgin	8 x 10	AP	.50
7630.	Young Woman	10 x 8	NYGS	.50
THIEME, ANTHONY		American		
7631.	Along Cape Ann	12 x 15	CFA	3.00
7632.	Autumn in New England	25 x 30	AA	10.00
7633.	Aviles Street	25 x 30	CFA	12.00
		16 x 20	CFA	5.00
		12 x 15	CFA	3.00
7634.	Bear Skin Neck	25 x 30	AA	10.00
7635.	Blue Door	18 x 22	CFA	7.50
		12 x 15	CFA	3.00
7636.	Blue Shutters	20 x 24	CFA	10.00
7637.	Breaking Sunlight	25 x 30	CFA	15.00
7638.	Bridge	25 x 30	CFA	12.00
		14 x 17	CFA	3.00
7639.	Dreamy Lagoon	25 x 30	CFA	12.00
		16 x 20	CFA	5.00
		12 x 15	CFA	3.00
7640.	Early Morning	12 x 15	CFA	3.00
7641.	Fisherman's Haven	25 x 30	CFA	12.00
		16 x 20	CFA	5.00
		12 x 15	CFA	3.00
7642.	Foggy Morning, Rockport	12 x 15	CFA	3.00
7643.	Getting Ready	18 x 22	CFA	7.50
		12 x 15	CFA	3.00
7644.	Going Out	25 x 30	AA	10.00
7645.	Going Out Fishing	12 x 15	CFA	3.00
7646.	Hauling Nets	12 x 15	CFA	3.00

7647.	In the Bahamas	25 x 30	AA	10.00
		12 x 15	CFA	3.00
7648.	Indian Summer	25 x 30	AA	10.00
7649.	Late Afternoon	12 x 15	CFA	3.00
7650.	Lobsterman and Gulls	25 x 30	IA	12.00
7651.	Mexican Village	12 x 15	CFA	3.00
7652.	Morning by the River	25 x 30	CFA	12.00
		16 x 20	CFA	5.00
7653.	New England Street Scene	12 x 15	CFA	3.00
7654.	New England Winter	12 x 15	CFA	3.00
7655.	North Easter	25 x 30	CFA	12.00
		14 x 17	CFA	3.00
7656.	Rainy Day in Rockport	25 x 30	CFA	15.00
		12 x 15	CFA	3.00
7657.	Rockport Wharf	12 x 15	CFA	3.00
7658.	Silverlight	12 x 15	CFA	3.00
7659.	Southern Waters	25 x 30	IA	10.00
		16 x 20	IA	5.00
		12-1/2 x 15	IA	3.00
		12 x 15	CFA	3.00
7660.	Spanish Patio	20 x 24	CFA	10.00
7661.	Summer Morn	12 x 15	CFA	3.00
7662.	Sunlit Surf	12 x 15	CFA	3.00
7663.	Taxco Road	12 x 15	CFA	3.00
7664.	View of Taxco	12 x 15	CFA	3.00
THOMA, HANS		German	1839-1924	
7665.	At the Lake of Garda	10 x 8	HYGS	.50
7666.	Early Morning in the Black Forest	20 x 29-1/2	NYGS	20.00
7667.	Field Flowers	29 x 22	NYGS	22.00
7668.	Idylle at Bernau	30 x 25	CFA	18.00
7669.	Landscape near Main	22-1/2 x 28	AR	15.00
		22 x 28	CFA	15.00
THOMAS, E.				
7670.	Field and Stream	24 x 48	DAC	10.00
7671.	Homeward Bound	24 x 48	DAC	10.00
7672.	Miller's Home	24 x 48	DAC	10.00
7673.	Red Water Mill	24 x 48	DAC	10.00
THOMPSON, JEROME B.		American	1814-1886	
7674.	Old Oaken Bucket	24 x 38-1/2	IA	12.00
		18 x 28	IA	12.00
		16 x 20	IA	6.00
THOMPSON, WORDSWORTH				
7675.	Departing Guests	21-1/2 x 36	NYGS	15.00
THON				
7676.	Light in Autumn	18 x 36	IA	18.00
7677.	Moment in Venice	17-1/2 x 36	IA	18.00
THORNTON, DR.				
7678.	Group of Carnations	12 x 10	IA	1.00

7679.	The Pontic Rhododen-dron	12 x 10	IA	1.00
7680.	Sacred Egyptian Bean	12 x 10	IA	1.00
7681.	Tulips	12 x 10	IA	1.00

THURNER

7682.	Ranunculus	11 x 11	CFA	2.00

TIEPOLO, GIOVANNI BATTISTA Italian   1696-1770

7683.	Adoration of the Child, Jesus	15 x 10	IA	3.00
7684.	Alexander and the Daughters of Darius	13 x 11	IA	3.00
7685.	Alexander and the Family of Darius	15 x 11	IA	3.00
7686.	Apollo Pursuing Daphne	23-1/2 x 30	NYGS	16.00
7687.	Baptism of Constantinus	15 x 8	IA	3.00
7688.	Communion of St. Lucy	15 x 7	IA	3.00
7689.	Coronation with Thorns	11 x 12	IA	3.00
7690.	Danae	11 x 15	IA	3.00
7691.	Education of the Virgin	15 x 9	IA	3.00
7692.	Fortitude and Wisdom	10 x 15	IA	3.00
7693.	Heliodorus and Onias	11 x 13	IA	3.00
7694.	Immaculate Virgin	15 x 8	IA	3.00
7695.	Iphigenia's Sacrifice	8 x 15	IA	3.00
7696.	Justice and Peace	11 x 13 oval	IA	3.00
7697.	Madonna of the Goldfinch	20 x 16	NYGS	7.50
7698.	Magnanimity of Scipio	15 x 11	IA	3.00
7699.	Martyrdom of St. John of Bergamo	15 x 11	IA	3.00
7700.	Martyrdom of St. Agatha	15 x 11	IA	3.00
7701.	Minuet	11 x 15	IA	3.00
7702.	Neptune Offering Wealth to Venice	6 x 15	IA	3.00
7703.	Oriental's Head	14 x 11	IA	3.00
7704.	A Page	14 x 11	IA	3.00
7705.	Portrait of Antonio Riccobono	13 x 11	IA	3.00
7706.	Procuratore Giovanni Querini	15 x 11	IA	3.00
7707.	Reynold in Armida's Garden	9 x 15	IA	3.00
7708.	Road to Calvary	11 x 13	IA	3.00

7709.	St. Catherine of Siena	15 x 11 oval	IA	3.00
7710.	St. Maximus and St. Oswald	16 x 9	IA	3.00
7711.	Tarquinius and Lucretia	15 x 11 oval	IA	3.00
7712.	Temptations of St. Anthony	11 x 14	IA	3.00
7713.	Timocleia and the Thracian	10" oval	NYGS	.50
7714.	Trained Dogs	11 x 15	IA	3.00
7715.	Transportation of the Holy House of Loreto	15 x 10	IA	3.00
7716.	Triumph of Zephir and Flora	16 x 11	IA	3.00
7717.	Two Dying Warriors	15 x 10	IA	3.00
7718.	Two Flying Putti	11 x 13	IA	3.00

TINTORETTO (ROBUSTI, JACOPO) Italian   1518-1594

7719.	Christ at the Sea of Galilee	21 x 30-1/2	NYGS	16.00
7720.	Doge Mocenigo	8 x 10	AP	.50
7721.	Marriage of Bacchus and Ariadne	11 x 13	IA	3.00
7722.	Miracle of St. Mark	11 x 14	IA	3.00
7723.	Presentation of Maria in the Temple	11 x 13	IA	3.00
7724.	Tarquin and Lucretia	9 x 7	NYGS	.50
7725.	Trinity Adored by the Heavenly Choir	20 x 18	NYGS	10.00

TITI, TIBERIO   Italian   1573-1627

7726.	Portrait of Leopold Medici as a Baby	11 x 15	IA	3.00

TITIAN (TIZIANO VECELLIO)   Italian   1477-1576

7727.	Apollo and Daphne	7 x 15	IA	3.00
7728.	Assumption of the Virgin	15 x 9	IA	7.50
7729.	Cardinal de Granvella	10 x 8	NYGS	.50
7730.	Caterino Comaro as St. Catherine of Al	15 x 10	IA	3.00
7731.	Danae	10 x 15	IA	3.00
7732.	Doge Nicolo Marcello	13 x 11	IA	3.00
7733.	Duke of Norfolk (Supposed)	13 x 11	IA	3.00
7734.	Head--Detail of No. 7733	15 x 11	IA	3.00
7735.	Flora	17 x 14	IA	3.00
		10 x 8	AP	.50
7736.	Head--Detail of No. 7735	16 x 11	IA	3.00

7737.	Isabella of Portugal	20 x 16-1/2	AR	12.00
7738.	Lavinia, the Artist's	23 x 18	HNA	5.95
	Daughter	20 x 16	NYGS	10.00
		9 x 7	NYGS	.50
7739.	Madonna and Child with St. John and St. Anthony	10 x 15	IA	3.00
7740.	Magdalene	15 x 11	IA	3.00
7741.	Man with the Glove	12 x 11	IA	3.00
7742.	Paul III and his grandsons, Alessandro and Ottavio	13 x 11	IA	3.00
7743.	Pope Paul III	15 x 11	IA	3.00
7744.	Portrait of a Lady, known as "La Bella"	15 x 11	IA	3.00
7745.	Portrait of a Man	8 x 10	CFA	1.00
7746.	Portrait of a Young Woman at the Mirror	13 x 11	IA	3.00
7747.	Presentation of Mary	9 x 6	NYGS	.50
7748.	Queen Isabella	20 x 16	CFA	12.00
7749.	Rape of Europa	8 x 9	NYGS	.50
7750.	Reclining Venus (Venus of Urbino)	10 x 15	IA	3.00
7751.	Head--Detail of No. 7750	15 x 11	IA	3.00
7752.	Sacred and Profane Love	11 x 27	IA	10.00
		11 x 15	IA	3.00
7753.	Nude Figure--Detail of No. 7752	14 x 11	IA	3.00
7754.	Dressed Figure-- Detail of No. 7752	11 x 15	IA	3.00
7755.	Head of Nude-- Detail of No. 7752	15 x 11	IA	3.00
7756.	Head of Dressed Figure--Detail of No. 7752	15 x 11	IA	3.00
7757.	St. Vincenzo of Ferreri	13 x 11	IA	3.00
7758.	Strozzi Child	8 x 10	AP	.50
7759.	Tribute Money	26 x 19-1/2	NYGS	12.00
		25 x 18	IA	24.00
		17-1/2 x 13	NYGS	5.00
		10 x 8	AP	.60
7760.	Venus and the Lute Player	10 x 13	NYGS	.50

TOBEY

7761.	Earth Circus	25-1/2 x 19	NYGS	15.00
7762.	Golden City	20 x 30	ESH	15.00
7763.	Homage to Rameau	8 x 10	ESH	1.00

TOMA, GIOACCHINO		Italian	1838-1891	
7764.	Ashes Rain	9 x 15	IA	3.00
TOMANECK, JOSEPH		American	1889-	
7765.	Getting Acquainted	18 x 22	CFA	10.00
TOMLIN, BRADLEY		American	1899-1953	
7766.	Number 20	8 x 10	MMA	.35
TONELLI, SIRIO				
7767.	Portrait of Christ	17 x 13	IA	3.00
		13 x 10	IA	1.00
		10 x 8	IA	.50
		8 x 7	IA	.20
TORAN, ALFONSO T.		American	1898-	
7768.	Asian Art (4)	10 x 8	DAC	.80 ea.
7769.	Chinese Screen	25 x 31	NYGS	7.50
		16-1/2 x 20-1/2	NYGS	3.00
		9-1/2 x 12	NYGS	1.00
7770.	Moonglow	8 x 10	DAC	1.20
7771.	Moonlight Reflection	8 x 10	DAC	1.20
7772.	Sails in the Sunset	8 x 10	DAC	1.20
7773.	Sunbeams	8 x 10	DAC	1.20
7774.	Sunset Glow	8 x 10	DAC	1.20
7775.	Sunset Silhouette	8 x 10	DAC	1.20
TORBIDO, IL (INDIA, FRANCESCO) Italian			1483-1561	
7776.	Young Man with a Flageolet	14 x 11	IA	3.00
TORI, ANGELO See BRONZINO				
TORINO				
7777.	Carmen	16 x 20	ESH	5.00(Pr.)
7778.	Juanita	19-1/2 x 23-1/2	ESH	10.00(Pr.)
7779.	Manuela	19-1/2 x 11-1/2	ESH	5.00(Pr.)
TOULOUSE-LAUTREC, HENRI DE French			1864-1901	
7780.	Alfred La Guigne	14 x 11	NYGS	3.00
7781.	Aristide Bruant	22 x 17	AR	5.00
7782.	Aristide Bruant (Poster)	27 x 18	PENN	1.00
7783.	Au Cirque	13 x 9	NYGS	7.50
7784.	Au Moulin Rouge	20 x 24	DAC	6.00
		16 x 18	AP	5.00
		14 x 16	IA	6.00
7785.	Bar	23 x 18	HNA	5.95
7786.	Black Gloves	12 x 9	CFA	7.50
7787.	La Chambre Separee	21-1/2 x 18	NYGS	12.00
7788.	Chilperic	21 x 26	HNA	5.95
7789.	Le Chocolat Dancing	8 x 6	CFA	1.00
7790.	Clown Resting	12 x 9	CFA	7.50
7791.	Clownesse	24 x 20	PENN	1.00
7792.	The Clowness Cha-U-Kao	23 x 17	NYGS	12.00
		10 x 8	ESH	1.00
7793.	Les Coulisses	13 x 9	NYGS	7.50
7794.	Country Drive	6 x 8	CFA	1.00
7795.	Dancer, Gabrielle	9 x 7	NYGS	.50
7796.	Danseuse	23 x 18-1/2	NYGS	10.00

7797.	Desire Dihau	9 x 7	NYGS	.50
7798.	Divan Japonais	22 x 17	AR	5.00
7799.	Divan Japonais			
	(Poster)	24 x 18-1/2	NYGS	10.00
7800.	Le Docteur Tapie de			
	Celeyran	15 x 7	IA	3.00
7801.	Ecuyere	9 x 7	NYGS	4.00
7802.	Eldorado	12 x 9	CFA	7.50
7803.	Englishman	8 x 6	CFA	1.00
7804.	La Goulue	23 x 17-1/2	MMA	3.00
		14-1/2 x 10	NYGS	12.00
		10 x 8	ESH	1.00
7805.	La Grande Loge	10 x 8	ESH	1.00
7806.	Jane Avril	24 x 18	PENN	1.00
				1.98(Pr.)
7807.	Jane Avril (Poster)	26-1/2 x 18	PENN	1.00
7808.	Jane Avril Dancing	23 x 12	ESH	10.00
		10 x 5	CFA	1.00
7809.	Jane Avril Leaving	32 x 24	CFA	15.00
	Moulin Rouge	28 x 15	NYGS	12.00
7810.	Jockey	6 x 9	CFA	1.00
7811.	Marcel Linder			
	Dancing	8 x 10	ESH	1.00
7812.	Marcel Lender			
	(Detail)	10 x 8	ESH	1.00
7813.	Madame de Honorine	24 x 17	PENN	1.00
7814.	Mlle. Lender	10 x 8	ESH	1.00
7815.	Maxime Dethomas	14 x 11	NYGS	3.00
7816.	Messalina	18 x 13	CFA	5.00
7817.	Milliner	13 x 11	IA	3.00
7818.	La Modiste	24 x 19	NYGS	12.00
7819.	M. Bolleau au Cafe	20 x 16	PENN	1.00
				1.98(Pr.)
7820.	Mr. Warner at the			
	Moulin Rouge	10 x 8	ESH	1.00
7821.	Moulin Rouge	24 x 20	PENN	1.00
7822.	Moulin Rouge	14 x 16	NYGS	6.00
7823.	Moulin Rouge			
	(Poster)	28 x 17	PENN	1.00
7824.	Pony Trap	8 x 10	ESH	1.00
7825.	Profile of a Woman	24 x 20	PENN	1.00
7826.	Quadrille at the			
	Moulin Rouge	18 x 23	HNA	5.95
7827.	Reine de Joie	22 x 17	AR	5.00
7828.	Seated Clown	22 x 17	PENN	1.00
7829.	Seated Model	24 x 19	PENN	1.00
7830.	Sortie de Theatre	14-1/2 x 10-1/2	NYGS	5.00
7831.	La Toilette	14-1/2 x 10	NYGS	12.00
		9 x 7	NYGS	.50
7832.	Une Table au Moulin			
	Rouge	8 x 10	ESH	1.00
7833.	Woman in a Wicker			
	Chair	26 x 18	DAC	6.00

7834.	Yvette Guilbert	12 x 9	CFA	7.50
		10 x 6	CFA	1.00
		8 x 5	CFA	1.00
TRAINI, FRANCESCO		Italian	1320-1364	
7835.	Triumph of Death	10 x 15	IA	3.00
7836.	Detail of No. 7835	11 x 15	IA	3.00
TRAVER, MARIAN				
7837.	Snow Bound	25 x 30	IA	7.50
TROYON, CONSTANT EMILE		French	1810-1865	
7838.	Game-Keeper and his Dogs	14 x 11	IA	3.00
7839.	Pasturage	8 x 10	AP	.50
TRUBNER				
7840.	Housebuilders	17 x 27	NYGS	20.00
TRUMAN, HERBERT		English		
7841.	Quayside, St. Ives	17 x 22-1/2	RL	5.00
TRUMBULL, JOHN		American	1756-1843	
7842.	Alexander Hamilton	18 x 14-1/2	NYGS	10.00
7843.	Declaration of Independence	20 x 30	NYGS	12.00
		8 x 10	AP	.50
TURA, COSME (COSIMO)		Italian	1430-1495	
7844.	Member of the Este Family	8 x 10	AP	.50
TURNER, JOSEPH MALLORD WILLIAM English			1775-1851	
7845.	Carthage	8 x 10	NYGS	.50
7846.	Fighting Temeraire	18 x 23	HNA	5.95
		8 x 10	AP	.50
7847.	Grand Canal, Venice	29-1/2 x 39	NYGS	20.00
		9 x 13	CFA	4.00
		8-1/2 x 12-1/2	AR	4.00
7848.	Hastings, about 1835	8 x 10	AP	.25
7849.	Lake Geneva	9 x 13	CFA	4.00
7850.	Lake Vierwaldstaetter	9-1/2 x 15	AR	4.00
7851.	Lake von Bergen	8-1/2 x 11	AR	4.00
7852.	Mortlake Terrace	17-1/2 x 23-1/2	NYGS	12.00
7853.	Music Party, Petworth	27 x 20	NYGS	18.00
7854.	Petworth Park	10 x 22-1/2	AP	6.00
7855.	Sunset in Venice	8-1/2 x 12-1/2	AR	4.00
7856.	Sunset on the Grand Canal	9 x 13	CFA	4.00
7857.	Venice	9 x 13	CFA	4.00
7858.	Venice: Dogana and San Giorgio Maggiore	22 x 30	NYGS	15.00
7859.	Venice, the Giudecca	8-1/2 x 12-1/2	AR	4.00
7860.	Venetian Scene	18-1/2 x 28	AP	12.00
TYNG, GRISWOLD		American	1883-	
7861.	Abraham Lincoln	28 x 22	CFA	7.50

- U -

UCCELLO, PAOLO (DONO, PAOLO DI) Italian		1397-1475	
7862. Battle of San	15 x 27	IA	10.00
Romano	10 x 17	IA	3.00
7863. Nativity (Stained			
Glass Window)	11" circle	IA	3.00
7864. Portrait of Elisabeth			
of Montefeltro	15 x 8	IA	3.00
7865. Resurrection of			
Christ (Stained			
Glass Window)	11" circle	IA	3.00
7866. Rout of San Romano	19 x 34	CFA	20.00
7867. Selling of the Conse-			
crated Wafer	8 x 15	IA	3.00
UCHERMANN, KARL	Norwegian	1855-	
7868. Playing Whelps	14 x 19	ESH	7.50
UDERMAN, J., JR.			
7869. Apple Blossoms	12 x 9	DAC	1.20
7870. Magnolias	12 x 9	DAC	1.20
7871. Pansies	12 x 9	DAC	1.20
7872. Rhododendron	12 x 9	DAC	1.20
UFER, WALTER	American	1876-	
7873. Solemn Pledge	8 x 10	AP	.50
UHDE, KARL HERMANN FRITZ VON German		1848-1911	
7874. The Children's			
Friend	24 x 36-1/2	IA	15.00
7875. Come Lord Jesus, Be			
Our Guest	19 x 23-1/2	IA	7.50
7876. His Omnipresence	18-1/2 x 23-1/2	NYGS	7.50
UPRKA, JOZA	Czeckoslovakian	1862-	
7877. Moravian Peasants	8 x 10	AP	.50
UTRILLO, MAURICE	French	1883-1955	
7878. Au Point de Vue	24 x 18	AR	12.00
7879. La Banlieue	24 x 30	DAC	8.00
	12-1/2 x 18	ESH	10.00
	11 x 14	DAC	2.00
	7 x 9	DAC	.80
7880. La Basilique du	22-1/2 x 18	ESH	10.00
Sacre-Coeur	10 x 8	ESH	1.00
7881. Behind the Moulin			
de la Galette	8 x 10	ESH	1.00
7882. Berlioz House	8 x 10	AP	1.00
7883. La Butte de Mont-			
martre	15-1/2 x 19	NYGS	7.50
7884. Le Cabaret	14-1/2 x 17-1/2	AP	5.00
7885. Cafe du Nord	24 x 30	DAC	8.00
7886. La Caserne	20 x 24	CFA	15.00
7887. Cathedral	8 x 10	ESH	1.00
7888. Christmas in Mont-	18 x 26-1/2	NYGS	12.00
martre	11 x 14	NYGS	3.00
	6 x 7-1/2	NYGS	1.00

7889.	Church at St. Hilaire	14 x 18	AP	6.00
7890.	Church at Saint-Severin	18 x 23	HNA	5.95
7891.	Church of LaFerte-Milon	24 x 18	IA	7.50
7892.	Church of Sacre-Coeur	18 x 23	HNA	5.95
7893.	Corsican Landscape	20 x 26	CFA	15.00
7894.	Courtyard	20 x 24	NYGS	10.00
7895.	Eglise de Bourgogne	22 x 18-1/2	NYGS	10.00
7896.	Eglise de Coude Couchey	18 x 21	AP	7.50
		17-1/2 x 21	IA	7.50
7897.	Eglise de Royan	31 x 11-1/2	NYGS	12.00
		20 x 7	NYGS	5.00
7898.	Eglise de Sauviat	16 x 22	NYGS	16.00
7899.	Eglise de Strins	24 x 30	DAC	8.00
7900.	Faubourg Parisien	20 x 24	DAC	6.00
7901.	Flowers in a Blue Jug	10 x 8	ESH	1.00
7902.	Le Lapin	15 x 19	CFA	7.50
7903.	Le Lapin Agile	19-1/2 x 24	AR	12.00
		18 x 23	HNA	5.95
		17 x 24	NYGS	12.00
		11 x 14	DAC	2.00
		7 x 9	DAC	.80
7904.	Lapin Agile in the Snow	19 x 30	ESH	15.00
7905.	Maison Mimi	19-1/2 x 24	NYGS	15.00
		11 x 14	NYGS	3.00
		6 x 7-1/2	NYGS	1.00
7906.	Mimi Pinson's House in the Snow	8 x 10	ESH	1.00
7907.	Montmartre	22 x 30	AR	18.00
		21 x 29	CFA	15.00
		19 x 21-1/2	NYGS	16.00
		15 x 20	AP	6.00
		11 x 14	NYGS	3.00
		6 x 7-1/2	NYGS	1.00
7908.	Moulin de la Galette	24 x 30	DAC	8.00
		17 x 20	NYGS	10.00
		12 x 15	NYGS	15.00
		11 x 14	DAC	2.00
		8 x 10	ESH	1.00
		7 x 9	DAC	.80
7909.	Parisian Suburb	24 x 30	DAC	8.00
7910.	Petit Cafe, Mont-martre	13 x 20	NYGS	7.50
		11 x 14	NYGS	3.00
		6 x 7-1/2	NYGS	1.00
7911.	La Place Ravignon	11 x 14	NYGS	10.00
7912.	Pontoise	18 x 13	NYGS	16.00
7913.	Portfolio (4)	24 x 8	DAC	2.00 ea.
		11 x 5-1/2	DAC	.80 ea.

7914.	Porte St. Martin	21 x 24	NYGS	12.00
		19-1/2 x 24	AR	12.00
7915.	Restaurant au Mont	11 x 14	NYGS	3.00
	Cenis	6 x 7-1/2	NYGS	1.00
7916.	Rheims Cathedral	35 x 24-1/2	ESH	18.00
7917.	Rue Artez	20 x 24	DAC	6.00
7918.	Rue a Sannois	13 x 20	NYGS	7.50
		11 x 14	NYGS	3.00
		6 x 7-1/2	NYGS	1.00
7919.	Rue Jeanne D'Arc	17 x 22-1/2	AP	10.00
7920.	Rue Jeanne D'Arc	17 x 22-1/2	ESH	10.00
	in the Snow	8 x 10	ESH	1.00
7921.	Rue Lepic a Mont-	31 x 11-1/2	NYGS	12.00
	martre	20 x 7	NYGS	5.00
7922.	Rue Mont Cenis	24 x 30	DAC	8.00
		13 x 17-1/2	AR	6.00
		13 x 17	CFA	7.50
		11 x 14	DAC	2.00
		8 x 10	ESH	1.00
		7 x 9	DAC	.80
7923.	Rue Moulin Rouge	20 x 30	CFA	15.00
7924.	Rue Ordener	21-1/2 x 29	NYGS	15.00
7925.	Rue St. Vincent	19 x 30	AA	15.00
7926.	Rue Saint Rustique	31 x 11-1/2	NYGS	12.00
		20 x 7	NYGS	5.00
7927.	Rue Seveste	17 x 21	NYGS	10.00
7928.	Rue Tholoze	8 x 10	ESH	1.00
7929.	Rue de Venice	23-1/2 x 16-1/2	AR	12.00
7930.	Rue de Village	21 x 26	NYGS	15.00
7931.	Rural France	18 x 22	NYGS	10.00
		11 x 14	NYGS	3.00
7932.	Sacre Coeur de Mont-	28 x 21	NYGS	15.00
	martre	25 x 20	DAC	6.00
7933.	St. Vincent Street	6 x 9	CFA	1.00
7934.	Snow on Montmartre	17-1/2 x 23-1/2	NYGS	12.00
		11 x 14	NYGS	3.00
7935.	Snowy Street	6 x 9	CFA	1.00
7936.	Spring in Montmartre	18 x 21-1/2	NYGS	10.00
7937.	Le Square Saint-Pierre	10 x 8	ESH	1.00
7938.	Steps	9 x 6	CFA	1.00
7939.	Suburban Street	18 x 22	NYGS	10.00
		11 x 14	NYGS	3.00
		6 x 7-1/2	NYGS	1.00
7940.	La Tour Saint	31 x 11-1/2	NYGS	12.00
	Jacques	20 x 7	NYGS	5.00
7941.	Village Lane	6 x 8	CFA	1.00
7942.	Village Street	14 x 17	CFA	4.00
7943.	Winter in Paris	24 x 30	DAC	8.00
		11 x 14	DAC	2.80

- V -

VAELTL, OTTO
7944. Summer Flowers   26 x 22-1/2   ESH   8.00
VALADON, SUSANNE   French   1867-1938
7945. Gladioli   10 x 8   ESH   1.00
VALCKENBORGH, LUK VAN   Flemish   1540-1625
7946. Autumn Landscape   11 x 20   CFA   7.50
    11-1/2 x 19-1/2   NYGS   7.50
7947. Harvest Time   27-1/2 x 47   AJ   20.00
    21 x 36   AJ   12.00
    12-1/2 x 21   AJ   7.50
7948. Summer Landscape   12 x 21   NYGS   7.50
VALLET, MATH.   French   1901-1949
7949. Baby in Cradle   13 x 11   CFA   3.00
VANCE, JAMES
7950. Mexico (4)   16 x 21 Sheet   IA   3.00 ea.
    Floating Gardens
    Flower Pickers
    Market Day at Patzcuaro
    Shopping at Mercado
VAN DER GOES See GOES, HUGO VAN DER
VAN DER LEUR, J.
7951. Spring Splendor   24 x 30   CFA   10.00
VANDERLYN
7952. George Washington   24 x 19   DAC   6.00
VANDER MEULEN, PIETER See MEULEN, PIETER VAN DER
VAN DER WEYDEN, ROGIER   Flemish   1399-1464
7953. Adoration of the Three
    Kings   16-1/2 x 46   IA   24.00
7954. Annunciation   18-1/2 x 19-1/2   ESH   10.00
    8 x 5   IA   3.00
7955. Portrait of a Lady   13-1/2 x 10   NYGS   7.50
    11 x 8   NYGS   .50
7956. Portrait of a Young
    Woman   18-1/2 x 12-1/2   NYGS   16.00
7957. Triptych Sforza   9 x 15   IA   3.00
VAN DYCK, (SIR) ANTHONY (OR ANTHONIS) Flemish 1599-1641
7958. Angels (Detail of
    Rest on the
    Flight)   7 x 9   IA   1.50
7959. Apostle Peter   22 x 17-1/2   ESH   7.50
7960. Apostle Thomas   22 x 17-1/2   ESH   7.50
7961. Armored Warrior   24 x 18   DAC   6.00
7962. Charles I and Hen-
    riette of England   11 x 14   IA   3.00
7963. Count Henry Van   20 x 18   CFA   10.00
    Der Bergh   20 x 17-1/2   NYGS   7.50
7964. Crucifix   15 x 10   IA   3.00
7965. Duke of Richmond   14 x 11   IA   3.00
7966. Genoese Lady with
    her Daughter   15 x 11   IA   3.00

7967.	John of Montfort	15 x 11	IA	3.00
7968.	Madonna and Child			
	with St. Anthony	13 x 11	IA	3.00
7969.	Nativity	14 x 11	IA	3.00
7970.	Nobleman	9 x 6-1/2	AR	3.50
7971.	Philip, Lord Wharton	28 x 22	NYGS	12.00
7972.	Portrait of the			
	Prince Rodoxanakis	14 x 10	IA	3.00
7973.	Portrait of a			
	Painter	10 x 8	AR	3.00
7974.	Rest on the Flight	22 x 24	IA	12.00
	into Egypt (For	21 x 25	NYGS	12.00
	Detail see No.	17 x 19-1/2	IA	5.00
	7958)			
7975.	Self-Portrait	14 x 11	IA	3.00
7976.	Viscount of Stafford	14 x 11	IA	3.00
VAN EYCK, HUBERT		Flemish	1366-1426	
7977.	Annunciation	26 x 10	NYGS	12.00
7978.	Crucifixion	15 x 10	IA	3.00
VAN EYCK, JAN		Flemish	1390-1440	
7979.	Marriage of Arnol-			
	fini	25 x 18	CAC	12.00
7980.	Portrait of Cardinal			
	Albergati	13 x 10	IA	3.00
7981.	Virgin of Autun	20 x 18	ESH	10.00
		11 x 11	IA	3.00
VAN FALENS, C.				
7982.	Alte de Chasseurs	14 x 18	CFA	12.00
7983.	Rendezvous de Chasse	14 x 18	CFA	12.00
VAN GOGH, VINCENT		Dutch	1853-1890	
7984.	Les Alpiles	18 x 22-1/2	NYGS	10.00
7985.	Alyscamps	8 x 10	MMA	.35
7986.	Artist's Bedroom at	16-1/2 x 21	NYGS	4.00
	Arles			
7987.	Auvers	15 x 30	NYGS	12.00
7988.	Auvers, Vue de			
	Village	17-1/2 x 21	NYGS	6.00
7989.	Bedroom at Arles	18 x 22-1/2	ESH	10.00
		8 x 10	ESH	1.00
7990.	Bell Lilies in a	30 x 24-1/2	ESH	15.00
	Copper Vase	20 x 15-1/2	NYGS	4.00
		10 x 8	ESH	1.00
7991.	Bench	11 x 13	IA	3.00
7992.	La Berceuse	26 x 20	PENN	1.00
		20-1/2 x 16	NYGS	4.00
7993.	Blooming Apple			
	Orchard	12 x 16	NYGS	3.00
7994.	Blue Iris	9 x 7	NYGS	.50
		8 x 6	CFA	1.00
7995.	Boats, 1888	15 x 21	NYGS	15.00
7996.	Boats of Saintes-	25 x 31-1/2	NYGS	18.00
	Maries	18 x 23	NYGS	10.00

		16-1/2 x 20-1/2	NYGS	5.00
		16 x 20	NYGS	4.00
		6 x 9	NYGS	.50
7997.	Boats Docked	6 x 8	CFA	1.00
7998.	Boats on Beach	8 x 10	ESH	1.00
		6 x 8	CFA	1.00
7999.	Breakfast Table	17-1/2 x 23	NYGS	10.00
8000.	Bridge	23 x 28	CFA	18.00
		19 x 26	NYGS	10.00
		16 x 19-1/2	NYGS	6.00
		15 x 19-1/2	NYGS	5.00
8001.	Bridge and Road	7 x 9	NYGS	.50
8002.	Bridge at Arles	23-1/2 x 25-1/2	IA	18.00
		18 x 19-1/2	ESH	10.00
		8 x 10	ESH	1.00
		7 x 9	NYGS	.50
8003.	Bridge at Asnieres	16 x 22-1/2	ESH	10.00
8004.	Cafe at Arles	17-1/2 x 25	AR	12.00
		17 x 25	CFA	12.00
8005.	Cafe at Night	22-1/2 x 18	ESH	10.00
		10 x 8	ESH	1.00
8006.	Cafe, Evening	22-1/2 x 18	NYGS	10.00
		20 x 15-1/2	NYGS	5.00
8007.	Champs	8-1/2 x 11	NYGS	4.00
8008.	Chestnut Blossoms	13 x 16	CFA	5.00
		10 x 8	ESH	1.00
8009.	Church at Auvers	23 x 18	HNA	5.95
		18 x 14	CFA	4.00
8010.	Cloister Garden	28-1/2 x 36	NYGS	24.00
8011.	Cornfield	12 x 16	NYGS	3.00
8012.	Cornfield near Arles	24 x 31	CFA	18.00
8013.	Cornfield near Dunes	7 x 9	NYGS	.50
8014.	Cornfield with Cypresses	27 x 34-1/2	NYGS	18.00
8015.	Cornfield with Rooks	8 x 10	ESH	1.00
8016.	Cottages	18 x 23	HNA	5.95
8017.	Cottages at Cordeville	18 x 22-1/2	ESH	10.00
		8 x 10	ESH	1.00
8018.	La Crau	17-1/2 x 21-1/2	ESH	10.00
		8 x 10	ESH	1.00
8019.	Cypress in the Field	25 x 32	CFA	18.00
8020.	Cypress Road	22-1/2 x 17-1/2	ESH	10.00
8021.	Cypresses	20 x 16	AJ	7.50
8022.	Dr. Gachet	22-1/2 x 18-1/2	NYGS	10.00
8023.	Drawbridge	6 x 8	CFA	1.00
8024.	Drawbridge at Arles	16 x 20	PENN	1.00
		15 x 15	NYGS	4.00
8025.	Dutch Landscape	20 x 24	PENN	1.00
8026.	Field at Arles	19 x 24	PENN	1.00
8027.	Field at Auvers	5 x 10	CFA	1.00
8028.	Field with Yellow Wheat	8 x 10	ESH	1.00

8029.	Fishing Boats at Saintes-Maries	18 x 23	CFA	10.00
8030.	Flowering Almond Branch	10 x 8	ESH	1.00
8031.	Flowering Chestnut Branch	8 x 10	ESH	1.00
8032.	Flowering Tree	22 x 18	IA	10.00
8033.	Flowers in a Copper-Vessel	17-1/2 x 14	PENN	1.00
8034.	Garden at Daubigny	15 x 30	ESH	15.00
8035.	Garden of Dr. Gachet	8 x 10	ESH	1.00
8036.	Girl in a Straw Hat	23 x 18	HNA	5.95
8037.	Les Glaieuls	22 x 12	NYGS	16.00
8038.	Green Corn	17-1/2 x 22	ESH	10.00
8039.	Gypsy Camp	20 x 24	PENN	1.00
				1.98(Pr.)
		16-1/2 x 19	NYGS	4.00
8040.	Gypsy Caravan	18 x 22	IA	10.00
		17-1/2 x 22	ESH	10.00
		8 x 10	ESH	1.00
8041.	Gypsy Encampment	14 x 16	CFA	4.00
		6 x 7	CFA	1.00
8042.	Harvest	23 x 28	NYGS	22.00
8043.	Haystacks	15 x 30	CFA	15.00
8044.	House at Auvers	23-1/2 x 19-1/2	PENN	1.00
				1.98(Pr.)
8045.	Houses at Auvers	23 x 28	IA	15.00
8046.	L'Homme a L'Oreille Coupee	24 x 20	PENN	1.00
				1.98(Pr.)
8047.	Hospital Corridor	8 x 10	MMA	.35
8048.	Iris	20 x 16	PENN	1.00
				1.98(Pr.)
8049.	Irises	22-1/2 x 18	ESH	10.00
		7 x 9	NYGS	.50
8050.	LeJardin de Daeigny	12 x 23	PENN	1.00
8051.	Le Jardin de L'-Hopital	7 x 8	CFA	1.00
8052.	Landscape at Auvers	25 x 31-1/2	NYGS	18.00
		18 x 23	HNA	5.95
8053.	Landscape with Bridge	23 x 26	CFA	18.00
8054.	Landscape with Cypress	27 x 34-1/2	IA	18.00
		22 x 28	IA	18.00
8055.	Landscape with Cypress Tree	7 x 8	NYGS	.50
		6 x 8	CFA	1.00
8056.	Landscape with Green Corn	24 x 30	DAC	8.00
8057.	Laurier Roses	23 x 28	NYGS	18.00
		18 x 22	CFA	10.00
8058.	Little Gardens--Montmartre	8 x 10	ESH	1.00

8059.	Little Pear Tree in Bloom	28-1/2 x 18	NYGS	15.00
8060.	Madam Roulin and Child	16-1/2 x 14	AR	5.00
8061.	Man Sowing	18 x 22-1/2	AJ	10.00
8062.	La Meule	8-1/2 x 11	NYGS	4.00
8063.	Montmartre, the Gas Lamps	8 x 6	CFA	1.00
8064.	Mountains	8 x 10	MMA	.35
8065.	La Mousme	24 x 18	PENN	1.00
		20 x 16-1/2	NYGS	7.50
		7-1/2 x 6-1/2	NYGS	.50
8066.	Olive Grove	16 x 20	NYGS	5.00
		8 x 10	ESH	1.00
8067.	Open Air Cafe	22 x 18	CFA	10.00
8068.	Orchard	22 x 27	NYGS	12.00
		8 x 10	ESH	1.00
8069.	Painter	18 x 16	CFA	6.00
8070.	Peasant	27 x 21-1/2	NYGS	22.00
		9 x 7	NYGS	.50
8071.	Pere Tanguy	9 x 7	NYGS	.50
8072.	Pink and White	23-1/2 x 30	NYGS	22.00
		16 x 20	NYGS	4.00
8073.	Plains at Auvers	16 x 32	AR	15.00
		10 x 20	AR	5.00
8074.	Poppy Field	25 x 31	CFA	18.00
		24-1/2 x 31	NYGS	18.00
8075.	Portfolio (6)	11 x 14	PENN	1.00 set
8076.	Portrait of Armand Roulin	20 x 16	NYGS	4.00
8077.	Portrait of the Artist	24 x 20	IA	12.00
8078.	Portrait of a Young Man	25 x 20-1/2	NYGS	15.00
		24 x 20	DAC	6.00
		16 x 12	DAC	2.00
8079.	Postman Roulin	28 x 22	NYGS	15.00
8080.	Purple Iris	18 x 22-1/2	MMA	3.00
8081.	Restaurant de la Sirene	21 x 25	NYGS	12.00
		20 x 24	PENN	1.00
				1.98(Pr.)
		18 x 23	HNA	5.95
8082.	Roses and Anemones	20 x 20	ESH	7.50
		12 x 12	ESH	4.00
8083.	Schoolboy	12 x 11	IA	3.00
8084.	Self-Portrait	24 x 20	AJ	12.00
		16 x 13	AJ	6.00
8085.	Self-Portrait	17 x 14	NYGS	10.00
		12 x 9	NYGS	.50
		9 x 7	NYGS	.50
8086.	Self-Portrait (Hat)	10 x 8	ESH	1.00
8087.	Self-Portrait (Pipe)	16-1/2 x 14-1/2	ESH	10.00
		10 x 8	ESH	1.00

8088.	Sidewalk Cafe at	22 x 18	NYGS	10.00
	Night	20 x 15-1/2	NYGS	5.00
8089.	Souvenir de Mauve	20 x 16	NYGS	5.00
8090.	Sower in the Field	18 x 22-1/2	NYGS	10.00
8091.	Stairway at Auvers	16 x 23	NYGS	10.00
8092.	Starlight over the			
	Rhone	20 x 25	NYGS	10.00
8093.	Starry Night	18 x 23	MMA	6.50
		18 x 22	ESH	10.00
		8 x 10	ESH	1.00
8094.	Still Life (Fruit)	16-1/2 x 20	IA	7.50
		16 x 20	CFA	7.50
8095.	Still Life with			
	Gloves	12 x 16	NYGS	3.00
8096.	Still Life with Onions	12 x 16	NYGS	3.00
8097.	Still Life with Pears	18 x 23	NYGS	7.50
8098.	Street in Auvers	28-1/2 x 36	NYGS	15.00
		16 x 20	NYGS	5.00
8099.	Sunflowers (Blue	33-1/2 x 26-1/2	IA	18.00
	Background)	30 c 23-1/2	NYGS	16.00
		20-1/2 x 16	IA	5.00
		20 x 15-1/2	IA	4.00
8100.	Sunflowers	33-1/2 x 26-1/2	NYGS	18.00
		32 x 24	CFA	18.00
		24 x 18	PENN	1.00
				1.98(Pr.)
		22 x 17	ESH	10.00
		20 x 15-1/2	NYGS	5.00
		15 x 12	AR	3.00
		10 x 8	ESH	1.00
8101.	Sunflowers (Yellow	32-1/2 x 25	IA	18.00
	Background)	22 x 16-1/2	IA	10.00
		20-1/2 x 15-1/2	IA	5.00
		20 x 15-1/2	IA	4.00
8102.	Sunny Midi	15-1/2 x 20	AJ	7.50
8103.	Sunset at Arles	8 x 10	ESH	1.00
8104.	Tarascon Coach	8 x 10	MMA	.35
8105.	Thatched Cottages	7 x 9	CFA	1.00
8106.	Three Trees	18 x 22	NYGS	10.00
8107.	Tree in Bloom	22 x 18	AJ	10.00
8108.	Vegetable Gardens	24-1/2 x 32	IA	15.00
		24-1/2 x 31-1/2	NYGS	15.00
		22-1/2 x 28-1/2	NYGS	12.00
		17-1/2 x 21	IA	10.00
		16 x 20	NYGS	4.00
8109.	View of Arles	22 x 28	NYGS	18.00
8110.	View of Arles with			
	Iris	20-1/2 x 25	IA	15.00
8111.	View of Auvers	8 x 10	ESH	1.00
8112.	View of Les Stes.-			
	Maries-de-La Mer	22-1/2 x 18-1/2	NYGS	10.00

8113.	Vincent's House at Arles	17-1/2 x 23	ESH	10.00
8114.	Vineyard	17-1/2 x 22-1/2	AJ	10.00
		17 x 22	CFA	10.00
8115.	Walk at Twilight	20 x 18-1/2	NYGS	7.50
8116.	Walk in Alyscamp Park	16 x 20	NYGS	5.00
8117.	Walk in the Evening	12 x 11	IA	3.00
8118.	Wheatfield	5 x 10	CFA	1.00
		7 x 9	NYGS	.50
8119.	White Roses	30-1/2 x 24	NYGS	18.00
		26 x 20-1/2	IA	7.50
		26 x 20	PENN	1.00
				1.98(Pr.)
		23 x 18	HNA	5.95
		17 x 14	CFA	5.00
		10 x 8	MMA	.35
8120.	Yellow Chair	10 x 8	ESH	1.00
8121.	Zouave	14-1/2 x 12	NYGS	3.00
8122.	Zouave Officer Milliet	14-1/2 x 12	NYGS	3.00

VAN HUYSUM, JAN See HUYSUM, JAN VAN
VAN OSTADE, See OSTADE, ADRIAEN VAN
VAN SPAENDENCK

8123.	Rose a Cent Feuilles	18 x 13	CFA	10.00
8124.	Rose de Provins	17 x 13	CFA	10.00

VANNI, ANDREA   Italian   c.1332-1414

8125.	St. Catherine	15 x 11	IA	3.00

VANNI, LIPPO   Italian   1344-1372

8126.	Madonna and Child	15 x 10	IA	3.00

VANNUCCI, PIETRO See PERUGINO
VARIN, RAOUL   French

8127.	Baseball, 1865	17 x 23-1/2	PENN	1.00
8128.	Broadway, New York, 1834	17 x 23	CFA	60.00
8129.	Broadway and City Hall, N.Y., 1819	18 x 29	CFA	75.00
8130.	Chicago, 1865	17-1/2 x 22-1/2	PENN	1.00
8131.	New York, 1835	17 x 23	CFA	60.00
8132.	New York, 1848	18 x 23	CFA	60.00
8133.	New York, 1852	18 x 29	CFA	75.00
8134.	New York from the East River	18 x 23	CFA	60.00
8135.	New York from the North River, 1839	12 x 33	CFA	60.00
8136.	Printing House Square, N.Y., 1864	18 x 23	CFA	60.00
8137.	St. Paul's Church, 1831	18 x 23	CFA	60.00

VAROTARI, ALESSANDRO See PADOVANINO, IL
VECELLIO, TIZIANO See TITIAN
VECCHIETTA, LORENZO DI PIETRO Italian 1412?-1480

8138.	Il Beato Andrea			
	Gallerani	16 x 10	IA	3.00
VELASQUEZ, DIEGO RODRIGUEZ		Spanish	1599-1660	
8139.	Cardinal Gaspar	8 x 10	AP	.25
8140.	Christ on the Cross	10 x 8	ESH	1.00
8141.	Coronation of the			
	Virgin	10 x 8	ESH	1.00
8142.	Drinkers	18 x 23	HNA	5.95
		13 x 18	IA	3.00
8143.	Immaculate Conception	28 x 21	NYGS	18.00
8144.	The Infanta	22 x 17	AR	12.00
8145.	Infanta in White	22 x 17	CFA	12.00
8146.	Infanta Maria			
	Margarita	13 x 11	IA	3.00
8147.	Infanta Maria Theresa	10 x 8	NYGS	.50
8148.	Infanta Margarite			
	Maria	11 x 9	NYGS	.50
8149.	Infante M. Therese	8 x 10	AP	1.00
8150.	Infante Margareta	25 x 19	CFA	12.00
	Theresa	23-1/2 x 18-1/2	IA	15.00
		23 x 18	HNA	5.95
		20 x 16	CFA	5.00
		20 x 15-1/2	AJ	7.50
		8 x 10	AP	.50
8151.	Infante Marguerite	8 x 10	AP	1.00
8152.	Infante Philip			
	Prosper	20 x 15	NYGS	7.50
8153.	Maids of Honor	18 x 15-1/2	AP	5.00
8154.	Man with a Wine			
	Glass	8 x 7	NYGS	.50
8155.	Merrymakers	13 x 18	NYGS	5.00
8156.	Les Meninas	8 x 10	AP	.50
8157.	Philip IV of			
	Spain	15 x 11	IA	3.00
8158.	Pope Innocent X	14 x 11	IA	3.00
8159.	Head--Detail of			
	No. 8158	15 x 11	IA	3.00
8160.	Queen Mary Anne	13 x 11	IA	3.00
8161.	St. Jerome	15 x 10	IA	3.00
		11 x 6	NYGS	.50
		10 x 8	AP	.25
8162.	St. Mary of Egypt	14 x 11	IA	3.00
8163.	Self-Portrait	15 x 10	IA	3.00
8164.	Surrender of Breda	15 x 18	NYGS	5.00
8165.	Tapestry Weavers	13-1/2 x 18	NYGS	5.00
8166.	Venus and Cupid	19 x 27-1/2	AR	12.00
		19 x 27	CFA	18.00
VELDE, WILLEM (OR ADRIEN) VAN DE		Dutch	17th century	
8167.	Entrance to a Port	8 x 10	NYGS	.50
VENETO, BARTOLOMEO (FRA)		Italian	1502-1530	
8168.	Portrait of a			
	Gentleman	15 x 11	IA	3.00

8169.	Portrait of a Man	10 x 8	NYGS	.50
VENEZIANO, DOMENICO		Italian	1390-1461	
8170.	The Florentine	20 x 13	AR	12.00
8171.	Martyrdom of St. Lucia	10 x 9	IA	3.00
8172.	Portrait of a Girl	21 x 14	NYGS	12.00
8173.	Virgin Enthroned with Child and Saints	11 x 11	IA	3.00
8174.	St. Lucy--Detail of No. 8173	15 x 11	IA	3.00
VERLINDE, CLAUDE		French	1921-	
8175.	La Danse	18 x 26	RL	12.50
8176.	Vikings	16 x 40	RL	20.00
VERMEER, JAN (VAN DELFT)		Dutch	1632-1675	
8177.	Artist in his Studio	22 x 19	ESH	10.00
		10 x 8	ESH	1.00
8178.	Artist in the Studio	23 x 18	HNA	5.95
8179.	Artist's Studio	24 x 20	CFA	7.50
		10 x 8	AP	.50
8180.	Cook	8 x 10	AP	.50
8181.	Diana and the Nymphs	11 x 12	IA	3.00
8182.	Girl Interrupted in Her Music	15-1/2 x 17	NYGS	10.00
8183.	Girl with a Turban	10 x 8	AP	.50
8184.	Girl with Yellow Turban	19 x 16	IA	12.00
		18-1/2 x 16	IA	5.00
8185.	Kitchen Maid	17 x 16	CFA	10.00
8186.	Lace-Maker	24 x 18	DAC	6.00
		17-1/2 x 15-1/2	NYGS	7.50
		10 x 8	AP	.50
		9 x 8	IA	1.00
8187.	Lady at the Virginals	16 x 14	CFA	4.00
8188.	Lady with a Lute	8 x 10	AP	.50
8189.	Lady and Gentleman Drinking Wine	16-1/2 x 20	AR	5.00
8190.	The Letter	22-1/2 x 17-1/2	DAC	6.00
		19-1/2 x 16	NYGS	3.00
8191.	Loveletter	24 x 18	DAC	6.00
		16-1/2 x 14-1/2	NYGS	10.00
8192.	Milkmaid	24 x 20	PENN	1.00
				1.98(Pr.)
		23 x 20	DAC	6.00
		8 x 7	NYGS	.50
8193.	Music Lesson	8 x 10	AP	.50
8194.	Seamstress	24 x 20	PENN	1.00
				1.98(Pr.)
8195.	Tasting Wine	23-1/2 x 28	NYGS	75.00
8196.	View of Delft	8 x 10	AP	.50
8197.	Webster Church at Amsterdam	7 x 12	AR	3.50

8198.	Wine Test	27 x 32	IA	15.00
		17 x 20	IA	10.00
8199.	Wine Tester	17 x 20	CFA	12.00
8200.	Woman Reading	8 x 10	AP	.50
8201.	Woman Weighing Gold	16-1/2 x 14-1/2	NYGS	7.50
8202.	Woman with Water Jug	10 x 9	NYGS	.50
8203.	Young Woman with Jug	10 x 9	NYGS	.50
VERNET, CARLE		French	1758-1836	
8204.	Hunting Scene in England	11 x 30-1/2	ESH	15.00
VERNET, HORACE		French	1789-1863	
8205.	Barouche	13-1/2 x 22-1/2	ESH	10.00
8206.	Pony Trap	8 x 10	ESH	1.00
VERNET, JOSEPH		French	1712-1789	
8207.	Bordeaux No. 9	21 x 29	CFA	25.00
8208.	Le Choix de Poisson	12 x 16	CFA	15.00
8209.	Domino Francisco	12 x 16	CFA	15.00
8210.	Marseille No. 4	21 x 29	CFA	25.00
8211.	Les Pecheurs a la Ligne	12 x 16	CFA	15.00
8212.	Les Pecheurs Fortunes	12 x 16	CFA	15.00
8213.	Toulon No. 6	21 x 29	CFA	25.00
8214.	Vue Proche de Genes	12 x 16	CFA	15.00
8215.	Vue Proche de Mont	12 x 16	CFA	15.00
VERONESE, PAOLO (CALIARI, PAOLO)		Italian	1528-1588	
8216.	Feast in the House of Levi	10 x 22	IA	10.00
		7 x 9	NYGS	.50
8217.	Marriage of St. Catherine	15 x 11	IA	3.00
		9 x 7	NYGS	.50
8218.	Martyrdom of St. Justine	10 x 12	IA	3.00
8219.	Self-Portrait	9 x 7	NYGS	.50
8220.	Sermon of St. John	9 x 7	NYGS	.50
VERROCCHIO, ANDREA DEL		Italian	1435-1488	
8221.	Baptism of Christ (with Leonardo)	13 x 11	IA	3.00
8222.	Heads of Angels (with Leonardo)	12 x 15	IA	3.00
VERSPRONCK, JAN CORNELISZ		Dutch	1597-1662	
8223.	Little Girl in Blue	8 x 10	AP	.25
VERTES, MARCEL		Hungarian	1895-	
8224.	After the Performance	18 x 21-1/2	PENN	1.00
8225.	Cheval au Cirque	19 x 14	NYGS	12.00
8226.	Les Saltimbanques	16 x 24	CAC	9.00
8227.	Serenade	27 x 15	PENN	1.00
				1.98(Pr.)
8228.	Two Ballerinas	23 x 18	PENN	1.00
8229.	Young Mother and Child	24 x 18	PENN	1.00

VIDAL

8230.	Enchanted Lotus	25-1/2 x 36	NYGS	15.00
VIÉ, GABRIEL		French	1888-	
8231.	Pont de Montvert	20 x 26	RL	12.50
8232.	St. Claude	20 x 26	RL	12.50
8233.	Souvenir de Seg-			
	maringen	18 x 22	RL	7.50
8234.	White Village	18 x 22	RL	7.50
VIGÉE-LEBRUN, ELISABETH	See LEBRUN, ELISABETH VIGÉE			
VILLON, JACQUES		French	1875-1963	
8235.	Anger	18-1/2 x 22	ESH	10.00
8236.	En Colere	18 x 12	NYGS	8.00
8237.	Portrait	13 x 10-1/2	NYGS	15.00
8238.	Yellow Accent	19-1/2 x 23-1/2	NYGS	12.00
VINCENT, H.A.				
8239.	Lifting Fog	20 x 28	CFA	7.50
8240.	New England Harbor	16 x 20	CFA	2.50
VINCI, LEONARDO DA	See LEONARDO DA VINCI			
VISSCHER				
8241.	Map of the World	18 x 21	PENN	1.00
VIVES-ATSARA		Spanish	1919-	
8242.	Pottery Vendor	25 x 20	RL	10.00
VIVIN, LOUIS		French	1861-1936	
8243.	Notre Dame	6 x 8	CFA	1.00
8244.	Railroad in the			
	Village	20 x 24	PENN	1.00
VLAMINCK, MAURICE DE		French	1876-	
8245.	A. Chatou	8 x 10	ESH	1.00
		6 x 8	CFA	1.00
8246.	Automne	15 x 18	NYGS	16.00
8247.	Banks of the Seine			
	near Chatou	18 x 22	ESH	10.00
8248.	Bateau a Voile	21-1/2 x 26	NYGS	18.00
8249.	Blue Vase	21 x 25	NYGS	15.00
8250.	Boats on the Seine	16 x 22	CFA	12.00
8251.	Bridge at Meulan	18-1/2 x 24	PENN	1.00
8252.	Chartres	16-1/2 x 19	NYGS	7.50
8253.	Cottage	14 x 17	CFA	5.00
8254.	Cottages	18 x 23	HNA	5.95
8255.	French Farmhouses	25 x 32	CFA	18.00
		18 x 22	PENN	1.00
				1.98 (Pr.)
8256.	Frigate	18 x 22-1/2	ESH	10.00
8257.	Haystack	5 x 7	NYGS	.50
8258.	Hiver	13 x 16	NYGS	16.00
8259.	House in the Woods	8 x 7	NYGS	.50
8260.	Landscape	18 x 24	ESH	10.00
8261.	Landscape	15 x 19-1/2	AP	5.00
8262.	Landscape in the			
	Snow	8 x 10	AP	1.00
8263.	Loaf of Bread	7 x 9	NYGS	.50
8264.	Lupins and Poppies	26 x 21	NYGS	18.00

287

8265.	Main Street	9 x 7	NYGS	.50
8266.	Old Port of			
	Marseille	19-1/2 x 24	PENN	1.00
8267.	Orage	16 x 18-1/2	NYGS	16.00
8268.	Paysage	17 x 20-1/2	NYGS	16.00
8269.	La Petite Gare	17-1/2 x 21	NYGS	16.00
8270.	Pond	8 x 10	ESH	1.00
8271.	Portrait of a Woman	9 x 6	NYGS	.50
		8 x 7	NYGS	.50
8272.	Red Field	17-1/2 x 22	ESH	10.00
		8 x 10	ESH	1.00
8273.	Red Trees	24 x 30	ESH	15.00
8274.	La Route	20 x 26	NYGS	15.00
		18 x 23	ESH	10.00
8275.	St. Maurice-Les-	18 x 22-1/2	ESH	10.00
	Charency	8 x 10	ESH	1.00
8276.	Seine at Carrieres	18-1/2 x 22-1/2	ESH	10.00
8277.	Seine at Chatou	18 x 22	ESH	10.00
		8 x 10	ESH	1.00
8278.	Snowy Countryside	6 x 8	CFA	1.00
8279.	Snowy Village	14 x 18	CFA	7.50
8280.	Still Life with			
	Flowers and Fruits	18 x 23	HNA	5.95
8281.	Still Life with Fruit	17 x 24	PENN	1.00
8282.	Street Scene	21 x 25	NYGS	15.00
8283.	Thatched Cottages	18 x 22	ESH	10.00
		8 x 10	ESH	1.00
8284.	Through the Village	16-1/2 x 22-1/2	ESH	10.00
8285.	Town on a River	22 x 27	NYGS	18.00
8286.	Vase of Flowers	20-1/2 x 16	PENN	1.00
8287.	Village Church	8 x 10	ESH	1.00
8288.	Village Landscape	19-1/2 x 24	PENN	1.00
				1.98(Pr.)
8289.	Village Lane	17-1/2 x 20-1/2	NYGS	10.00
8290.	Village Street in			
	Winter	8 x 10	ESH	1.00
8291.	Wheat Landscape	19 x 24	PENN	1.00
8292.	Winter Landscape	18 x 24	PENN	1.00
		8 x 10	AP	1.00
		6 x 8	CFA	1.00

VOGEL VON VOGELSTEIN, KARL CHRISTIAN German 1788-1868

8293.	Suffer Little Children	23-1/2 x 18	IA	7.50
		14 x 10	IA	3.00
8294.	The Master's Chil-			
	dren	28 x 36	CAC	18.00

VOGLER, KURT   German   1893-

8295.	Golden Harvest	20 x 29	CFA	7.50
8296.	Road in the Mountains	20 x 29	CFA	7.50
8297.	Rocky Mountain Lake	20 x 29	CFA	7.50

VOGT-VILSECK, MAX

8298.	Sheep in the Valley	23 x 35-1/2	IA	15.00

VOIGT
| 8299. | Dancer | 20 x 17 | CFA | 12.00 |

VOLK, DOUGLAS .... American 1856-1935
| 8300. | Portrait of Lincoln | 8 x 10 | AP | .50 |

VOLKAMER
| 8301. | Fruits, Antique (4) | 12 x 7 | CFA | 5.00ea. |

VOLKMANN, H.
8302.	Ballet Dancers (4)	14 x 11	IA	2.00ea.
		8 x 6	IA	1.00ea.
8303.	Little Princess	20 x 16	IA	6.00
		14 x 11	IA	2.50

VOLPI, ALFREDO .... Brazilian .... Contemporary
| 8304. | Casas | 25 x 12-1/2 | NYGS | 10.00 |

VOLTERRANO, IL (FRANCESCHINI, BALDASSARE) Italian
1611-1689
| 8305. | Cupid Sleeping | 15 x 10 | IA | 3.00 |
| 8306. | One of Arlotto's Jokes | 10 x 15 | IA | 3.00 |

VON HESS
| 8307. | At Lake Chiemsee | 19-1/2 x 17 | NYGS | 5.00 |

VON MUNCHHAUSEN See MUNCHHAUSEN
VON SALIS, C.
| 8308. | Landscape in the Alps | 21 x 30 | CFA | 12.00 |

VOS, MARTIN DE .... Flemish 1531-1689
| 8309. | Apollo and the Muses | 10 x 15 | IA | 3.00 |

VU-CAO-DAM .... Vietnamese 1908-
8310.	Blue Madonna	21-1/2 x 16	RL	12.50
8311.	Lotus Bowl	24 x 16-1/2	RL	15.00
8312.	Yellow Madonna	21-1/2 x 16	RL	12.50

VUILLARD, JEAN EDOUARD .... French 1868-1940
8313.	La Cargo a Quai	21 x 21	CFA	30.00
8314.	Mother and Child	8 x 10	ESH	1.00
8315.	Mother and Sister of the Artist	8 x 10	MMA	.35
8316.	Les Premiers Pas	14 x 11	DAC	2.80
8317.	Vase of Roses	10 x 8	ESH	1.00

- W -

WAGNER, H.
8318.	Antelope	18 x 24-1/2	IA	18.00
8319.	Cranes	18 x 24-1/2	IA	18.00
8320.	Horses on the Strand	23 x 31-1/2	IA	12.00
8321.	Mother and Son	15-1/2 x 21	IA	4.00
8322.	Running Horses	18 x 24-1/2	IA	18.00
8323.	Southern Harbor	18 x 35	CFA	15.00
8324.	Two Horses	18 x 24-1/2	IA	18.00

WALCH, CHARLES .... French 1898-1948
| 8325. | Cock | 22-1/2 x 17 | ESH | 10.00 |

		10 x 8	ESH	1.00
8326.	First Snow	18 x 21-1/2	ESH	10.00
8327.	Still Life	10 x 8	ESH	1.00
8328.	Wild Flowers	22-1/2 x 18	ESH	10.00

WALDMULLER, FERDINAND GEORGE Austrian 1793-1865

8329.	Almhutte	12 x 10	NYGS	10.00
8330.	Beethoven	28 x 22-1/2	NYGS	22.00
8331.	Lake Wolfgang	12 x 10	NYGS	10.00
8332.	Vienna Woods	22 x 27	NYGS	18.00

WALKER, LESLEY

8333.	Race	16 x 20	CFA	5.00
8334.	Sovereign of the Seas	16 x 20	CFA	5.00
8335.	With a Following Breeze	16 x 20	CFA	5.00

WALKOWITZ, ABRAHAM   American   1880-

8336.	Rest Day	7 x 21	AR	3.00

WALL-HILL, WILLIAM G.   1792-1862

8337.	Fort Edward	14 x 21	IA	2.50
8338.	New York from Governor's Island	14 x 21	IA	2.50
8339.	View near Fort Miller Bridge	14 x 21	IA	2.50
8340.	View near Hudson	14 x 21	IA	2.50

WALTER

8341.	Ilonka	19-1/2 x 23-1/2	ESH	10.00 (Pr.)
8342.	Old Farm	23-1/2 x 31-1/2	ESH	10.00 (Pr.)

WALTERS, SAMUEL   1811-1882

8343.	The "Independence"	20 x 29	AA	12.00
8344.	The "Roscoe"	20 x 29	AA	12.00

WALTHER

8345.	Peonies	10 x 8	ESH	1.00
8346.	Roses	10 x 8	ESH	1.00

WARD, EDMOND F.

3847.	Enter the Law	18 x 24	AA	10.00

WARD, VERNON D.   English   1905-

8348.	Anemones	17 x 13-1/2	RL	2.50
8349.	Autumn Group	17 x 13-1/2	RL	2.50
8350.	Clearing Day	13 x 20	CFA	7.50
8251.	Dahlias	17 x 13-1/2	RL	2.50
8352.	English Roses and French Porcelain	17 x 22	IA	5.00
8353.	Flight over Skye	16 x 22	RL	5.00
8354.	Light of June	17 x 22	IA	5.00
8355.	Peonies and Porcelain	17 x 22	IA	5.00
8356.	Shovellers Frightened	16 x 22	RL	6.00
8357.	Spring Ecstacy	18 x 22	RL	7.50
8358.	Spring Fragrance	17 x 13-1/2	RL	3.50
8359.	Spring Serenade	13 x 17	RL	2.50
8360.	Summer Gold	17 x 22	IA	5.00

8361.	Wild Alarm	18-1/2 x 22	RL	6.00
8362.	Wings of Spring	16 x 24	RL	7.50

WARNER, J.

8363.	Paris Scenes (4)	20 x 24	DAC	6.00 ea.
		9 x 12	DAC	1.20 ea.

WARREN, ED

8364.	Toreador No. 1	20 x 9	AA	5.00
8365.	Toreador No. 2	20 x 9	AA	5.00

WARSHAWSKY, ABEL GEORGE   American   1883-

8366.	La Belle Bretonne	20 x 16	IA	6.00
8367.	La Fenetre Bleu Tr.-The Blue Window	25 x 32	IA	7.50

WATENPHUL, MAX

8368.	Still Life	25 x 31	CFA	18.00

WATERS, BILLIE   English   1896-

8369.	Crested Grebe and Water Lilies	19 x 15	RL	7.50

WATKINS, FRANKLIN   American   1894-

8370.	Fire Eater	20 x 12	NYGS	5.00

WATSON, R.W.

8371.	Autumn	16 x 20	CFA	2.50
8372.	Summer	16 x 20	CFA	2.50
8373.	Winter	16 x 20	CFA	2.50

WATTEAU, JEAN ANTOINE   French   1684-1721

8374.	After the Hunt	22 x 13	CAC	10.00
8375.	The Art Gallery (Pair)	29-1/2 x 26-1/2	NYGS	50.00 Pair or 28.00 ea.
	Left Side Right Side			
8376.	Autumn	22 x 13	CAC	10.00
8377.	Bird-Nesting	14 x 10	CAC	7.50
8378.	Buffoon	9 x 12	CAC	2.50
8379.	La Collation	12 x 9	IA	10.00
8380.	La Danse	28 x 33	NYGS	28.00
		18 x 24	CAC	10.00
		10 x 15	IA	10.00
8381.	Danse en Plein Aire	9 x 12	IA	10.00 (Grav.)
8382.	Embarkation for Cythera	21-1/2 x 31-1/2	NYGS	15.00
		12 x 18	NYGS	5.00
		10 x 15	IA	3.00
		7 x 11	NYGS	.50
8383.	L'Escarpolette Tr.--The Swing	14 x 11 12 x 10	CAC IA	7.50 10.00
8384.	Fete D'Amour	9 x 12	IA	10.00 (Grav.)
8385.	Fete Champetre	9 x 12	IA	10.00 (Grav.)
		8 x 10	AP	.50

8386.	"Finette"	9 x 7	IA	3.00
8387.	French Comedians	10 x 12	NYGS	.50
		6 x 7	NYGS	.50
8388.	Gallant	14 x 10	CAC	7.50
8389.	La Gamme D'Amour	8 x 10	ESH	1.00
8390.	Gersaint's Signboard	18 x 23	HNA	5.95
8391.	Gilles	13 x 11	IA	3.00
8392.	Girl Seated	9 x 7	CFA	4.00
8393.	Guitarist	14 x 10	CAC	7.50
8394.	Hunting Party	22 x 13	CAC	10.00
8395.	Huntress	9 x 12	CAC	2.50
8396.	L'Indifferent	12 x 9	CFA	2.50
		10 x 8	ESH	1.00
		10 x 7	IA	3.00
8397.	Lecon D'Amour	9 x 12	IA	10.00 (Grav.)
8398.	Lecon de Musique	9 x 12	IA	10.00 (Grav.)
8399.	Life in the Country	19-1/2 x 28	NYGS	15.00
8400.	Little Musician	12 x 9	CFA	2.50
8401.	Le Mezzetin	20-1/2 x 16	AA	5.00
		8 x 6	NYGS	.50
8402.	Party in a Park	12 x 18	CAC	5.00
8403.	Pastorale	22 x 18	NYGS	15.00
		13 x 11	IA	3.00
		10 x 9	NYGS	.50
8404.	Pilgrim	14 x 10	CFA	4.50
8405.	Pipe	14 x 10	CAC	7.50
8406.	Shepherdess	9 x 12	CAC	2.50
8407.	Spring	22 x 13	CAC	10.00
8408.	Spring Song	14 x 10	CAC	7.50
8409.	Summer	22 x 13	CAC	10.00
		15-1/2 x 12	NYGS	12.00
8410.	Trumpeter	11 x 14	CAC	7.50
8411.	Two Cousins	14 x 12	CAC	7.50
8412.	Winter	13 x 22	CAC	10.00
WATTS, GEORGE FREDERICK		English	1817-1904	
8413.	Hope	20 x 16	CAC	5.00
		14 x 11	CAC	3.00
		12 x 9	CAC	2.00
8414.	Sir Galahad	28 x 14	CAC	6.00
		20 x 12	CAC	3.50
WAUGH, FREDERICK		American	1861-1940	
8415.	A Bit of the Cape	30 x 36	NYGS	18.00
		11 x 14	NYGS	3.00
8416.	Breakers	26 x 36	IA	15.00
8417.	Coast of Maine	27 x 36	NYGS	15.00
8418.	March--North Atlantic	16 x 24	NYGS	7.50
8419.	New Jersey Coast	15-1/2 x 21-1/2	IA	7.50
8420.	Open Sea	27 x 35-1/2	NYGS	15.00
8421.	Polar Bear	8 x 10	AP	.50

8422.	Pounding Surf	22 x 28	NYGS	10.00
		17 x 21	NYGS	7.50
		11 x 24	NYGS	3.00
8423.	Wild Weather	15 x 24	PENN	1.00
8424.	Windward Shore	27 x 35-1/2	NYGS	15.00
		11 x 14	NYGS	3.00
WEAVER, ARTHUR		English	1918-1961	
8425.	Black Gold	21 x 32	RL	12.50
8426.	Hoylake Golf Course	16 x 22	RL	7.50
8427.	Royal and Ancient	16 x 22	RL	7.50
WEBER, MAX		American	1881-	
8428.	Flower Piece	24 x 20	AA	10.00
8429.	Geranium	8 x 10	MMA	.35
8430.	In the Temple	21 x 14	AR	3.00
8431.	Interior with Still Life	9 x 7	NYGS	.50
8432.	Still Life, 1950	19-1/2 x 23-1/2	PENN	1.00
8433.	Still Life--Flowers	8 x 6	NYGS	.50
8434.	Summer	19 x 14-1/2	NYGS	5.00
WEBER, ROY		American	1909-	
8435.	Boogie Beat	11 x 14	AR	7.50
WEBSTER				
8436.	Love's Token	14 x 10	CFA	1.50
8437.	Love's Young Dream	14 x 10	CFA	1.50
8438.	Proposal	14 x 10	CFA	1.50
8439.	Stolen Meeting	14 x 10	CFA	1.50
WECUS, WALTER VON		German	1893-	
8440.	Ragusa	22 x 27-1/2	ESH	12.00
8441.	Sailing the Mediterranean	22 x 18	ESH	7.50
WEHLE, JOHANNES		German	1848-1930	
8442.	And They Followed Him	19-1/2 x 31	IA	10.00
		7 x 11	IA	1.20
WEIMANN, PAUL				
8443.	Winter Landscape	20-1/2 x 29	ESH	10.00
WEISGARD				
8444.	Children's Fairy Tales (6)	11 x 14	PENN	1.00 set
	Goldilocks and the Three Bears			
	Jack and the Beanstalk			
	Little Red Riding Hood			
	Pinocchio			
	Snow White and the Seven Dwarfs			
	Tom Thumb			
8445.	Circus Animals (6)	14 x 11	PENN	1.00 set
	Bears on Skates			
	Giraffes			
	Jumbo Elephant			
	Monkey Musicians			
	Performing Horse			
	Trained Seal			
8446.	Farm Animals (6)	14 x 11	PENN	1.00 set

Bunny and Mother
Cows and Sheep
Farm Fowl
Kitten and Mother
Puppies and Mother
Sow and Piglets
8447. Mother Goose Set "A"
      (6)   11 x 14   PENN   1.00 set
Little Bo Peep
Little Boy Blue
Old Mother Hubbard
Peter, Peter, Pumpkin Eater
Ride a Cock Horse
Three Little Kittens
8448. Mother Goose Set "B"
      (6)   14 x 11   PENN   1.00 set
Hey Diddle Diddle
Humpty Dumpty
Jack and Jill
Mary had a Little Lamb
Old Woman Who Lived in a Shoe
Rock-a-Bye Baby
8449. Nursery Prints (4)   11 x 14   PENN   1.00 set
The Fox and the Little Red Hen
Kittens in Toyland
Pups in Playland
Puss 'N' Boots

WEISSENBRUCH, JOHANNES HENDRIK Dutch 1824-1903
8450. Holland Landscape   19 x 31   CFA   12.00
WELTERS, G.
8451. Breaking Wave   20 x 40   IA   12.00
8452. Sunlit Sea   24 x 34-1/2   IA   12.00
WENCK, PAUL   American   1892-
8453. Grand Canyon,
      Arizona   26-1/2 x 36   NYGS   12.00
WENCKE
8454. Mixed Flowers   17 x 14   CFA   3.00
8455. Sunflowers   14 x 17   CFA   3.00
WESSON, EDWARD   English   1910-
8456. Fishing Harbor in
      Cornwall   10 x 8   CFA   1.00
WEST, BENJAMIN   American-English   1738-1820
8457. Penn's Treaty   8 x 10   AP   .50
WESTALL, W.
8458. Eton College   7 x 10   CFA   6.00
8459. Sion House   7 x 10   CFA   6.00
WETMORE-KING, MAUDE
8460. Magnolias   28 x 32   NYGS   10.00
WHEAT, JOHN
8461. Good Old Winter
      Time   18 x 26   PENN   1.00
8462. Red Bridge   13-1/2 x 35   NYGS   12.00

8463.	September Harvest	13-1/2 x 35-1/2	NYGS	12.00
8464.	Summer Winds	20 x 36	NYGS	12.00
WHEATLEY, FRANCIS		English	1747-1801	
8465.	Harvest Time	28 x 36	NYGS	12.00
		20 x 26	NYGS	7.50
WHISTLER, JAMES ABBOTT MC NEILL		American 1834-1903		
8466.	At the Piano	8 x 10	AP	.50
8467.	Battersea Bridge	8 x 10	AP	.50
8468.	Mother of the Artist	20 x 24	NYGS	7.50
		18 x 24	DAC	6.00
		13-1/2 x 15-1/2	DAC	2.00
		11 x 14	NYGS	3.00
		8 x 10	AP	.50
		8-1/2 x 9-1/2	NYGS	.50
WHITE, ETHELBERT		English	1891-	
8469.	Autumn, Arundel Park	18 x 22	RL	7.50
8470.	Hillside Farm	17 x 22	RL	7.50
8471.	New Fence	18 x 22	RL	7.50
WHITE, ORRIN A.		American	1883-	
8472.	Autumn Morn	25 x 31	NYGS	10.00
		16-1/2 x 21	NYGS	5.00
		9 x 11-1/2	NYGS	1.00
8473.	Autumn Reflections	25 x 31	NYGS	10.00
		16-1/2 x 21	NYGS	5.00
		9 x 11-1/2	NYGS	1.00
WHITNEY, E.A.				
8474.	Fishing Village	8 x 10	AA	.90
8475.	Lobsterman's Cove	8 x 10	AA	.90
8476.	Saddle River	8 x 10	AA	.90
8477.	Visitor	8 x 10	AA	.90
WHORF, JOHN		American	1903-	
8478.	Beachcombers	15 x 20	NYGS	7.50
8479.	Brightening Seine	13-1/2 x 19	NYGS	5.00
8480.	Winter by the Sea	12-1/2 x 19	NYGS	5.00
WIECZOREK, MAX		American	1863-1955	
8481.	Head of Christ	20 x 16	IA	4.00
		18 x 13	NYGS	4.00
		10 x 7	NYGS	.50
8482.	Mater Dolorosa	20 x 16	IA	4.00
		17-1/2 x 13	NYGS	4.00
		10 x 7	NYGS	.50
WIED, MAXIMILIAN DE				
8483.	American Views, 1841 (6)		RL	55.00 set
	Encampment of Piekann Indians	12 x 17-1/2		
	Fort Clark	12 x 17		
	Fort Pierre on the Missouri	9-1/2 x 12-1/2		
	Steamer "Yellow-stone"	10 x 12-1/2		

	View of Rocky			
	Mountains	12 x 17		
	White Castles	10-1/2 x 17		
WIEGAND				
8484.	Indian Summer	20 x 16	CAC	2.50
8485.	Mother Earth	21 x 25	CAC	10.00
8486.	November Glow	14 x 29	CAC	7.50
8487.	Peonies	20 x 16	CAC	5.00
8488.	Shimmering Fields	20 x 16	CAC	2.50
8489.	Silvery Birches	14 x 29	CAC	7.50
WILA				
8490.	Corzo	16 x 12	IA	1.50
8491.	Lucero	16 x 12	IA	1.50
8492.	Piconera	22-1/2 x 15-1/2	IA	5.00
8493.	Platero	16 x 12	IA	1.50
8494.	Pollino	16 x 12	IA	1.50
8495.	Revoltosa	22-1/2 x 15-1/2	IA	5.00
WILKE, PAUL ERNST				
8496.	Going to Sea	20 x 29	CFA	7.50
8497.	In the Harbor	20 x 29	CFA	7.50
WILKS, BEN				
8498.	Magic City No. 1	18 x 36	CFA	20.00
8499.	Magic City No. 2	18 x 36	CFA	20.00
8500.	Mystic Mosque	17 x 44	CFA	25.00
WILKS, MAURICE CANNING		Irish	1910-	
8501.	Break in the Clouds	18 x 23	RL	7.50
8502.	Donegal Bay	19 x 23	RL	7.50
8503.	Errigal Mount from			
	Gola Island	16 x 21	RL	3.50
8504.	Kerry Cottages	16 x 21	RL	5.00
8505.	Middle Lake, Kil-			
	larney	19-1/2 x 23	RL	7.50
8506.	Sunshine and Shadow,			
	Co. Donegal	16 x 19	RL	3.50
WILLARD				
8507.	Spirit of '76	26 x 20	CAC	7.50
		20 x 16	CAC	5.00
		12 x 9	CAC	2.00
		10 x 8	AP	.50
WILLIAMS, G.				
8508.	In the Trossachs	24 x 30	AA	10.00
WILLIAMS, WALTER		American	1920(?)-	
8509.	Peaceful Glade	24 x 48	AA	15.00
WILLIAMSBURG PRINTS				
8510.	Birds (Catesby)(12)	24 x 18	DP	100.00 set or 10.00 ea.
8511.	Florals (Furber Wythe House Prints) (12)	24 x 18-1/2	DP	75.00 set or 7.50 ea.

WILSON, A.J.

8512.	Lakeside Sentinels	18 x 23	RL	6.00

WINANTS, A.J.

8513.	Evening Landscape	29 x 37	CFA	18.00

WINDISCH-GRAETZ, F.J.N. Austrian 1905-

8514. Spanish Riding School

(6)	12 x 8-1/2	NYGS	15.00
Capriole			set or
Croupade			3.00 ea.
Passage			
Piaffe			
Pirouette			
Volte			
(4)	12 x 18	NYGS	20.00
Pas de Deux I			set or
Pas de Deux II			6.00 ea.
Pas de Trois I			
Pas de Trois II			

WINTER, FRITZ German Contemporary

8515.	Africana	28 x 30	NYGS	18.00
8516.	Bright Yellow	20 x 21-1/2	NYGS	18.00

WINTERHALTER, FRANZ XAVIER German Contemporary

8517.	Empress Eugenie and	25 x 36	NYGS	12.00
	Her Ladies of	18 x 26	NYGS	7.50
	Honour	8 x 10	ESH	1.00

WINTZ, RAYMOND French 1884-1956

8518.	Blue Door	30 x 24	NYGS	10.00
		22 x 17-1/2	NYGS	4.00
		11 x 8	CFA	1.00
8519.	Blue Harbour,			
	Brittany	22 x 18	RL	6.00
8520.	Breton Window	22 x 17-1/2	RL	6.00
8521.	Fishing Boats	21-1/2 x 17-1/2	NYGS	4.00
8522.	Geranium	18 x 22	RL	6.00
8523.	Harbour Street	21-1/2 x 17	NYGS	4.00
		10 x 8	CFA	1.00
8524.	Joinville	23 x 27-1/2	NYGS	12.00
8525.	Luminosite Marine	17-1/2 x 22-1/2	RL	6.00
8526.	Open Door	20 x 24	NYGS	7.50
8527.	Return of the Tunny			
	Boat	7 x 11	CFA	1.00
8528.	Sunny Morning,			
	Ploumanach	19 x 25	RL	7.50
8529.	Vue Tranquille	19 x 22-1/2	RL	10.00

WITZ, CONRAD Swiss 1398-1447

8530.	Annunciation	28 x 28-1/2	NYGS	28.00
8531.	Mourning under the			
	Cross	10-1/2 x 14	NYGS	15.00
8532.	St. Christopher	23 x 18	HNA	5.95

WOLSTENHOLME, DEAN 1757-1837

8533.	Essex Hunt near			
	Epping	25 x 32-1/2	AA	12.00

WOMACKA, WALTER	German	1925-	
8534. On the Shore	16 x 19	AP	5.00
WONG, TYRUS	Chinese-American	1910-	
8535. Bamboo	30 x 9-1/2	IA	7.50
8536. Calligraphic Rhythm	12 x 39	IA	10.00
8537. Enchanted Isle (2)	14 x 18	IA	7.50 ea.
8538. Fantasy (2)	14 x 18	IA	7.50 ea.
8539. Imaginary Landscape (2)	14 x 18	IA	7.50 ea.
8540. Pine	30 x 9-1/2	IA	7.50
8541. Plum	30 x 9-1/2	IA	7.50
8542. Tai-Ling in the Rain	16 x 20-1/2	IA	5.00
WOOD, CHRISTOPHER	English	1901-1930	
8543. Blue Boat	16 x 22	CFA	10.00
	15-1/2 x 22	NYGS	12.00
WOOD, GRANT	American	1892-1942	
8544. American Gothic	24 x 20	DAC	6.00
	20-1/2 x 17	NYGS	7.50
	16 x 12	DAC	2.00
	9-1/2 x 7-1/2	NYGS	.50
8545. Fall Plowing	12 x 16	NYGS	5.00
8546. Midnight Ride of Paul Revere	18 x 24	NYGS	10.00
8547. Spring in Town	20 x 18	NYGS	7.50
8548. Spring Landscape	18 x 21-1/2	NYGS	7.50
	8-1/2 x 11	NYGS	1.50
8549. Stone City	21 x 27-1/2	NYGS	10.00
	16 x 21	NYGS	5.00
8550. Woman with Plants	18 x 16	NYGS	7.50
8551. Young Corn	12 x 16	NYGS	5.00
WOOD, ROBERT	American	1889-	
8552. Along the Pacific	24 x 36	DAC	8.00
	18 x 26	DAC	6.00
	12 x 16	DAC	2.00
8553. Autumn Glade	24 x 36	IA	12.00
	16 x 22	IA	3.50
	12 x 16	IA	2.00
8554. Autumn Leaves	24 x 40	DAC	8.00
8555. Autumn Mood	16 x 20	IA	3.00
8556. Autumn Sunset	24 x 36	DAC	8.00
	18 x 26	DAC	6.00
	12 x 16	DAC	2.00
8557. Brook	16 x 20	IA	3.00
8558. California Desert	25 x 30	IA	10.00
8559. Carmel Coast	24 x 32	IA	10.00
	16 x 20	IA	3.00
8560. Desert Grandeur	24 x 36	DAC	8.00
	12 x 18	DAC	2.00
8561. Desert in Spring	24 x 36	IA	12.00
	16 x 22	IA	3.50
8562. Dreamer's Cove	25 x 30	IA	10.00

8563.	Early Fall	24 x 36	IA	12.00
8564.	Early Snow	24 x 36	IA	12.00
		12 x 16	IA	2.00
8565.	Early Spring	24 x 36	DAC	8.00
		18 x 26	DAC	6.00
		12 x 16	DAC	2.00
8566.	English Countryside	24 x 48	DAC	10.00
8567.	Evening in the Tetons	24 x 36	IA	12.00
8568.	Fields of Blue	12 x 16	IA	2.00
8569.	Golden Maples	26 x 36	IA	12.00
		16 x 22	IA	3.50
8570.	Golden Shore	16 x 20	IA	3.00
8571.	Golden West	24 x 36	IA	12.00
8572.	Grand Teton	24 x 48	DAC	10.00
		24 x 36	DAC	8.00
		18 x 26	DAC	6.00
		12 x 16	DAC	2.00
8573.	High Glory	25 x 30	IA	10.00
8574.	In the Tetons, Wyoming	25 x 30	IA	10.00
8575.	Lupines and Owl Clover	21 x 47	DAC	8.00
8576.	Majestic Peaks	24 x 36	DAC	8.00
		18 x 26	DAC	6.00
		12 x 16	DAC	2.00
8577.	Mill Stream	24 x 36	DAC	8.00
		12 x 16	DAC	2.00
8578.	Montana Mountains	24 x 36	IA	12.00
8579.	Mount Adams, Colorado	25 x 30	IA	10.00
8580.	Mountain Campers	24 x 36	DAC	8.00
		12 x 16	DAC	2.00
8581.	Mountain Home	24 x 48	DAC	10.00
		12 x 30	DAC	4.00
8582.	Mountain Lake	24 x 36	IA	12.00
8583.	Mount Shasta	24 x 48	DAC	10.00
		24 x 36	IA	12.00
		12 x 30	DAC	4.00
8584.	Mountain Stream	24 x 36	DAC	8.00
		18 x 26	DAC	6.00
		12 x 16	DAC	2.00
8585.	North Country	24 x 30	IA	12.00
8586.	Ocean Breeze	24 x 48	IA	12.00
8587.	October Gold	21 x 47	DAC	8.00
		24 x 36	IA	12.00
		12 x 30	DAC	4.00
8588.	October Morn	24 x 48	DAC	10.00
		24 x 36	DAC	8.00
		18 x 26	DAC	6.00
		12 x 16	DAC	2.00
8589.	Old Mill	24 x 48	DAC	10.00

		24 x 36	DAC	8.00
		18 x 26	DAC	6.00
8590.	Owens Valley	24 x 48	DAC	10.00
8591.	Pacific Sunset	12 x 30	DAC	4.00
		12 x 16	IA	2.00
8592.	Palette of Autumn	28 x 36	IA	15.00
8593.	Path of Gold	25 x 30	IA	10.00
		12 x 16	IA	2.00
8594.	Pine Grove Lake	21 x 47	DAC	8.00
		11 x 24	DAC	2.80
8595.	Pine Lake	24 x 36	IA	12.00
8596.	Point Lobos	12 x 16	IA	2.00
8597.	Rocky Coast	21 x 47	DAC	8.00
		11 x 24	DAC	2.80
8598.	Rustic Homestead	24 x 36	DAC	8.00
		18 x 26	DAC	6.00
		12 x 16	DAC	2.00
8599.	Sea and Sand	16 x 22	IA	3.50
8600.	Seafarers	21 x 47	DAC	8.00
8601.	Sea Splendor	12 x 16	IA	3.00
8602.	Silver Sea	24 x 48	DAC	10.00
8603.	Snow in the Catskills	24 x 48	DAC	10.00
		24 x 36	DAC	8.00
		18 x 26	DAC	6.00
		12 x 16	DAC	2.00
8604.	Springtime	24 x 36	IA	12.00
		16 x 22	IA	3.50
		12 x 16	IA	2.00
8605.	Sundown	24 x 36	IA	12.00
8606.	Sunset, Dana Point	25 x 30	IA	10.00
8607.	Sunset Shore	24 x 40	DAC	8.00
		12 x 18	DAC	2.00
8608.	Texas Blue Bonnets	25 x 30	AA	10.00
8609.	Texas Spring	24 x 36	IA	12.00
8610.	Winter in the	25 x 30	IA	10.00
	Cascades	12 x 16	IA	2.00
8611.	Winter's Arrival	12 x 16	IA	2.00
8612.	Winter Sunset	12 x 16	DAC	2.00
8613.	Yosemite	24 x 48	DAC	10.00
		12 x 30	DAC	4.00

WOODSON, JACK
8614.	River Boats (4)	11 x 14	DAC	2.80 ea.
	Hapland			
	Hudson			
	Robert E. Lee			
	Whipporwill			

WOODVILLE, RICHARD C.   American   1825-1855
| 8615. | First Step | 25 x 27-1/2 | NYGS | 12.00 |

WORTHINGTON, NETTER
| 8616. | Italian Costume | | | |
| | Figures (4) | 14 x 8 | DAC | 2.40 ea. |

WRIGHT, GEORGE
8617.	Getting the Scent	17 x 25	CFA	5.00
8618.	Tally-Ho	17 x 25	CFA	5.00

WYANT, ALEXANDER American 1836-1892
8619.	Forenoon in the Adirondacks	8 x 10	NYGS	.50

WYATT, HENRY English 1794-1840
8620.	Alfred Lord Tennyson	20 x 16-1/2	NYGS	7.50

WYETH, ANDREW American Contemporary
8621.	Christina's World	16 x 24	IA	7.50
8622.	Ground Hog Day	18 x 23	HNA	5.95
8623.	Hunter	8 x 10	AP	.50
8624.	Marshall Point Lighthouse	13 x 18	PENN	1.00
8625.	Young America	13-1/2 x 19	IA	7.50

- Y -

YATES, CULLEN American 1866-1945
8626.	Spring on the Delaware	9 x 8	NYGS	.50

YECKLEY, NORMAN
8627.	Arroyovista	24 x 36	DAC	8.00
		12 x 18	DAC	2.00
8628.	Spring Formal	24 x 36	DAC	8.00
		12 x 18	DAC	2.00

YELINE, O.
8629.	Swiss Chalets	24 x 48	DAC	10.00

YOS
8630.	Amalfi	14 x 17-1/2	IA	3.00
8631.	Autumn	24 x 32	IA	10.00
8632.	Black Forest	14 x 18	IA	3.00
8633.	Brook	14 x 17-1/2	IA	3.00
8634.	By the Lake	24 x 36	IA	7.50
8635.	Huron River	16 x 20	IA	2.50
8636.	Konigsee	24 x 32	IA	10.00
		18 x 23-1/2	IA	6.00
8637.	Lake Como	14 x 18	IA	3.00
8638.	Lake Garda	14 x 18	IA	3.00
8639.	Midsummer	24 x 36	IA	7.50
8640.	Orchard Lake	16 x 20	IA	2.50
8641.	Peaceful Valley	14 x 17-1/2	IA	3.00
8642.	Portofino	14 x 17-1/2	IA	3.00
8643.	Quiet Path Through the Woods	23 x 31	CFA	12.00
8644.	Spring	19-1/2 x 39	IA	5.00
8645.	Spring by the Lake	13 x 17	CAC	3.00
8646.	Spring in the Black Forest	18 x 24	IA	5.00
8647.	Spring in the Forest	23 x 31	CFA	12.00
8648.	Sunny Autumn	19-1/2 x 39	IA	5.00

8649.	Sylvan Lake	16 x 20	IA	2.50
8650.	Walnut Lake	16 x 20	IA	2.50

YOUNG
8651.	Winter Sunlight in Wicklow	17-1/2 x 22	NYGS	7.50

YOUNG-HUNTER
8652.	Santa Fe Trail	26 x 47	CFA	24.00
		18 x 33	CFA	12.00
		8 x 10	AP	.50

- Z -

ZABALETA, RAFAEL   Spanish   Contemporary
8653.	Interior Y Baisaje	24 x 19	NYGS	12.00

ZAMPIERI, DOMENICO   See DOMENICHINO

ZAMPIGHI, EUGENIO
8654.	Famous Hunting Story	21 x 30	IA	10.00

ZARITSKY, JOSEPH   Israeli   1891-
8655.	Tel Aviv, 1936	17 x 23-1/2	NYGS	12.00

ZATZKA
8656.	Flight into Egypt	19-1/2 x 27-1/2	IA	7.50
8657.	Holy Family	38-1/2 x 26	IA	12.00
8658.	Nativity	19-1/2 x 27-1/2	IA	6.00

ZENDEL, GABRIEL   French   1906-
8659.	Composition with Fruit	18 x 24	NYGS	12.00

ZIMMERMAN, ERNST   German   1856-1901
8660.	Christ and the Fisherman	21 x 26	IA	6.00
		17 x 24	IA	2.50
		8 x 10	NYGS	.50

ZINKEISEN, ANNA   Scotch   1901-
8661.	All Things Praise Thee	21 x 15	RL	6.00
8662.	Country Drive	20 x 24	NYGS	12.00
8663.	Drive in the Afternoon	20 x 24	NYGS	12.00
8664.	Esplanade	20 x 24	NYGS	12.00
8665.	In Regency Times	20 x 24	NYGS	12.00
8666.	Nocturno	20 x 24	NYGS	12.00
8667.	Petruchka	20 x 24	NYGS	12.00
8668.	Restive Mount	20 x 24	NYGS	12.00
8669.	Rotten Row	20 x 24	NYGS	12.00
8670.	Spring Morning, the Gossips	21-1/2 x 18	RL	10.00
8671.	Tea at Five	20 x 24	NYGS	12.00

ZOCCHI, GINO   Italian   1900-
8672.	Bright Future	19 x 13	CFA	12.00
8673.	Never Losing Hope	19 x 13	CFA	12.00

ZORACH, WILLIAM   American   1887-
8674.	The Cove	15 x 22	NYGS	5.00
8675.	Five Islands, Maine	12-1/2 x 19	NYGS	5.00

ZORN
8676.	On the Stairs	8 x 10	AP	.50

8677.	Farmer's House in the Wood	12 x 9		CAC	2.00
8678.	Going to Ammaus	18 x 24		CAC	7.50
8679.	The Way to Emmaus	26-1/2 x 35		IA	15.00
		18-1/2 x 25		IA	7.50
		12 x 16		IA	4.00
		8-1/2 x 11		IA	1.00
ZURBARAN, FRANCISCO DE		Spanish		1598-1662	
8680.	Chestnuts in a Basket	6 x 7		CFA	1.00
8681.	St. Francis	24 x 13		AP	10.00
8682.	Still Life	19 x 39		CFA	15.00

Index of Titles

Numbers refer to Item Numbers

Autos, Old 3171
Autumn 288, 508, 724, 907, 929, 4133, 8371, 8376, 8631
Autumn, Arundel Park 8469
Autumn Abundance 757
Autumn Afternoon 4198
Autumn at Argenteuil 5225
Autumn Birches, Loch Lomond 3520
Autumn Bluebird 5789
Autumn Day 7085
Autumn Farewell 6306
Autumn Flowers 450, 2783
Autumn Garden 3191
Autumn Glade 8553
Autumn Glory 4973
Autumn Group 8349
Autumn Honeymoon 3548
Autumn Idyll 5698
Autumn in Kinnordy 5699
Autumn in New England 7344, 7632
Autumn in Paris 1127
Autumn in Vermont 2298
Autumn Landscape 4444, 7946
Autumn Leaves 2800, 5559, 7300, 8554
Autumn Mood 8555
Autumn Morn 225, 230, 8472
Autumn Morning 4199
Autumn Oaks 3665
Autumn Pleasures 6751
Autumn Reflections 7262, 8473
Autumn Sunset 8556
Autumn's Bounty 2170
Autumn's Paint Box 3691
Autumnal Landscape 997
Auvers 7987
Auvers, Vue de Village 7988
Avant le Rideau 3566
Ave Maria 933, 4326
Avenue, 7301
Avenue, Middleharnis, Holland 3400
Avenue de l'Opera in 1900 6088
Avenue of Trees 3401
Aveyron 4442
Avignon 4634
Aviles Street 7633

Awaiting the Tide 3097
Awakening 3830, 6980
Aylesbury Plain 5471

B. von Hartenstein 3442
Babies 4044
Baby in Cradle 7949
Baccarat Party 2046
Baccanale 1495, 1669
Bacchante 6159, 6729
Bacchus 6424
Bachelor's Friends 2966
Bachelor's Hall 48
Bacino from the Giudecca 1035
Bacino from S. Giorgio Maggiore 1034
Backgammon Players 5580
Backstage 3855, 4074
Backwater 7177
Bad Kreuznach 4635
Bad One 6891
Bahama Chores 3739
Bahama Morning 3740
Bahamas 3146
Baie de Menton 4636
Baigneuses 1171
Bailey's Beach 3156
Baiser a la Derobe 2453
Bakery 104
Bal a Gougival 6440
Le Balcon 457
Balcony 4555, 5850
Baldassare Monaco 5768
Bali Beauties 7028
Balinese Dancer 4122, 4123
Ballerina 1786, 3857, 4449, 5851
Ballerinas 314
Ballet 28, 781, 782, 1788, 1903, 3055
Ballet Class 1789
Ballet Dancer 1790
Ballet Dancer: Fourth Position 1791
Ballet Dancers 8302
Ballet Encore 1792
Ballet Espagnol 4556
Ballet Girl 1793
Ballet Girls on Stage 1794
Balloon 3172, 3173
Baltimore, View of 2551, 4238

307

4820
Beach at Saint-Adresse 5228
Beach at Tahiti 2575
Beach at Trouville 746, 5230
Beach Promenade 2048
Beachcombers 8478
Beachhead 3856
Beagle 99
Beans-Eater 1109
Bear Skin Neck 7634
Bearsville Store 6055
Il Beato Andrea Gallerani
8138
Beatrice Cenci 6426
Beatrice D'Este 4300
Beaufort at Worcester Lodge
4478
Beauty Adjusting Combs 3715
Beauty of Flowers 1271,
1272
Beauty with Attendant 3716
Becalmed 6302
Becques 5117
Bedroom at Arles 7989
Beechen Alley 3090
Beer-Drinking Monk 2310
Beethoven 8330
Beethoven's Sonata 309
Before Dinner 936
Before the Ballet 1795
Before the Mirror 5602,
7596
Before the Race 1796, 3567
Before the Rain 2317
Before the Start 2049, 4165,
5432
Before the Thrust 5852
Before the Wind 4492
Begonia Venusta 6129
Beheading of St. John the Baptist
1072
Behind the Curtain 1797
Behind the Moulin de la Galette
7881
Behind the Plow 3888
Behold, I send You Forth 7578
Behold the Man 4545
Beilstein 4639
Belfry at Douai 1496
Bell Flowers 2784
Bell Lilies in a Copper Vase
7990
Bell Mare 6892

La Bella Greca 1563
Bella Vista 3770
Belle Bretonne 8366
Belpermoos 672
Belvoir Hounds Excercising in
the Park 5433
Bench 7991
Bengal Girls 6
Ben Lomond from Loch Ard
5005
Benjamin Franklin 2116
Berceuse 7992
Bergere 6447
Berkshire Snows 497
Berlioz House 7882
Bern 4640
Bernina 1972
Bernkastel 4641
Bessie 6168
Bete du Soleil 219
Bethsabea Bathing 6361
Betrothal of St. Catherine
1584
Between Showers 4347
Between the Acts 1629
Bevy of Quails 3386
Bicycle 4291
Big Brother 3568
Big Circus 1277
Big Cloud 4464
Big Cutters 2318
Big Elms 2299
Big Julie 4267
Big Maples 5596
Big Sky 7478
Big Tree 2576, 7381
Biglen Brothers Racing 2189
Billard 784
Bindo Altoviti 6248
Birches 3091
Bird Garden 3915
Bird Lovers 3608
Bird Searching 2904
Bird Tower at Bellevue 1234
Bird-Nesting 8377
Birds' Wings Glide over the
Moon 5140
Birds 2848, 2849, 4164,
5790-5823, 8510
Birds, Sketches of 1899
Birth of the Baptist 2443,
2671
Birth of the Flag 5211

Birth of the Virgin 2672,
4405, 7049
Birth of Venus 686
Bit of the Cape 8415
Black Bass 7081
Black Board 1728
Black Cockers 1681
Black Dress 3831
Black, Figured Amphora 2269
Black Fishes 937
Black Forest 5428, 8632
Black Forest Idyll 3310
Black Gloves 7786
Black Gold 8425
Black Knight 5434
Black Palette 2978
Blackberry Patch 3005
Blackfriars 1905
Blanket of Snow 1365
Blast Furnace 3175, 7035
Blenheim Leaving Star Hotel
3161, 6149
Blessing 1336
Blessing Strive 3369
Blind Bird 2905
Blind Leading the Blind 901
Blindman's Buff 2851, 5691
Blond Cocker Spaniel 100
Blond Boy 3858
Blonde Girl 192
Blooming Apple Orchard 7993
Blooming Desert 7538
Blooming Orchard 3725
Blossom Time 2547, 5554,
5588
Blossom Valley 2900
Blossoming Garden 4909
Blossoming Palo Verde Tree
7539
Blossoming Plum Tree 6089
Blossoming Smoke Tree 7540
Blossoms 4474
Blossoms in the Twilight 3916
Blossoming Tree by the River
5719
Blossom-Headed Parakeet 2803
Blotter 1729
Blouse Roumaine 4910
Blue and White 2805, 2948
Blue Baloon 7463
Blue Barque 5237
Blue Basket 4268
Bluebell Time 4850

Bluebell Wood 2254
Bluebells 1647
Bluebells (Glockenblume) 1648
Blue Bird 1373
Blue Birds 1374
Blue Boat 8543
Blue Bonnet Time 7009
Blue Bonnet Trail 7010
Blue Bonnets 4994
Blue Bowl 2935
Blue Boy 2529, 5853
Blue Butterfly 1755
Blue Clown 4065
Blue Coast 2319
Blue Compote 4432
Blue Dancer 7388
Blue Danube 5711
Blue Door 3410, 7635, 8518
Blue Door, Newlyn 3152
Blue Fox 4612
Blue Girl Reading Book 4499
Blue Grosbeak 247
Blue Gulf Stream 113
Blue Harbor 7178
Blue Harbour, Brittany 8519
Blue Harmony 103
Blue Head 3917
Blue Horizon 925, 1268
Blue Horses 4613
Blue Iris 7994
Blue-Jay 242, 248, 2806,
5793
Blue Kimono 5712
Blue Lake 1485
Blue Madonna 7066, 8310
Blue Marine 2320
Blue Mozart 2050
Blue Night 3918
Blue Nude 4911
Blue Oak 1906
Blue Ridge Mountains of
Virginia 4543
Blue Room 4912, 7597
Blueroom Prints 1031
Blueroom Proofs 1030
Blue Saloon 7563
Blue Shutters 7636
Blue Studio, St. Ives 7244
Blue-Umber 5486
Blue Vase 1175, 3176, 8249
Blue Vase on Dark Background
6311
Blue Waters 15, 4493

318

Danseuses Saluant 1835
Danseuses sur un Banquette 1836
Dante, Portrait of 2764, 7283
Danza di Amorini e Ratto di Proserpina 24
Danza Gitana, Granada 2773
Daphine Flower 1649
Darby and Joan 6983
Dark Stranger 6298
David 5092
David Showing Goliath's Head 1076
Davos in the Snow 3905
Dawn 5501
Dawn in the Glade 1503
Dawn over the Marshes 116
Day of Devotion 2329
Daybreak 5667
Days before Rapid Transit 3346
Days of Adventure 1744
Days of Chivalry 4046
Days of God 2584
Dead Bird 2958
The Dead Christ 396
Dead Tree 5386
Deadline of the Range 6903
Dearest Dolls 1727
Death 3359, 4018
Death and Burial of Adam 6036
Death and Obsequies of St. Francis 2719
Death of St. Francis 2720
Death of the Knight of Celano 2718
Death of the Virgin 2445
Deauville 2064
Deauville, 1935 2065
Deborah and Nietzsche 1738
Debut 2210
December 2846
Declaration of Independence 7843
Decor for the Ballet "Palm Beach" 2066
Dedham Mill 1456
Deep Canyon 7541
Deer 3964
Deer at the Water Hole 7490
Deer Hunter 3982
Deer Hunting 971

Deer in Flower Garden 4614
Deer in the Forest 4615
Deer Isle Islets, Maine 4775
Dejeuner Provencal 1928
Delfina Flores 6649
Delft Bowl 5493
Delft Vase 5534
Delight 2814
Della Fortuna 5311
Delphi 3994
Delphic Sibylle 5093
Delphiniums 4852, 7518
Delphiniums and Lillies 3890
Delphiniums and White Peonies 2910
Democritus 1582
Demoiselles 2432
Demoiselles D'Avignon 5879
Dempsey and Firpo 418
Dentist 4389
Dents du Midi 4652
Departing Fishermen 3100
Departing Guests 7675
Departure 376, 4799
Departure of the Bocentauro 3028
Departure of the Mayflower 23
Deposition 1077, 2721
Deposition from the Cross 150, 1543, 2765, 5613
Derby View, Vermont 2302
Derwentwater 7248
Descent from the Cross 151, 4406, 6365
Desert Beauty 2968
Desert Cacti 7542
Desert Calm 4995
Desert End 7543
Desert Foliage 425
Desert Grandeur 8560
Desert Horizon 7544
Desert in Spring 8561
Desert Mood 4996, 4997
Desert Peace 4998
Desert Smoke Tree 7545
Desert Smoke Tree in Bloom 7546
Desert Song 5029
Desert Study 7547-7550
Desert Valley 7551
Design--Study in Relief 238
Designer 1339
Desire Dihau 7797

987
Empidocles of Agrigentum 7280
Empire of Light 4525
Empress Fugenie and her Ladies
of Honour 8517
Empress Helen and the Inven-
tion of the Cross 6040
En Colere (Anger) 8236
En Presentation 5419
Enchanted Hour 3702
Enchanted Isle 8537
Fnchanted Lotus 8230
Enchanted Pool 674
Enchanted Road 3726
Enchanted Valley 1964
Enchanting Sun 2603
Enchantment 2816
End of Day 1731
End of a Perfect Day 4535
End of Skein 6984
End of Summer 7346
End of the Hunt 5509
End of the Mall 6840
End of the Trail 2504
Endeavor II and Ranger 2840
Enduring Charms 6633
Enfant au Bourelet 6848
Enfant a l'Ecuelle 2959
Enghien in the Snow 6216
English Countryside 8566
English Family Outing 3064
English Officer 6241
English Rose 7377
English Roses and French
Porcelain 8352
English Setters 3143
Englishman 7803
Enter the Law 8347
Entertainment in a Garden
4521
Entombment 6254
Entombment of Christ 153,
397
L'Entracte 1021
L'Entree des Masques 1838
Entrance to a Port 8167
Entrance to a Village 2585,
6097
Entry into Jerusalem 154,
2722
Environs du Jas de Bouffan
1185
Environs of Rome 2641

Epoque Heureuse 7503
Equals Infinity 3929
Equatorial Jungle 6818
Equestrians 4776
Equestrienne 2998
Eritrian Sibylle 5095
Erlach 4656
Eros and Psyche 2656, 6028
Errand Woman 1340
Errigal Mount from Gola
Island 8503
Escape 3838
Escarpolette (Swing) 2456,
5694, 8383
Espacio Azul 5728
Espana 553
Esplanade 8664
Essex Hunt near Fpping 8533
L'Estaque 788, 1186
Esther and Ahasverus 4332
Ete, La Plage des Sables
4824
Eternal East 6753
The Fternal Father 1978
Etienne Chevalier adoring the
Madonna 2446
Eton College 8458
Etude 1187
Etude de Cavalier 1887
Eucalyptus Trees 7136
European Cities 70
Evander and Aeneas 2697
Eve of St. Nicholas 7439
Evening 5669, 7107
Evening Enchantment 1285
Evening Glow 5214
Evening Glow in Ireland 478
Evening Grosbeak 5801
Evening in the Country 5510
Evening in the Tetons 8567
Evening Landscape 8513
Evening Solitude 2255
Evening's Comfort 3124, 5825
Evensong 864
Eventails 5558
Eventide 592
Evolene 4657
Exaltation 2817
Excursionist 6466
Exhibition Poster 1015
Expectation 7411
Express 570
Expression I 7453

Flamenco Dancer #1 6841
Flamingoes 675, 5802
Flatford Mill 1457
Flatford Mill on the River
   Stour 1458
Flemish Kermis 6849
Flemish Landscape 6958
Fleurs 3967, 4468
Fleurs Decoratives 6782
Fleurs des Champs 5139
Flight 6413
Flight at Morn 118
Flight into Egypt 155, 2653,
   2723, 2770, 3399, 3541,
   6783, 8656
Flight over Skye 8353
Flooded Meadow 3388
Floods at Marly in 1875 7312
Flora 715, 7735, 7736
Flora-Dora Girls 7504, 7505
Floral and Fruit 5523, 5524,
   5525
Floral Fantasy 7219
Floral Magic 502
Floral Rhapsody 325
Floral Still Life 2795
Florals 4394, 8511
Florence, Mercato dell'Pulci
   4809
Florence, Mercato di S. Pietro
   4810
Florence, Italy: Piazza 3191
Florence, Piazza S. Spirito 4811
Florence, Ponte Vecchio 4812
Florence, seen from the Boboli
   Gardens 1505
Florence, La Singagoga 4813
Florence, Via Alzani 4814
Florence, Via Orivolo 4815
Florence, Volta dei Tintori
   4816
Florentine 8170
Florida Jay 253
Flower Basket 1997
Flower Fiesta 1580
Flower Garden and Bungalow,
   Bermuda 3469
Flower Gatherers 1935
Flower Girl 3931, 5312
Flower Market 2222, 3574,
   5626, 7466
Flower Market, Madagascar
   3765

Flower Petals 4922
Flower Piece 927, 1888,
   7220, 7221, 8428
Flower Scenes 6204
Flower Seller 5891, 6650
Flower Shop 5463
Flower Study 1897, 1898
Flower Subjects 1976
Flower Vendor 106, 5648,
   6651, 7394, 7456
Flower Vendors 4859
Flower Vendors by the Seine
   2365
Flower Vendors, Paris 2366
Flowering Acaceas 427
Flowering Almond Branch
   8030
Flowering Chestnut Branch
   8031
Flowering Dogwood 2818
Flowering Tree 8032
Flowers 603, 1120, 1190,
   2067, 5400, 5530, 5539,
   5892, 6086, 6314, 6784, 6819
Flowers 1903, 5893
Flowers and Bowl of Fruit
   2590
Flowers and Cat 6472
Flowers and Fruit 1191,
   2290, 4807, 6954
Flowers and Fruits 1286,
   4923
Flowers and Music 2211
Flowers and Music with Piano
   2212
Flowers and Music with Violin
   2213
Flowers and Pineapple 4419
Flowers from my Garden
   2172
Flowers in a Blue Jug 7901
Flowers in a Blue Vase 898,
   6315
Flowers in a Brown Vase 899
Flowers in a Copper Vessel
   8033
Flowers in a Delft Vase 1192
Flowers in a Jug 1193, 5515
Flowers in a Vase 1910, 6785
Flowers of the Hunt 49
Flowers on a Grey Background
   856
Flowery Palm Trees 6098

Fluelen 4664
Flute Concert 5062
Flute Player 2272, 4081, 4566
Fluyder Children 4208
Flying Codonas 1619
Flying Geese 2262
Flying Swans 5567
Fog Warning 3470
Foggy Morning, Rockport 7642
Follow Me 1606
Follow Thou Me 7020
Fontainebleau Woods 1960
Footballers 1949
Foothills in Flower 5627
Foothills of the Rockies 2776
For a Song 1388 ·
For all my Fancy Dwells on Nancy 6986
For Fifty Years 6987
Forces of Life and the Spirit Triumphing over Evil (Unesco Mural) 5894
Ford 444
Forenoon in the Adirondacks 8619
Forest at Coubron 1506
Forest Blossoms 851
Forest Cyclamen 1654
Forest of Arden 6969
Forest Scene 6959
Forest Secrets 1969
Forest View 3503
Forget-Me-Nots 1655
Fornarina 6294
Fort Edward 8337
Fortitude and Wisdom 7692
Fortune Teller 4174, 5840
Forum of Trajan and Church of S. Maria 5022
Forum, seen from the Palatinos 1507
Fountain 1936
Fountain in Triente 6227
Fountains 6660
Four Birds 3390
Four Dancers 1841
Four Designs 6256
Four Fortunes of the Maize 277
Four Girls 4180
Four Horses 3718

Four Philosophers 6850
Four Saints 187, 188
Four Seasons 6687
Fourth of July Parade 3538
Fox Hunting 50, 51
Fox Hunting Scenes 3360
Fox Island, Maine 3149
Foyer de la Danse a l'Opera 1842
Fragment 5150
Fragment of a Triptych 5151
Fragments of Elegance 4375
Fragrance of Spring 7087
Fragrant Flowers 283
Fragrant June 2238
Francesco della Opere 5774
Francesco Maria della Rovere 6257
Francis I 1430
Franklin, Benjamin 2116
Franklin D. Roosevelt 7012
Frate Guido di S. Galgano 3057
Frederick of Urbino as a Child 326
Free as the Wind 33
Freedom of the Plains 611
Freight Ships on River 5754
Freisia 2787
French Comedians 8387
French Farmhouses 8255
French Park 5351
French Provincial Subjects 4294
French Quarter, New Orleans 367
French Window 2433
French Winter Scene 6099
Fresco, 1951 5152
Fresco with Horses 2273
Freshmen 3840
Fribourg 4665
Friends 1956
Frigate 8256
Fritzi and Fred 6057
Frolic 7356
From the Bridge 4778
From Garden and Orchard 6183
From Manhattan Bridge 2491
From my Garden 521
From my Window 1396
From the Old West 34

Gersaint's Signboard 8390
Getting Acquainted 7765
Getting Ready 7643
Getting the Scent 8617
Gettysburg Address 3648
Gift Bearers 691
Gilles 8391
Ginevra Bentivoglio 6676
Giocollieri 4801
La Gioconda 4304
Giovane Romana 6072
Giovanna Tournabuoni 2678
Giovanni Bentivoglio 6677
Giralda, Sevilla 4353
Girl 1122
Girl Adjusting Earrings 6479
Girl and her Cat 3862
Girl and her Duenna 5448
Girl at Folies Bergere 4568
Girl at her Studies 2461
Girl at Ironing Board 1843
Girl at the Piano 5833
Girl from Brittany in Prayer
2591
Girl Gleaner 5122
Girl in Blue 5834
Girl in a Chair 5895
Girl in Pink 5187, 6480,
7385
Girl in Red 4181
Girl in a Straw Hat 8036
Girl in Violet 6481
Girl Interrupted at her Music
8182
Girl Looking through Opera
Glasses 1844
Girl Lying at Water's Edge
6482
Girl of China 3863
Girl on a Beach Ball 5896
Girl on a Divan 5897
Girl on a Wall 5898
Girl Peeling Potatoes 194
Girl Pilgrim 2976
Girl Reading 2462, 4924,
6483
Girl Reading by the Waterside
1508
Girl Seated 8392
Girl with Anemones 4925, 4926
Girl with Basket 3805
Girl with Battledore 1341
Girl with a Birdcage 2173

Girl with Black Tie 5188
Girl with Blue Birds 4501
Girl with Braids 5189
Girl with a Broom 6367
Girl with Cat 2685, 6484
Girl with Cherries 6952
Girl with a Dog 6520
Girl with Dove 7457
Girl with a Drinking Cup
5760
Girl with a Falcon 6485
Girl with a Finch 7594
Girl with a Flower 6077
Girl with Flowers 2686,
4182, 6317
Girl with Flowers in her Hair
6761
Girl with Flowing Hair 6486
Girl with a Hat 6487
Girl with a Jug 5899
Girl with a Kitten 2434,
5759
Girl with Lillies 4183
Girl with Mandolin 5900
Girl with Mandoline 2174
Girl with a Marmot 2463
Girl with Red Bow 1509
Girl with Rose 4184
Girl with Swing 3326
Girl with Tambourine 5476
Girl with a Turban 8183
Girl with a Watering Can
6488
Girl with Yellow Turban 8184
Girl Writing a Letter 5359
Girls in Open Air 6489
Girls Picking Flowers 6490
Girls Throwing Flowers 3417
Girls under the Trees 4502
Giselle First Act Curtain
446
Gisze, Merchant George
3445
Gitana Playing the Mandolin
1510
Giudoriccio of Fogliano 4868
Giuliano De'Medici 6167
Glade Water 2950
Gladiola 451
Gladiolas 4503
Gladioli 1288, 2068, 2820,
7945
Gladiolus 5592

Grandeur of Summer 1438
Grandmother 195
Grandmother and Child 2969
Grandmother's Bouquet 5526,
5527
Grandmother's Pride 3806
Grands Boulevards 6491
Grandview 1003
Grant Avenue, San Francisco
3864
Grapes and Pear 627
Gravelines 1912
Gravesend 5598
Gray and Gold 1581
Gray Morning 3708
Grazing Reindeer 6208
Greased Lightning 4284
Great Clock, Rouen 3620
Great Hall of the Bulls 6210
Great Metropolitan Stakes 7036
Great Pine 1199, 1913
Greek Fishing Boats 2312
Green Corn 8038
Green Dancers 1845
Green Dish 4420
Green Grapes and Strawberries
628
Green Grapes and Zinnias 629
Green Lantern, Carmel-by-the-
Sea 1129
Green Meadows 2525
Green Pasture 5628
Green Pastures 5732
Green Planes 5487
Green Pumpkin 4930
Green Seascape 6713
Green Slices 5488
Green Still Life 5903
Green Valley 4670
Green Vase 3193
Green Violinist 1287
Green-Winged Teal 5804
Greenwich 3621
Greeting the Sunrise 3694
Gretel 3812
Greylag on the Loch 5215
Gribourg 4671
Grille 5904
Grindelwald 4672
Grindelwald mit Wetterhorn
3756
Griselda Legend 4515
Grist Mill 1613

Grocer's Daughter 5190
Ground Hog Day 8622
Ground Swell 3510
Group of Carnations 7678
Group of Dancers 1846
Group Portrait 2011
Grouse Shooting 7185
Guardian Angel 2427, 6137
Guardian of the Coast 7031
Guardian of the Flock 5125
Guernica 5905
Guerrier 4469
Guillaume Juvenal des Ursins
2447
Guitar 4459, 5906
Guitar and Bottle 5907
Guitar and Flowers 2982
Guitar and Grapes 5908
Guitar and Music Sheet 1352
Guitar and Sombrero 4569
Guitar Clown 2027
Guitar Player 6492
Guitare 4270
Guitarist 2983, 8393
Gulf Stream 3471
Gypsies 3865
Gypsy 3078
Gypsy Camp 8039
Gypsy Caravan 8040
Gypsy Encampment 8041
Gypsy Girl 6724
Gypsy Girl at the Fountain
1511
Gypsy Life 5436
Gypsy Wagon 6101
Gypsy with Mandolin 1512
Gypsy Woman and Child 5191
Gypsye 544

H. M. the Queen in Coronation
Robes 5634
Hail Mary 2593
Hail Victory 5505
Hair Dresser 107
Haitian Dancers 2947
Half-Nude 6030
Half-Way House 7223
Les Halles, Paris 2368
Halting at an Inn 5039
Hambletonian 2841
Hamilton, Alexander 7842
Hamlet 1889

Hammerstein's Roof Garden
2780
Hampstead Heath 1460
Handball 7211
Handel 5654
Hands 4011
Hands of a Praying Apostle
2153
Hansel 3813
Happy Childhood 1770
Happy Days 3675
Happy Family 4049
Happy Hollow 7338
Happy Hours 1901, 6187
Happy Springtime 1771
Harbinger of Spring 894
Harbor 947, 1914, 3114,
3549, 7268
Harbour at East Lake 5212
Harbor at Honfleur 3749, 7200
Harbor at Rockport, Mass.
4673
Harbor in Brittany 4674
Harbour of Algier 1941
Harbour of Barcelone 333
Harbor of Joinville 1018
Harbour of Naples 4825
Harbour of Saint-Tropez 604,
7269
Harbor Pattern 7126
Harbour, St. Ives 3297
Harbor Scenes 2567
Harbour Street 8523
Harbor Towns 3741
Harbor Traffic 2889
Harbor View--Phlox 524
Harlem River 1962
Harlequin 1847, 1915, 2984,
5909, 5911
Harlequin, 1917 5910
Harlequin,]923 5912
Harlequin and Boy 5913
Harlequin and Companion 5914
Harlequin and Dog 6786
Harlequin and Mandolin 6194
Harlequin and Mirror 5915
Harlequin on Horseback 5916
Harlequin Sonata 846
Harlequin with Guitar 6195
Harlequin with Mask 5918
Harlequin's Carnival 5153
Harlequin's Family 5917
Harmony 2941

Harp of the Winds 4858
Harp of Trees 7242
Harvest 630, 4322, 5593,
8042
Harvest Time 3598, 7947,
8465
Hastings, about 1835 7848
Hat Seller 447
Hauling Nets 7646
Haus Am See 7587
Hawaii, 1963 6299
Hawking 511, 512
Hawthorne, N.Y. 6024
Hay Harvest 911
Hay Wagon 7488
Hay Wain 1459
Haying 7116
Haying Time 2303
Haymakers 2069, 2930
Haymaking 912, 4319
Haymaking, 1940 90
Haystack 8257
Haystack at Sunset 5249
Haystacks 2592, 8043
Haytime in the Cotswolds 353

He Prayeth Best Who Loveth
Best 7579
Head 4194
Head of an Apostle 2130
Head of Cherub 4477
Head of a Child 6657, 7050
Head of Christ, 7021, 8481
Head of a Clown 949
Head of a Girl 2960, 4854
Head of a Lion 1890
Head of Lynn 6171
Head of a Saint 1153
Head of St. Anne 4310
Head of a Woman 1848, 5919
Head of the Artist's Mother
2681
Head of the Saviour 4301
Head of the Virgin 4453
Head of Vengeance 6225
Head of Winter 7615
Head of a Young Girl 4526
Heading for Home 4876
Heading South 5568
Head of Angels 6613, 8222
Heads of Two Clowns 6787
Heads or Tails 6908
The Healer 1607

8046
Honey Taster 2347
Honeymoon by the Bay 3550
Honeymoon by the River 3551
Honeymoon in Paris 3554
Honeymoon in the Snow 3555
Honeymoon in the Spring 3556
Honfleur 1125
Honfleur Harbor 2071
Hong Kong 2350
Hon. Mrs. Ashley 4209
Hon. Mrs. Graham 2532
Hooded Merganser 5805
Hooded Warbler 5806
Hoop, Jr. 7485
Hope 6232, 8413
Hope of the World 1473
Horas du Pin 2072
Horse and Acrobat 4802
Horse and Butterfly 1353
Horse and Carriage 3065
Horse and Eagle 4617
Horse and Groom 3392
Horse Fair 596
Horse on Red Ground 4804
Horse Race 2658
Horse Trolley 573
Horse Wrangler 4381
Horseman 4803
Horsemen and Herdsmen with
   Cattle 1625
Horses 893
Horses, Thoroughbred 7072
Horses at Market 2659
Horses Gamboling 3719
Horses in a Storm 6727
Horses in the Rain 496
Horses in Winter 4374
Horses on the Strand 8320
Hospital Corridor 8047
Hostess 5714
Hot Jazz 3768
House at Auvers 8044
House in the Woods 8259
House of Cards 1342
House of the Hanged Man 1221
House of Pere Lacroix 1200
House of the Vestals 4895
House on the Bay 1201
House on the Hill 1201
House on Pamet River 3511
Housebuilders 7840
Houses 2405

Houses at Auvers 8045
Houses at Honfleur 1513
Houses of Parliament 268
Hoylake Golf Course 8426
Hudson River Logging 3473
Humorist 5537
Humpty Dumpty 322
Hunt 3115
Hunt and Coaches, Small 54
Hunt Breakfast 430
Hunter 8623
Hunters 7033
Hunting in Autumn 12
Hunting Morn 6990
Hunting Party 8394
Hunting Recollections 4124
Hunting Scene in England
   8204
Huntress 8395
Hunts and Coaches 431
Hurdy-Gurdy Boy 3601
Huron River 8635
Hyde Park 1916, 3066
Hyde Park Corner 6151
Hydropic Woman 2002

I and my Village 1289
I Orana Maria 2593
I Pledge Allegiance 7473
I Raro Te Oviri 2594
Ibiza 3317
Ice Cream Vendor 3577
Ice Glare 982
Ice Landscape 263
Icebound 5072
Ideas for Metal Sculpture, 1937
   5337
Ideas for Two-Figure Sculpture
   5338
Idle Hours 3045
Idol 4931
Idylle at Bernau 7668
Ikons 3641
Ile de France 4826
Ile de la Cite, Paris 2931
I'll Show the Way 6058
Ilonka 8341
Imaginary Landscape 6196,
   8539
Immaculata 5449
Immaculate Conception 5450,
   8143

335

Interior with Egyptian Curtain 4934
Interior with Flowers 4935
Interior with Still Life 8431
Interior Y Paisaje 8653
Interlude 4150, 5421
Intermission 4076
Intersecting Lines 3790
Into the Happy Lands 7339
Introduction 978
Intruder 3673
Inventions of Monsters 1675
Iphegenia's Sacrifice 7695
Iran Courtesan 3440
Iris 2133, 2203, 8048
Iris and Insects 2417
Iris, Convolvulus and Cherries 2416
Iris, Liserons and Cherries 2418
Irises 8049
Irish Setter with Teal 1684
Irish Setters 1683, 3144
Ironer 5920
Ironers 1849
Ironwood Tree 7555
Isabelle Brant, First Wife 6853
Isabella of Portugal 7737
Isaiah, Prophet 5098
Iserables 4677
Island of La Grande Jatte 7314
Isle 2227
Isle of Arran 3533
Isle of Istria 5317
Isola Bella Sbocco Sul Lago 4678
Isola Dei Pescatori Barche Alla Rivoca 4679
Isola Dei Pescatori 4680
Isola San Giorgio 948
Italian Costume Figures 8616
Italian Fantasy 1432
Italian Landscape 2539, 3418
Italian Landscape, Agnuzzo 3419
Italian Landscape, the Appennines 1726
L'Italienne 5921
Italy 7362

Jack 4050
Jack and the Beanstalk 3328

Jackie 5404
Jackson, General T.J. 2234
Jacobea of Baden 390
Jacob's Dream 566
Jade and China 3059
Jaleo, El 7044
Jamaica 3194, 3195
James Stuart, Son of Charles I 1059
Jane Avril 7806, 7807
Jane Avril Dancing 7808
Jane Avril Leaving Moulin Rouge 7809
Japanese Toy Tiger and Odd Objects 4070
Jardin de Daeigny 8050
Jardin de l'Hospital 8051
Jardins des Tuileries 3365
Jas de Bouffan 1202
Jazz Musicians 5741
Jazz Players 1950
Jean Bellows 7397
Jean Monet on a Mechanical Horse 5251
Jean Renoir Drawing 6496
Jean Renoir Sewing 6497
Jeanette 4187
Jeanne 5192
Jeanne D'Arc 6789
Jeanne Samary 6498
Jefferson, Thomas 5706
Jefferson, Thomas' Home, Monticello, Charlottesville, Va. 3183
Jenny Lind 4524
Jeremiah, Prophet 5100
Jerk Line 6911
Jerked Down 6912
Jester 3080
Jesus, the Children are Calling 1947
Jesus, the Children's Friend 7023
Jesus and St. John 5451, 7054
Jesus Feeding the Five Thousand 5452
Jesus, Light of the World 7024
Jesus of Nazareth 3703
Jesus Sleeping 4761
Jetty at Deauville 749
Jeune Baigneuse 6499
Jeune Ballerina 3579

337

2486
Madonna and Child with St. John
698, 4413, 5600, 7055
Madonna and Child with St. John
and St. Anthony 7739
Madonna and Child with Saints
5781
Madonna and Child with Two
Angels 6757
Madonna and Child with Two
Saints 2482, 4402
Madonna and Donor 1367
Madonna and Saints 2769,
4403, 6066
Madonna and Saints John and
Francis 4407
Madonna, Angels and St.
Francis 1400
Madonna, Child and Angels 4528
Madonna, Child and Saints
2484
Madonna "La Belle Jardiniere"
6261
Madonna del Cardelino 6262
Madonna del Dito 1981
Madonna dei Francescani (The
Virgin Adored) 2020
Madonna del Granduca 6265
Madonna del Sacco 7056
Madonna della Scala 1546
Madonna della Sedia (Madonna
of the Chair) 6266
Madonna della Serra 5756
Madonna della Stella 163
Madonna della Tenda 6267
Madonna Enthroned 1597
Madonna Enthroned and Saints
4872, 5056
Madonna in a Mystic Garden
4370
Madonna in the Rose Garden 4371
Madonna of the Apple
6658
Madonna of the Arbour 1585
Madonna of the Butterfly 2480
Madonna of the Carnation
4455
Madonna of the Chair 6266
Madonna of the Cherries 327
Madonna of Foligno 6263
Madonna of the Goldfinsh
7697
Madonna of the Grapes 5110

Madonna of the Harpies 7057
Madonna of the Iris 2138
Madonna of the Lilies 699
Madonna of the Linaiuoli 165
Madonna of the Magnificat 700
Madonna of the Maison d'Or-
leans 6268
Madonna of the Meadows 399
Madonna of the Olives 318
Madonna of the Pomgranate
703
Madonna of Port Lligat 1676
Madonna of the Rosary 1393,
7067, 7291
Madonna of the Rose Arbor
4372
Madonna of the Rose Bower
4456
Madonna of San Sisto (Sis-
tine) 6269
Madonna of Senigallia 6043
Madonna of the Seraphim 705
Madonna of the Street 2344
Madonna of the Trees 400
Madonna of the Veil 1982
Madonna Ornas 343
Madonna Surrounded by Animals
2139
Madonna with the Canopy 706
Madonna with the Green Cushion
7371
Madonna with the Pomgranate
6270
Madonna with Sleeping Child
4602
Madonna with the Soup 1720
Madonna with Sweet Pea 4899
Madonnina 2344
Madrid, Puente di Segovia
4356
Mafalda 7604
Magdalene 1979, 7740
Magdalen and Jesus 2738
Magic City 310, 8498, 8499
Magical Sunlight 6636
Magnanimity of Scipio 7698
Magnolia 455, 2649, 2942
Magnolia Blossoms 3073
Magnolias 3900, 4159, 5555,
7105, 7480, 7870, 8460
Maid of Honor 6857
Maids of Honor 8153
Main and Side Roads 3939

Main Street 8265
Maine Islands 4782
La Maison Blanche 848
Maison Dubois 4222
Maison du Pendu 1221
Maison Mimi 7905
Maize God 278
Majestic Peaks 8576
Majesty of the Mountains
5402
Major T. Bouch, M. F. H. , with
the Belvoir Hounds 5437
Major John Biddle 7526
Major Thomas Biddle 7527
Maker of Preserves 2985
Mal's Restaurant 4223
Male Torso 5102
Mallard, Anglesay 5216
Mallard Rising 3138
Mallorca 2223, 4690
Mallorca Harbor 4357
Malmoe City Hall, Averige
2373
Maloja 4691
Malvern Hall 1460
Mama, Papa is Wounded 7573
Man and Machinery 6653
Man at a Door 6373
Man in Brown Jerkin 6173
Man O'War 82, 5379, 5380
Man of War Cutter 3973
Man on a Tight Rope 3940
Man Resting 951
Man Sowing 8061
Man with an Axe 2598
Man with the Glove 7741
Man with a Golden Helmet
6374
Man with Guitar 5934
Man with a Hoe 5127
Man with a Medal 707
Man with a Wine Glass 8154
Man, Woman and Child 5154
Manchester Valley 6027
Mandarin Figures 1380
Mandello near Comer Sea 6886
Mandolin 386
Mandolin and Fruit 7209
Mandolin and Guitar 5935
Mandoline 799
Mandolins and Pineapplies 7569
Mandril 3999
Manhattan 3009

Manhattan Harbor 3010
Manhattan Nocturne 2492
Mannequins at the Races 2030
Manor House 5411
Manton from LaPausa 1391
Manuela 7779
Many Friends 1772
Many Views 3842
Map 2995, 6932
Map of the Americas 517
Map of the World 8241
Maple Sugaring in Vermont
7034
Marble Table 800
Marcel Linder Dancing 7811,
7812
March Gallery 4224
March--North Atlantic 8418
March Snow 6174
March Sun 6175
Les Marchandes des Modes 731
Marche St. Medard 1694
Marcus Aurelius 5638
Mardi Gras 350, 1222
Mare and Foal in the Paddock
4021
Mares' Tails in the Sky 7340
Margaret 2533
Margarethe Boghe, Wife of
Joris W. Vezelier 1426
Marguerite Reading 4937
Maria 5649
Maria de Medici, Daughter of
Cosimo I 885
Maria of Burgundy 4544
Mariachi in Blue 1879
Mariachi in Red 1880
Marianne 3585
Maribou 2908
Marie Adelaide 5481
Marie Antoinette and her
Children 4249
Marie Henry 2599
Marie Zephirine 5482
The Maries 166
The Maries at the Tomb 2021
Marika 5406
Marilyn 5407
Marimba Players 5650
Marina di Giorgio, Venezia
5319
Marine 801, 3750
Marine Collection 1733

Melon, Oranges and Green
Pears 632
Melton Breakfast 2894
Melton Hunt 1668
Member of the Este Family
7844
Memories 1951
Menagerie 5156
Meninas 8156
Manton 4694
Mentone 3105
Menuett 4140
La Mer a L'Estaque 1225
Merchant George Gisze 3445
Merry-go-Round 558
Merrymakers 920, 8155
Messalina 7816
Metropolis 311
Meule 8062
Mevagissey Harbour 4256
Mexican Boy 2495
Mexican Brother and Sister
2496
Mexican Children 460
Mexican Girl 2497
Mexican Panels 218
Mexican Pueblo 5577
Mexican Street Scene 7468
Mexican Village 7651
Mexico 2972, 3204, 3205, 3206,
3207, 7950
Mezzetin 8401
Michelstadt 4695
Middle Lake, Killarney 8505
Midi 3546
Midi de France 1226
Midnight Ride of Paul Revere
8546
Midsummer 2305, 8639
Mid-Winter 498
Mignon 3588
Military Horsemen, French
5718
Milk Jug, Apples and Lemon
1227
Milk Maid 2962, 8192
Mill 6375, 6965
Mill at Pontoise 1228
Mill at Zaandam 5254
Mill in Brittany 2601
Mill Stream 8577
Miller's Home 7672
Milliner 7817

Millinery Shop 1859
Millinery Shop at Promenade
4506
Miltenberg 4696
Mimi 3589
Mimi Pinson's House in the
Snow 7906
Mimi Spirit Woman and a Cat
Fish 261
Mimosa 2788, 5519
Minnesota Farm 1884
Minnesota in August 1885
Ming Horse 3155
Minuet 2556, 7701
Miracle of the Cross 1100
Miracle of St. Anthony 5788
Miracle of St. Dominic 2880
Miracle of St. Francis 1595
Miracle of St. Mark 7722
Miracle of St. Vincent Ferrer
1558
Miracle of the Source 2735
Miracoli di S. Bernardino
2407, 2408
Miraculous Infant of Prague
1316
Mirador 4034
Misanthrope 905
Miser 6188
Miss Bowles 6620
Miss Croker 4213
Miss Eleanor Urquhart 6242
Miss Harriet Ann Seale 3517
Miss Mary Hickey 6621
Miss Murray 4214
Miss Pearce 7528
Miss West 4216
Miss Willoughby 6739
Missal Page with Annunciation
2667
Mission near San Xavier Del
Bac, Tucson 7141
Mississippi Moon 7118
Mr. Warner at the Moulin Rouge
7820
Mistral: Cap D'Antibes 5255
Mrs. Davenport 6740
Mrs. James Montgomery 7529
Mrs. John Bacon 1471
Mrs. Mole-Raymond 4250
Mrs. Richard Yates 7514
Mrs. Waddell and Children
3120

Misty Morning 7187
Mixed Bouquet 6330
Mixed Flowers 8454
Mixed Flowers in a Vase 6528
Mixed Glads 525
Mixed Summer Bowl 3134
The Mocked Christ 2700
Mocking Bird and Magnolia 5807
Model 4321
Models from the Ballet 7605
Modern Ballet 4151
Modern French Bouquet 2932
Modern Madonna 5939
Modern Tempo 7395
Modiste 7818
Mois de Mai 3590
Molesey Weir 7320
Molucca Cockatoos 677
Moment in Venice 7677
Moment Musicale 5715
Mona Lisa 4304
Monaco 6692
Monarch of the Glen 4155
Monday in the Country 574
Monet's House at Argenteuil 5256
Monhegan Gold 7264
Monhegan Harbor 526, 554
M. Bolleau au Cafe 7819
Mont. Ste-Victoire au Deux Pins 1230
Montagne Sainte-Victoire 1229
Montana Mountains 3695, 8578
Monte Carlo 2077
Monte Rosa 4988
Monterey Wharf 7142
Montezuma Marshes 4881
Month of May 3980
Montmartre 6693, 7907
Montmartre, the Gas Lamps 8063
Montreux 4697
Monument Mountain 2118
Moon 5157
Moon Guitar 3720
Moonglow 7770
Moonlight 3018, 4860, 6141
Moonlight at Woods Island Light 3474
Moonlight on the Riviera 1269
Moonlight Reflection 7771
Moonlit Cove 6970

Moor and Bridge 7079
Moorland 3506, 7080
Moppets 5068
Moravian Peasants 7877
Morcote 4698
Moret-sur-Loing, Morning Sunshine 7321
Morges 4699
Morning 1519, 5673
Morning at the Louvre 6105
Morning by the River 7652
Morning: Dance of the Nymphs 1520
Morning Drive 575
Morning Gossip 6993
Morning Mist 7354
Morning Mystery 1292
Morning of the Hunt 5506
Morning Traders 1360
Mortlake Terrace 7852
Moses Defending the Daughters of Jethro 6760
Moses Striking the Rock 5455
Moss Rose 3649
Moss Roses 6529
Mother 3496, 5940
Mother and Child 3843, 4271, 5941, 5942, 5943, 6520, 6874, 8314
Mother and Child on the Beach 1521
Mother and Children 5543, 6531
Mother and Sister of the Artist 8315
Mother and Son 1740, 8321
Mother Earth 8485
Mother Goose 8447, 8448
The Mother of Christ 7026
Mother of the Artist 8468
Mother's Birthday 6348
Mother's Helper 6654
Motherhood 1328, 3047, 6791
Mothers 5944
Motion 5489
Moulin de la Galette 5945, 6235, 6532, 7908
Moulin Rouge 5330, 6694, 6826, 7821, 7822, 7823
Mount Adams, Colorado 8579
Mount Diablo, California Ranch 7143
Mount Equinox, Winter 3892

Nurnberg from the West 2141
Nurnberg Wife in Ball Dress
2142
Nurnberg Wife in Church Dress
2143
Nurnberg Wife in House Dress
2144
Nursery Decorations 5159
Nursery Prints 8449
Nurseryland 391
Nymph Echo 2263
Nymphes 6541

O Come Let us Sing unto the
Lord 7583
Oaks 6838
Oarsmen at Chatou 6542
Oast Cottage 1605
Oath of Love 2472
Oaxaca 6655
Oberammergau, Seide 2376
Oberengadin 4704
Objects on a Sofa 4071
Ocean Avenue, Carmel 1131
Ocean Breeze 8586
Ocean Racers 1749
October Gold 8587
October Meeting 5438
October Morn 8588
October Sunshine 3822
Odalisque 737, 1891, 4940
Odd Birds Bathing 5134
Odd Birds in a Tree 5135
Oellets and Clematites 4574
Off Concarneau 2266
Off Cowes, Isle of Wight 7253
Off San Francisco 2115
Off the Avenue 3300
Off the Coast of Arran 5008
Off the Highlands 5178
Off the Main Road 3349
Off the Western Land 5564
Offering 2276, 2605
Ohio Magic 7213
L'Oise near Pontoise 6106
Old and New 3677
The Old and the Young 6996
Old Archway 3734
Old Banjo 3878
Old Bridge 1921, 6662
Old Bridge, Venice 3735
Old Bruton Church (Williamsburg,

Va.) 1411
Old Canal Bridge 4705
Old Checkered House 5387
Old Church and Steps 4436
Old Companions 5827
Old Covered Bridge 499
Old Cremona 5828
Old Customs House, Monterey
7144
Old Dieppe 3627
Old Dock 4380
Old Dutch Church 3350
Old Dutch Mill 4286
Old English Charm 6637
Old Farm 8342
Old Farmer 5607
Old Fisherman 3116
Old Forester 7590
Old Guitarist 5952
Old Homestead 5388
Old House 4258
Old King 6792
Old Man and the Sea 3046
Old Man with a Child 2676
Old Man with a Red Hat 6377
Old Manor 4706
Old Mill 4289, 8589
Old Mill Stream 1952
Old Mission 2973
Old Models 3131
Old New Orleans 4079
Old Oaken Bucket 7674
Old Port of Marseilles 8266
Old Quarry 484
Old Red Mill 1735
Old Refrain 3132
Old Salt 5538
Old Stage Coach 3743
Old Surrey 5703
Old Temple 6663
Old Time Plains Fight 6415
Old Town, Mentone 6643
Old Watermill at Storrington
2422
Old Weaver 2974
Old Well 3112
Old Woman Dozing over a Book
4514
Old Woman in Church 4280
Olevano Romano 1522
Olive Grove 8066
Olympia 4575
On Lake Maggiore 774

357

7445
Return of the Mythe 7296
Return of the Terre-Neuvier
751
Return of the Tunny Boat
8527
Return to Harbor 7254
Returning Victor 6878
Reunion of the Saints 2155
Reverence 2476
Reverie 2177, 2610, 4948
Reveries 5675
Revoltosa 8495
Revolution of the Viaduct 3950
Revue 7259
Rexworthy Billiard Parlor 53
Reynold in Armida's Garden
7707
Rheims Cathedral 877, 7916
Rhododendron 7872
Rhythm and Melody 1160
Rialto 1047
Rialto Bridge 4287
Rich Harbour 3951
Richard, Duke of Gloucester
3
Richmond Park 354
Ride on a Wagon 580
Rider 4806
Rider of the Rough String 6924
Rider on the Coast 2611
Riders on the Beach 2612,
4152
Riders on the Coast 2613
Ring-Necked Pheasant 5811
Rio dei Mendicanti at Venice
3035
Rio Hondo 3604
Rio di S. Lorenzo 26
Ripe Sheaves 2500
Rising Sun 5723
Ritz 4885
Rivals 6999
Rivaplana 4719
River 5267
River Bank 6115
River Boats 8614
River Landscape 3985, 4838
River Marne 4120
River Memories 21
River Meuse 3751
River Regulizing Territory 3952
River Scene, Quimper 6683

River Seine 2546, 7324
River View 2887
River Village 2306
Riverside Village 4720
Riviera 4398, 4721
Riviera Fantasy 1434
Riviera Splendor 237
Road 6116
Road along the Railway 6117
Road by the Sea 1490
Road in Snow at Honfleur 5268
Road in the Mountains 8296
Road to Calvary 176, 4861,
7708
Road to the Cove 7192
Road to Ennery 6118
Road to LaFrette 4839
Road to the Hills 2307
Road to Louveciennes 6119
Road to the Sea 7232
Road with Palm Tree 6229
Roadmenders of Rue de Berne
4588
Roadside Chat 3411
Roadside Cottage, Lough Inagh
3356
Roadside Dwellings 7405
Robert de Civrieux 7046
Robin 5812
Robin, American 2798
Rock-Bound Coast 2187
Rock Crystal 5017
Rockland Harbor, Maine 3514
Rockport 3747
Rockport Wharf 7657
Rocks of Belle Isle 5269
Rocky Coast 8597
Rocky Landscape 1245
Rocky Mountain Lake 8297
Rocky Mountains 1614
Rocky Point 6646
Rolling Hills 5735
Rolling Wheatfields 3727
Roma, Arco di Constantino
4722
Roma, Piazza San Pietro 4723
Roma, Tempie e Chiesa 4724
Roman Garden 6666
Roman Parade 6879
Roman Ruins 5641, 5642, 5643,
5644
Roman Ruins with Pyramid
5645

Romance 5677
Romantic River 5744
Romantic Rome 3801
Romantic Still Life 465
Rome 3266, 3267
Rome Eternal 75
Romeo and Juliet 1068
Rommelpot Player 3085
Romney, Kent 3628
Rond Point 2036
Roofs in Springtime in Suburb 1246
Rooftops 4379
Roosevelt, Franklin D. 7012
Roosevelt, Theodore 4171
Rooster 5166, 5967, 6608
Roping a Grizzly 6925
Roping a Wolf 6926
Roscoe 8344
Rose 532
Rose a Cent Feuilles 8123
Rose and Blue 6559
Rose and Recorder 1354
Rose Bouquet 5115
Rose-Breasted Grosbeak 2833, 5813
Rose du Bengale 6332
Rose de Bordeau 6333
Rose d'Enfante 6334
Rose de France 6335
Rose d'Hudson 6336
Rose de Provins 8124
Rose Goddess 3060
Rose of France 1666
Rosegtal Piz Roseg und Sella-gruppe 4725
Roses 92, 286, 762, 2096, 4162, 4219, 4220, 6560, 8346
Roses and Anemones 8082
Roses and Basket of Eggs 643
Roses and Blue Jug 2292
Roses and Eggs 644
Roses and Larkspur 2992
Roses and Tulips in a Vase 4589
Roses at Villaneuve 4003
Roses et la Mer 1273
Roses de Cumberland 6337
Roses des Indes 6338
Roses de Paris 6339
Roses in an Ochre Vase 6561
Roses Mousseuses 6562

Rosette Girl with Fan 4189
Rosier a Cent Feuilles 6340
Rosier Grandeur Royale 6342
Rosier des Parfumeurs 6341
Rosita 7460
Rothenburg 4726
Rotten Row 8669
Rouen Cathedral 5270
Rough Riders 7119
Rough Sea 6966
Rough Waters 3070
Round Table 812, 5064
Roundabouts 4727
Roundup 6827
Rout of San Romano 7866
Route 8274
Route Seven 4446
Route Tournante 1247
Rower's Lunch 6563
Rowers 4758
Rowing at Henley 2097
Royal Agricultural Beagles at Jarvis Quarry 4482
Royal and Ancient 8427
Royal Cockatoos 679
Royal Dragon 2430
Royal Hunt 5082
Royal Mail 6153
Royal Racer 1751
Royal Visitors in Watteau's Studio 5656
Rubaiyat 5678
Rubens and his First Wife 6862
Ruby-Throated Hummingbird 256
Rue Artez 7917
Rue de L'Abrevoir 5332
Rue Boulanger 6700
Rue Chevalier le Barre 541
Rue du Haut Pave 1700
Rue Jeanne d'Arc 7919
Rue Jeanne d'Arc in the Snow 7920
Rue Lepic a Montmartre 7921
Rue Mont Cenis 7922
Rue Moulin Rouge 7923
Rue Norvins 542, 5333
Rue Ordener 7924
Rue de Rivoli 1701
Rue Royale 6701
Rue Saint Rustique 7926
Rue St. Vincent 7925
Rue a Sannois 7918
Rue Seveste 7927

St. Ursula's Dream   1103
St. Veronica's Veil   4982
St. Victor and a Donor   2796
St. Vincent Street   7933
St. Vincenzo of Ferreri   7757
Saints Cosmas and Damian   466
Saints Cosmas and Damian before
   Lysias   183
Salisbury Cathedral   1461, 3630
Salisbury Cathedral from the
   Bishop's Garden   1462
Salisbury Cathedral, View of 1463
Salome with the Baptist's Head
   720
Saltimbanque Seated with a Boy
   5968
Saltimbanques   8226
Salton Sea   7558, 7559
Salute of the Robe Trade   6929
Salzburg   4004
Sampler   7609
Samplers   4765
San Carlos Church in Moonlight
   7148
San Cipriano, Corsica   5757
San Francisco, Cal.   3268, 3269,
   5070
San Francisco Harbor   7149
San Francisco Wharf   7150
San Giorgio Maggiore   2038
San Juan Capistrano Mission
   3720, 7151
San Marco, Venezia   4363
San Salvatore   4728
Sanary sur Mer   1092
Sand Cart   421
Sand Dunes   228
Sannox Bay, Arran   5132
Santa Barbara Mission   7152
Santa Clara Indian Girl   7448
Santa Fe Trail   8652
Santa Margarita   3737
Santa Maria della Salute   1048,
   4760
Santa Maria della Salute, Venice
   752
S. Maria Trastavere   5027
Santa Trinita Bridge at Florence
   2423
Santiago Madonna   5459
Sarlat   4729
Saskia   6387
Saskia at Toilet Table   6388

Satin Gown   2945
Saturday Night on the Ranch
   5032
Satyr and the Peasant   3754
Sauvetage   4344
The Saviour   1444, 3435,
   5430
Savonarola, Portrait of   5616
Saw Ohn Nyun   3887
Saying Grace   1336
Scandal and Tea   7000
Scarlet Ibis   257
Scarlet Tanager   5814
Scattering the Riders   6930
Scene de Ballet   1867
Scene in Venice   3038
Scenic Lane   7406
Schaffhausen   4730
Scheherazade   4450
School Boy   203, 8083
School Girl   204
School Master   2003
School of Athens   6286
School Recess   3319
School's Afire   581
School's Out   582, 1954
Schooner   3459
Schooner in Harbor   3825
Schooner "Newport"   449
Schweitzer, Albert   4036
Scissors Grinder   3744
Scourging of Christ   7365
Scout: Friend or Enemies?
   6416
Scribe   6283
Sculptor and Models   5971
Sculpture Group   779
Sculpture Relief--Ashurnaspirpal
   II   242
Sea at Etretat   5273
Sea at Le Havre   2101
Sea and Sand   8599
Sea Coast   5609
Sea Gulls   5571
Sea in Splendor   7267
Sea in Sunlight   39
Sea Splendor   8601
Sea Swallows   5815
Seacoast at Trouville   5274
Seacoast Honeymoon   3558
Seafarers   8600
Seaman's Den   40
Seamstress   8194

370

Street near Harbor 3461
Street Scene 993, 2389, 6230, 8282
Street Scene, Paris 2390
Strenuous Life 6934
Strike of a Steelhead 7193
String Quartet 5343
Stroll to the Lake 7430
Strozzi Child 7758
Strummin Days 41
Student 6395
Studies of Hands for Madonna 6243
Studies of Movements 6285
Studies of Pixie, an Exmoor Foal 5441
Studio 837, 1532, 3313, 5994
Studio View--Phlox 529
Studio with "La Danse" 4962
Study 5106
Study for Banjo Lesson 1141
Study for "The Dancing Class" 1869
Study for "Grande Jatte" 7204
Study in Half-Length 1870
Study--Morning Interlude 767
Study of an Apostle 1548
Study of a Dead Roller 2160
Study of a Nude 6181
Study of a Nude Male Model 7396
Study, St. Jerome 1166
Study of a Woman 2963, 4593
Study of a Young Man 6396
Stump Speaking 476
Stuppach Madonna 3020
Stymie 7486
Submarine Garden 1162
Suburban Street 7939
Suffer the Little Children 4014, 7584, 8293
Sugar Bowl with Fruit 838
Sugar Maples 3700
Suite Byzantine 5469
Suitor's Visit 7628
Summer 515, 744, 3547, 3881, 4147, 5283, 6671, 6831, 8372, 8409, 8434
Summer Bounty 5512
Summer Bouquet 2295, 2515
Summer Breezes 1752
Summer Day 4035, 7113
Summer Day in Rome 1967

Summer Dreams 1370
Summer Flowers 7944
Summer Glory 530
Summer Gold 8360
Summer Harvesters 906
Summer Holiday 1117
Summer Idyl 5589
Summer Idyll 5590
Summer in Amsterdam 3802
Summer in Devonshire 3109
Summer in Italy 6719
Summer Inlet 2563
Summer Landscape 1742, 2509, 4060, 7176, 5541, 7948
Summer Morn 7661
Summer Respite 43
Summer Sequel 7307
Summer Sports 870
Summer Storm 7498
Summer Symphony 6750
Summer Tanagers 5818
Summer Vista 3775, 4975
Summer Winds 8464
Summer's Day 5766
Summer's Glory 4061
Summer's Offering 2180
Summer's Pride 7379
Sun 5168
Sun and Rocks 985
Sun Animal 214
Sun on Baltic Beach 5725
Sunbeams 7773
Sunday Afternoon 2041, 6684
Sunday Afternoon on the Island of La Grande Jatte 7205
Sunday at Port En Bessin 7206
Sunday at Sannois 2233
Sunday by the Sea 2018
Sunday Devotion 2410
Sunday Fire Drill 584
Sunday in Paris 1134
Sunday in the Country 585
Sunday Morning 2119, 5651
Sunday on the Grande Jatte 7207
Sunday Ride 586
Sunday School Walk 208
Sunday Visitors 587
Sunday Walk 3963
Sunderland Hills 241
Sundown 8605
Sunflowers 453, 967, 2226, 3507, 5284, 6309, 7100, 7257, 7591, 8099, 8100,

8101, 8455
Sunflowers and Red Barn 986
Sunlight and Shadows in the
Desert 5002
Sunlit Patterns 4447
Sunlit Sea 8452
Sunlit Seas 7353
Sunlit Surf 7662
Sunlit Waters 5003
Sunny Autumn 3701, 8648
Sunny Bay 4735
Sunny Brittany 3826, 6081
Sunny Cove 773
Sunny Day 17, 299, 1033, 1324,
7592
Sunny Forest 2313
Sunny Forest Road 2519
Sunny Landscape 300
Sunny Midi 8102
Sunny Morning, Ploumanach
8528
Sunny Pastures 221
Sunny Terrace, Lake Como
7258
Sunny Valley 5736
Sunny Way 3093
Sunrise Flight 120
Sunrise in Hegau 1974
Sunrise in Ireland 481
Sunset 1389, 2161, 4792
Sunset, Dana Point 8606
Sunset at Arles 8103
Sunset Glory 3052
Sunset Glow 7774
Sunset in the Sand Country 7561
Sunset in Venice 7855
Sunset on the Grand Canal
7856
Sunset on the Snow 6347
Sunset Shore 8607
Sunset Silhouette 7775
Sunshine and Shadow, Co. Donegal
8506
Sunshine Lady 5610
Supper at Emmaus 4320, 6398,
7373
Sur la Pointe 5425
Surf, Sand and Rocks 2564
Surrender of Breda 8164
Susanna in the Bath 68
Susquehanna River 1602
Sussex Landscape 5473
Suzanne 3593

Swan Lake 44
Swans 5364
Swing 2456, 6441, 6578,
8383
Swiss Chalets 8629
Sybelle 6804
Sybil 1062
Sycamore Bend 1010
Sylphide 3580
Sylphides 45
Sylvan Honeymoon 3560
Sylvan Lake 8649
Sylvan Silence 3094
Sylvan Solitude 552
Symmetrical Accord 3795
Symphony 5344
Symphony of Flowers 2946
Synagogue in Jerusalem 1300
Syndics of the Drapers' Guild
6397
Syracuse 2105

Ta Matete 2614
Tabac Royal 4963
Table au Moulin Rouge 7832
Table Mise 5995
Taffy 7499
Tahiti, 1963 6300
Tahitian Girl Crouching 2617
Tahitian Landscape 2618
Tahitian Mountains 2619
Tahitian Village 2620
Tahitian Women 2621
Tai-Ling in the Rain 8542
Tailor 4393, 5377
Tales of a Grandfather 209
Tally-Ho 8618
Tangerines 657
Tango 1331
Tankard and Peaches 658
Taos Indian Boy 7449
Taos Indian Girl 7450
Tapa Cloth 7479
Tapestry Weavers 8165
Tapis Vert 839
Tarascon Coach 8104
Tarquin and Lucretia 7724
Tarquina 5322
Tarquinius and Lucretia 7711
Task Force of Two Navies 7239
Tasting Wine 8195
Tata Domingo 4373

Tavern on the Green   3595
Taxco Road   7663
Tay in June   486
Te Raau Rahi   2622
Te Rerioa   2623
Tea at Five   8671
Tea Pot   6185
Tea Rose   6237
Tea Table   840
Tea Time, Newlyn   3154
Teakettle with Eggs   659
Teal and Willows   5819
Teamwork   4169
Teddy Bear Beach   871
Teddy Bear Camp   872
Tel Aviv, 1936   8655
Tempest   4006
Tempio Borghese   6672
Tempio Calonna   6673
Tempio Corsini   6674
Tempio Doria   6675
Temple Dancer   2835
Temptations of St. Anthony
   7712
Ten P.M.   3903
Tender Burden   2251
Tenderfoot   6935
Tennessee   1011
Tennyson, Alfred Lord   8620
Tenterden, Kent   3632
Terpsichore   6880
Terrace   841, 6668
Terrace by the Sea   4743
Terrace Gardens at Richmond
   4007
Terrace in Summer   2181
Tete de Jeune Fille   5996
Tete de Jeune Homme   5997
Texas   3272-3275
Texas Blue Bonnets   8608
Texas Spring   8609
Thames Estuary   5365
Thanksgiving   4262
Thatched Cottages 8005, 8283
Theatre   110
Thebaid   7433
There's Danger Ahead when
   Sioux and Blackfeet Meet
   6936
Therese Berard 6579
They're Biting   3956
Third Class Carriage   1715
Thirty-six Gun Frigate   3975

This is My Love   2252
Thistle   535
Thoroughbreds   6756
Thoroughbreds at Large 4026
Three Ages of Man 4428
Three-Alarmer   588
Three Bs   387
Three Dancers   1871
Three Deer   4625
Three Elephants   6399
Three Generations   3809
Three Happy Pigs   324
Three Harlequins   3850
Three Horses   4626
Three Judges   6805
Three Kings Altar   755
Three Lawyers   1716
Three Linden Trees   2162
Three Little Girls   1961
Three Mallards 4886
Three Masks   3424
Three-Master   4793
Three Musical Ladies   4901
Three Musicians   5998
Three Philosophers   2703
Three Puppies   2624
Three-Quarter Coach   2042
Three Riders Attacked by Death
   2163
Three Scotties 1779
Three Setters   1686
Three Sisters   6178
Three Studies of the Virgin
   6288
Three Trees   8106
Three Women   4274
Three Women in Church 4279
Threshing   5474
Threshing Wheat   442
Through the Village   8284
Thunersee 4744
Tiberio   5019
Tiger   4627
Tiger Hunt   6832
Tight Dally and Loose Latgo
   6937
Time for Recreation   5767
Timeless City   3690
Times of Day   3088
Times Square   7130
Timocleia and the Thracian
   7713
Tinker Tailor   1780

Woman with a Pearl 1539
Woman with Plants 8550
Woman with Red Hair 5208
Woman with a Shawl 3909
Woman with Water Jug
   8202
Woman's Portrait 4598
Women and Sea 4797
Women Bathing 2634
Women in a Field 6596
Women of Galilee 6876
Women of Tahiti 2635
Women on the Beach 2636
Women Playing with a Goat
   6730
Women with Hats 6597
Women with Mangoes 2637
Wood on the Downs 5475
Woodcutter 3004
Wood-Gatherers 1540
Wood Ibis 259
Wooden Horses 4845
Woodland 3416
Woodland Festival 1116
Woodland Flowers 854
Woodland Gardeners 875
Woodland Rest 7225
Woodland Stream 1603, 2521
Woodland Traffic 876
Woodlands 979
Woodpeckers 2909
Wool Winder 2964
World of Silence 1164
Wounded Clown 6807
Writer 6179
Wynnstay Hunt 1028

Yacht, 1963 970
Yacht America 878
Yacht Basin 2113
Yacht Basin, Geneva 3728
Yachts at Deauville 2114
Yellow Accent 1737, 8238
Yellow and Pink Roses 6343
Yellow-Billed Cuckoo 5823
Yellow Bird 14
Yellow-Breasted Chat 260
Yellow Chair 4967, 8120
Yellow Coat 4509
Yellow Dahlias 1152
Yellow Flowers in a Blue Vase
   4275

Yellow Harlequin 1878
Yellow Horses 4631
Yellow Madonna 8312
Yellow Mums with Fruit 666
Yellow Roses 3061
Yellow Sails 7274
Yellow Triangle 3797
Yellow Tulips 610
Yellow Vermilion 5491
Yosemite 8613
You 5751
Young America 8625
Young Anglers 2425
Young Beggar 5461
Young Corn 8551
Young Field Hare 2167
Young Foal 5087
Young Girl 210, 1369, 3309,
   6078, 6598
Young Girl at an Open Half-
   Door 6401
Young Girl at Open Half-
   Window 6403
Young Girl at Piano 6599
Young Girl at a Window 6402
Young Girl Combing Her Hair
   6600
Young Girl Knitting 211
Young Girl Reading a Letter
   6305
Young Girl Singing into a Mir-
   ror 4329
Young Girl Waiting 5367
Young Girl with Arm Upraised
   6023
Young Girl with a Bird 2965
Young Girl with Daisies 6601
Young Girl with a Sheaf of
   Flowers 6602
Young Governess 1349
Young Man 216, 722, 6297
Young Man at Prayer 5054
Young Man in Seersucker Coat
   6180
Young Man with a Flageolet
   7776
Young Mother 264, 4042
Young Mother and Child 8229
Young Sailor with Cap 4968
Young Sculptress 4376
Young Shepherd 6603, 6625
Young Skippers 7409
Young Warrior 6870